From Stres.

MW00640185

Angus Jenkinson

ALSO IN THE 'BRINGING SPIRIT TO LIFE' SERIES:

Homemaking as a Social Art, Creating a Home for Body, Soul and Spirit
Veronika van Duin

The Journey Continues . . . , Finding a New Relationship to Death
Gilbert Childs with Sylvia Childs

From Stress to Serenity

Gaining Strength in the Trials of Life

Angus Jenkinson

Sophia Books

To Sally, Derwin, Hamish and Emily.
And all the family of humanity.

With grateful thanks to Jill Marshall
for typing and retyping.

Sophia Books
Hillside House, The Square
Forest Row, East Sussex
RH18 5ES

Published by Sophia Books 2003
An imprint of Rudolf Steiner Press

A catalogue record for this book is available from the British Library

ISBN 1 85584 157 6

Cover by Andrew Morgan Design
Typeset by DP Photosetting, Aylesbury, Bucks., in Bembo
Printed and bound in Great Britain by Cromwell Press Limited,
Trowbridge, Wilts.

The aim of philosophy is thoughts that are at peace.
Socrates

★

If a man speaks or acts with an harmonious thought
happiness follows him as his own shadow,
never leaving him.
Buddha

★

Oh well a Touch of Grey/Kind of suits you anyway.
That was all I had to say/It's all right . . .
I will get by/I will survive . . .
We will get by/We will survive.
From *Touch of Grey*, Robert Hunter of the Grateful Dead

★

Quiet I bear within me.
I bear within myself
Forces to make me strong.
Now will I be infused
With their glowing warmth.
Now will I fill myself
With my own will's resolve.
And I will feel the quiet
Pouring through all my being,
When by my steadfast striving
I become strong
To find within myself
The source of strength,
The strength of inner quiet.
Rudolf Steiner

A political victory, a rise in rents, the recovery of your sick, or the return of your absent friend, or some other favorable event, raises your spirits, and you think good days are preparing for you. Do not believe it. Nothing can bring you peace but yourself. Nothing can bring you peace, but the triumph of principles.

Ralph Waldo Emerson

★

Strong, calm people are always loved and revered.
They are like shade giving trees.

James Allen

CONTENTS

Acknowledgements   xi

CHAPTER 1   THE MISSION OF STRESS   2
The deeper meaning of stress   3
Stress as a personal guide   5
Causes of stress   9

CHAPTER 2   SELF-DIAGNOSIS: AN INNER WORKSHOP   11
I and the world   13
The mind's role in stress and calm   15
Becoming aware of stress   17
Signs of stress   19
We don't need to be stressed!   21
How distress develops   22
The effects of inadequate stress   26
Why it is important to value illness   27
Taking responsibility and making a change   28

CHAPTER 3   LIFESTYLE FUNDAMENTALS   30

CHAPTER 4   THE TRUE I AND THE EVERYDAY ME   49
Body, mind and spirit   51
Experiencing your soul   54
The true I   57
The I and freedom of choice   60
The I divided   61
The universal Cain and Abel   65
The meaning of individuality   69
How the I creates destiny   72
The meaning of stress and suffering   76
How to embrace destiny   78

CHAPTER 5   HOW STRESS CREATES SELF-LEADERSHIP   80
    I. Saturn: when uncertainty challenges   86
    II. Jupiter: when you need insight into complexity   90
    III. Mars: empowering yourself   92
    IV. Venus: the call of care   97
    V. Mercury: the call of flexibility   100
    VI. Moon: judgement and control in a world of activity   103
    VII. Sun: the need for moral maturity to confront the moral maze   110

CHAPTER 6   EXERCISES FOR INNER DEVELOPMENT   115
    Observation and sensitivity exercises   115
    Gaining self-knowledge through daily or life-retrospectives   122
    Thinking exercises   125
    Strengthening the will   127
    Finding emotional balance: equanimity   128
    Positivity   130
    Memory exercises   133
    Decisions and decision making   134
    Becoming more flexible   134
    Meditation   135

CHAPTER 7   STRESSES OF TEMPERAMENT   138
    The effect of the temperaments   139
    Exercise: recognizing your temperament   145

CHAPTER 8   LIFE AND WORK TECHNIQUES   148
    Creating positive mental and cultural attitudes   148
    Discuss good things together   151
    Time management   152
    Desk and work organization   156
    Taking the stress out of meetings   159
    Organizing change to minimize stress   163
    Using work rhythms to reduce stress   164

CHAPTER 9   WHEN PEOPLE SEND US CRAZY   166
    The pain of individuality and separation   167
    Vulnerability breeds aggression   169
    The mechanisms that make us vulnerable   171

The way out: taking true responsibility 178
Communication that connects 181
Healing relationships 189
Healing feelings and attitudes 191
We grow through others 194
Wonder, reverence and love 196

CHAPTER 10   TRIALS THAT GUIDE US TO OUR
             HIGHER SELF 199
Life as a 'trial by fire' 200
Life as a 'trial by water' 216
Finding balance and moral clarity 220
Life as a 'trial by air' 223
Crossing Thresholds 225
Your personal reflections 227

CHAPTER 11   MEDITATION 229
Thoughts for the days of the week 230
Seven practices to develop seven self-leadership qualities 232
A western way to meditate 235
Steps in meditation 236
Summary of how to meditate 240
Other ways to meditate 241
Specific meditations 242
Facing the future with courage 249

CHAPTER 12   THE BIG IDEAS 251
It matters how you think 252
Affirming goodness: from stress to strength to serenity 254
We live in a loveable universe 256
Love your neighbour 259

APPENDIX: RESOURCES 262
Stress reduction action plan 263
Notes 264
Readings 267
Illustration credits 270
Index of Names 271
Index of Meditations and Exercises 275

ACKNOWLEDGEMENTS

There is a saying that 'we are driven to study what we are deficient in'. There were dozens of people contributing to this book, including all those who put up with me—or quite rightly wouldn't—when I was irritable, complaining, worried or otherwise 'stressed', especially my work colleagues, wife and family. Researching and writing the book has also helped me. I think it may have helped avoid burnout and other stress symptoms. I have endeavoured to avoid including anything I have not tried and cannot endorse. Nevertheless, in considering the advice in this book, not only should you of course make your own choices and decisions, but please remember the advice of Confucius: 'The wise man does not appreciate a man because of what he says; nor does he depreciate what he says because of the man.'

My aim is to give suggestions for exercises and practices that help you not only to avoid distress but also to grow and develop. The ideas come from many sources and are echoed in many informed contemporary accounts. I am particularly indebted to Rudolf Steiner (1861-1925), a philosopher and artist who turned 'love of wisdom' into a practical and modern path of self-development towards freedom, for many of the development exercises.

Coen van Houten, who co-founded the Centre for Social Development, an adult development centre that provided excellent services for 30 years, originally introduced me to the seven fundamental stress patterns described in Chapter 5. I was then fortunate to develop this basic framework further in workshops with George Perry, a mediation consultant, and also Paul Maunsell, a McTimoney chiropractor and Bothmer gymnast. George Perry was particularly helpful in launching the research, practice and sharing that has been my maturing journey in the genesis of *From Stress to Serenity*.

My thanks also to Ann Druitt and my wife Sally Jenkinson as well as the Sophia Books team for invaluable editorial assistance.

For obvious reasons, most of the individual cases use pseudonyms to preserve confidentiality.

FROM STRESS TO SERENITY

CHAPTER 1

THE MISSION OF STRESS

All shall be well, and all shall be well, and all manner of things shall be well.

Julian of Norwich

Stress may be a stimulus or a burden, a fairground ride or a nightmare journey, but it can also be our partner and opponent in the inner game of life.

Despite its frequent unpleasantness, when approached in the right way, stress can become the means to learn and grow, for it has a positive mission. Stress symptoms can be our guide through the trials of life.

Just as the ordinary athlete uses exercise and challenge to develop physical muscles, so the inner athlete may develop calm, courage, imagination, balance, compassion, resilience, vision and presence of mind. Those who learn to pay attention to the physical, mental and spiritual signals that we call stress and discover how to respond will develop great personal gifts. Distress is only the outcome of failing to listen.

Though one man conquer a thousand men in battle a thousand times, he who conquers himself is the greatest warrior.
Buddha, *Dhammapada*, 103

From Stress to Serenity is therefore not only for those feeling stress or burnout and who are looking for a way to cope, it is also for everyone wishing personal, soul or spiritual development, or wanting to understand the *meaning and use* of stress. Sometimes it is just telling us to relax, like heat warning us away from a hot object. Yet, stress is also like a path of initiation arranged by nature or the gods or our own initiative to nurture our fullest potential, no fun at the time certainly, but ultimately an invaluable gift. Merely knowing this makes a difference. As Nietzsche commented, 'He who has a *why* to live for can bear almost any *how*.'

For leaders arise from this path, and leadership is much needed by humanity. Leadership waits not just in the corridors of power, but also in

Cheerfulness and pain: faces from mediaeval Lincoln Cathedral

every person, beginning with the process of really choosing how you will lead your own life—so developing life-wisdom and self-leadership.

The deeper meaning of stress

It is hard to be born as a human being, and hard to live the life of one. It is even harder to hear the path; and harder still to awake, to rise and to follow.

Buddha, Dhammapada, *182*

Engineers think of stress as anything that puts pressure on an object. In the same way, stress is anything that puts pressure on our inner responses. If we cannot respond, then the pressure becomes *distress* and potentially causes damage. (Fortunately even this may eventually have positive outcomes.) Stress is therefore simply the effect of a mismatch between life's trials and our individual capacities.

The mission of stress is to develop these inner, spiritual capacities (like positivity, tranquillity, resourcefulness, love and judgement). As they grow, so do we. Great personalities are those who have gained and use such qualities. This secret is not new.

The warning feeling of distress is a valuable stimulus to reflection, to the recognition that all is not well, and that change or development is needed. Furthermore, as I shall explain, it acts as a specific symptom that can point to exactly what needs to change.

Perhaps it is an overused point, or perhaps it is a point used so often because of its fundamental truth, that the Chinese word for 'crisis' consists of two ideograms meaning 'danger-opportunity'. Realizing that effort and even pain precede learning and personal growth was an important personal discovery for me. Even illness usually has value, typically as a rest or as a spur to a change in lifestyle. Instead of using drugs or other techniques to smother stress, there is another way.

There are western and eastern psychological traditions that refer to this as development through Fire. Indeed, alchemists, who evolved sophisticated meditations and exercises to transform their consciousness into the mature wisdom that they called the 'philosopher's stone', were also known as the 'Fire philosophers'. The great twentieth century psychologist Jung studied alchemical psychology extensively and considered its insights of the first importance. He commented, 'The genuineness or incorruptibility of the stone [i.e. the developed consciousness] is proved by the torment of fire and cannot be obtained without it. This leitmotiv runs all through alchemy.'[1] In other words, stress is essential for self-development. In a later chapter I will explore the 'trial by fire' in more detail, but its theme runs throughout this book.

The fire trial was an important image in alchemical literature

Normally, each period of change and transformation involves a crisis or even pain at the outset. But it is a curiosity of human nature that the more difficult the task, the more joy and fulfilment we get in its achievement.

That this represents hope will be important for many. Many people seek healing and another way of life. The word 'stress' appears on over ten million pages on the Internet. Contemporary advertising, self-development books, laws governing businesses, and even clip art (like this) are strong witnesses to the prevalence of anxiety, worry, burden, exhaustion, obsession and pain in the modern soulscape, as well as the wish to do something about it.

Stress as a personal guide

All that we are is the result of our thoughts; it is founded on our thoughts and made up of our thoughts. With our thoughts we make the world. If a man speaks or acts with a harmful thought, trouble follows him as the wheel follows the ox that draws the cart. All that we are is the result of our thoughts; it is founded on our thoughts and made up of our thoughts. With our thoughts we make the world. If a man speaks or acts with an harmonious thought, happiness follows him as his own shadow, never leaving him.

Buddha, Dhammapada, *1 & 2*

Each of us meets an individual world.

This world is tailored to and by our individual attitudes and aptitudes. For example, we tend to notice what we like or don't like, or what is important to us. We are also most affected by whatever helps or obstructs us. According to the scientists of the biology of cognition, Maturana and Varela, 'Every act of knowing brings forth a world.'

That is why stress is also so personal. One person is afraid of flying and another does it for a hobby. One person copes with thirty children and another can't manage one. One enjoys the quiet and another is bored. She seems to have tireless energy and enthusiasm while he spends any amount of time saying how busy he is. When we are unable to cope with what another can thrive on, this signals a need for personal growth.

The *amount* of stress is therefore not what creates distress but our *capacity* to cope with it. Some people easily cope with what would destroy others. Gandhi triumphed over the might of an empire. So a wise attitude to stress not only adjusts the environment to reduce stress, but also increases the capacity to cope.

Recent research suggests that the capacity to cope with stress and avoid depression may be biologically influenced. Certain genetic patterns make individuals more or less susceptible to stress. This is, however, only one of many examples of variation between people. Our biological constitution, life experience, life-style and unique outlook all affect our capacity to cope. What matters is responding to this current reality and deciding what to do about it.

Each time I experience stress it is a signal to reduce the pressure or develop increased capacity. Rather than just seeing stress as an ogre, you can productively imagine it as *the initiator of personal development* and of an improved lifestyle.

It is useful to think of stress as a *personal* coach. This guide helps us to achieve our fullest possible potential. For example, people who lack stress or challenge tend to become bored and eventually depressed. Then they begin to seek more challenge. The feeling of stress is then the guidance that shows where self-development is needed.

The mission of stress is to develop the capacities and lifestyle that end distress.

So, the first step in a more positive and productive relationship to stress is to recognize that its signals in the trials of life are a gift. How do you feel about *Ms Stress*, your personal life guide?

I believe that we almost always have the power and the imagination to do something about the stresses we meet, providing we are not lazy or locked in to bad habits (in which case the stress tends to increase until it matters enough to get our attention).

Furthermore, the unpleasantness of stress *nearly* always has beneficial aspects that make the temporary suffering worthwhile. Nelson Mandela's trials in prison under the apartheid regime were undoubtedly stressful, but they were also significant in creating a great man. Brian Keenan, who was kidnapped and held prisoner in Beirut for four and a half years, wrote, 'There were many other incidents in this hole in the ground. But each of them was an affirmation of human capacity to overcome despair.'

In an age when the pursuit of happiness is an assumed right, the idea of trials is not popular. Yet, these are central to self-development and have always been so recognized. Trouble builds character.

Viktor Frankl, after surviving the Nazi death camps, went on to develop logotherapy, one of the most influential psychological systems of the twentieth century. In his book, *Man's Search for Meaning*, which has been described as one of the ten most influential books in America, he comments on this experience: 'It is often just such an exceptionally difficult external situation which gives man the opportunity to grow spiritually beyond himself.'

The audience in a Shakespeare play such as *The Tempest* not only accepts the principle of trial, but I think it vicariously accompanies the stage characters. In Shakespeare, as in all great literature and not a few Hollywood movies, trials test and redeem characters. The members of the audience participate imaginatively in the drama's process and so by sympathy accompany the characters in their development. In this respect, I believe literature authentically reflects reality and serves to enrich its audiences.

World-renowned scholars Joseph Campbell, in the field of mythology, and Chris Vogler, in literature, have both described a recurrent theme that seems to bring meaning to human beings. It involves the hero being awakened to a task, refusal of that task until circumstances force them into it, and then a process of personal development, a kind of rite of passage in which they discover new faculties and in due course wisdom. This is typically called 'The Hero's Journey'.

According to Duane Elgin in *The Promise Ahead*:

> ...it is essentially the story of an individual who grows up by going through a series of tests that teach him or her about the nature of life. The person then brings this precious knowledge back to his or her personal life and life of the community.

She describes the journey's three stages of separation, initiation, and return in this way:

> It begins with the hero (or heroine) leaving home to search for the deeper meaning and purpose of life. This is the stage of separation. There eventually comes the stage when the hero undergoes a supreme test, whereby he is initiated into the nature and ways of the universe and no longer feels separate. With initiation, he experiences the deep unity and aliveness at the foundation of the universe and his sense of life-purpose in relation to it. He returns from his adventure with that hard-won knowledge and the capacity for personal renewal.

According to Campbell, the reason for this journey is to awaken in the individual a sense of wonder and participation in the mystery of the universe. This is indeed a recurring theme of this book. Experience tests our capacity, the feeling of stress or comfort giving us feedback on our personal development.

'Heroes' are people who have mastered stress and gained the capacity to act with wisdom. Perhaps they have developed indomitable courage and assurance, like Winston Churchill. Perhaps they have developed tireless compassion and care like Mother Theresa or St Francis. Perhaps, like Florence Nightingale, they not only have the energy ceaselessly to care but also the organizational ability and forcefulness to change the way things are done.

Heroes break their mental chains to refashion the world—as for example when Martha Graham fashioned a controversial new dance form or Emmeline Pankhurst challenged the social equity of women. When they do, they typically meet both trials and blocks. This it seems to me is akin to Christ's remark, 'I come not to bring you peace, but a sword,' the sword that cuts chains and barriers to human progress. When the Impressionists, such as Monet, rethought and re-created art they met a storm of protest, as did Stravinsky with his new ideas in music. Sometimes this opposition becomes violent, for example in the opposition to Aung San Suu Kyi, the Burmese politician, Martin Luther King or Joan of Arc.

Heroes are also realists. Admiral Jim Stockdale was the highest-ranking United States military officer in a prisoner of war camp during the height of the Vietnam War. He was tortured over twenty times and lived out the war without any rights, release date or certainty as to whether he would even survive. The story of his leadership and contribution to his fellow prisoners is inspiring. It is fascinating to note, however, that he credits his survival to two factors: that he never lost faith and he was never an optimist. The prisoners who died, he said, were those who kept believing that they would be out 'by Christmas'. On one occasion he reported, 'You must never confuse faith that you will prevail in the end—which you can never afford to lose—with the discipline to confront the most brutal facts of your current reality, whatever they might be.'

Fortunately I think we do not all have to experience giant trials. My sense is that most people get just what is quite enough! And this 'enough' may also be very significant, more indeed than we think. Heroes come in many forms: not all are famous; indeed most are not. When we pay our respects to the 'great', the universal and noticeable figures in history or in our times, we should not overlook the fine deeds and qualities of many 'ordinary' people.

I know a woman with endless ingenuity to respond to circumstances, a man capable of mastering highly complex systems, and many people with wonderful ability to solve social problems. It takes fortitude and care and creative energy for a parent to wake for the third or fourth time in the night, for the third or fourth or fortieth night in a row, to feed or calm a baby. It does not get written about in the history books, yet such care was a gift received by most great men and women when they were babies, and it has been the experience, mostly forgotten, of most of the six billion people alive on earth today. Nelson Mandela testifies to the love and support of his mother and of how she was the centre of his early existence. What part did her love have to play in the subsequent transformation of a bitter nation?

When a teacher enters a classroom and moves and inspires a class of children, it may not make it often into the papers, but Mandela acknowledges its importance to his education. For example, he describes how the taboo marriage of his popular Zoology teacher, Frank Lebentlele, to a woman from a different tribe undermined the parochialism that had previously imprisoned him. On another occasion he was inspired by the courage and dignity with which his black house-master, Reverend Mokitimi, insisted on his own responsibility and authority despite the attempted interference of the white headmaster wanting to 'solve' a problem. And his 'imagination was fired' by listening to stories of great Xhosa characters told by the village headmen as they gathered at the end of the days at the Xhosa leader's 'Great Place'. Did these people know what contribution they were making to the future of a nation? We rarely know how our lives might influence another's greatness.

Causes of stress

Life, the Universe and Everything.

Douglas Adams

There are three major causes of stress:

- The first of these is when we are out of tune with our environment, with nature and the natural world;
- The second is when we are out of tune with others;

- The third is when we are out of tune with our own spirit, the questing impulse towards self-fulfilment, self-actualization and self-transcendence through the divine.

In each case this might also be expressed as being separated from a fundamental aspect of the world in which we live. Separation or alienation is a primary cause of anxiety and hence stress.

As later chapters will show, responding positively to the challenges of stress grows and ripens a rounded and balanced resourcefulness that leads the emerging, free individual towards a wise and mutually loving relationship with the natural and life environment, people and spirit. This is the mission of stress and the way to turn stress into inner strength.

> Our deepest fear is not that we are inadequate
> Our deepest fear is that we are powerful beyond measure,
> It is our Light, not our darkness, that frightens us.
> We ask ourselves, who am I to be brilliant,
> Gorgeous, talented and fabulous?
> Actually, who are you not to be?
> You are a child of God.
> Your playing small doesn't serve the world.
> There's nothing enlightened about shrinking
> So that other people won't feel insecure around you.
> We are born to make manifest the Glory of God that is within us.
> It's not just in some of us; it's in everyone.
> And as we let our own Light shine,
> We unconsciously give other people permission to do the same.
> As we are liberated from our fears,
> Our presence automatically liberates others.
>
> Nelson Mandela

CHAPTER 2

SELF-DIAGNOSIS: AN INNER WORKSHOP

Just as a blade of grass will cut the hand if clumsily grasped, so a life badly
lived will destroy.

Buddha, Dhammapada, *311*

Simply being alive brings challenges. These are unavoidable. What matters is
how you respond. 'Just as a blade of grass will cut the hand if clumsily
grasped, so a life badly lived will destroy,' said Buddha (*Dhammapada* 311).

Most people find themselves facing either too much pressure or too little.
Ultimately there is only one way that this can be dealt with. Something needs
to change. Individuals must rise to the challenge, and the first step in this is
awareness. Jung commented that human beings would like to scale the
heights of the philosophical religion, but in fact are incapable of it. 'To grow
up to it is the most we can hope for. The Amfortas wound [in the Grail
legend] and the Faustian split ... are still not healed; his unconscious is still
loaded with contents that must first be made conscious before he can be free
of them.'

If there is not enough pressure I must, out of my own inner, creative
forces, find something to do. If there is too much stress I must once again take
charge of the situation. For example, I might rest, change my diet, find a
creative solution, or develop new skills and capacities. I must hold a balance
and take charge of my life, not have life take charge of me. This is self-
leadership.

I have overcome the world.

Jesus Christ

Taking charge of life does not mean imposing myself upon the world, it
means finding a right relationship with it. Using a biological metaphor, it
means fitting into the ecology of life.

Yet, I have noticed that instead of adjusting to the rhythm and tunes of life,
I have tried to make it fit me, however disjointed and unbalanced I am. For

example, I have gone to bed too late, and then used coffee to wake up. And then ended up again going to bed too late. I have passively sat watching television in my own little world instead of being imaginatively active or enjoying fellowship, for example by sharing and digesting the experiences of the day with my wife.

As James Allen puts it:

> You are the master of your thought, the moulder of your character, and the maker and shaper of your condition, environment, and destiny. As a being of power, intelligence, and love, and the lord of your own thoughts, you hold the key to every situation, and contain within yourself that transforming and regenerated agency by which you may make yourself what you will. You are always the master, even in your weakest and most abandoned state; but in your weakness and degradation you are the foolish master who misgoverns your household.

Running away from stress, for example into tranquillisers, television and 'getting-away-from-it-all' sunbathing holidays, often produces bounce-back problems (holidays are recognized as one of the highest stress times as well as a necessary chance to unwind). Yet, trying to impose a strict discipline to ensure that nothing can go wrong—disciplined savings, strict timetables and so on—seems to have other problems. There is an ugly but evocative description of characters who become too tight and cramped in character, that they are 'anal-obsessive'. And whatever we do, life tends to come up with the unexpected anyway!

The answer it seems to me lies in the kind of balanced right-living that Buddha described using the analogy of a musical instrument that needs to be strung neither too tight nor too loose. Renaissance thinkers also used musical analogy when they talked about the 'well-tempered' life. For good harmony in life and music means being able to bring a note that is true, in time with the rhythm and in relation to others. Whereas animals and plants innately belong through the wisdom of evolution to the natural order and ecology, the modern human seems to need to develop this social and environmental ecology consciously.

Ancient peoples also enjoyed a natural belonging and participation to a far greater extent than we do today. The anthropologist Levy-Bruhl singled out what he called participation mystique as the hallmark of the so-called primitive mentality. He meant by this a state of non-differentiation between subject and object that is strikingly different from modern, individualistic, western consciousness. Jung's comment on this was that whereas so-called primitive human beings lived in a world that was alive with ghosts and gods and with plants and animals that behaved like human beings, civilized human beings think themselves above such attitudes without recognizing how they are magically affected by all manner of people, things and circumstances. As a result, modern human beings no longer work with magic, such as amulets and animal sacrifices, but instead with tranquillisers, neuroses and rationalism (and, we might add, psychoanalysis and psychotherapy).

There is a simple experiment that you might be able to do that brings home how different modern life is. Yesterday night I went outside and stood in the field alongside our house (we live in a small village beside a farm). On one side there was the house, glowing with light, protected from the elements, an independent space. And around me in the dark there was the awesome and magical realm of nature: stars, wind, silence, coolness, and the occasional rustle. I felt what it would mean to live as a member of this order and the possibility to close it all off by going inside.

I and the world

> The inmost in due time becomes the outmost.
>
> *Ralph Waldo Emerson*

> Civilization is a projection of the mind.
>
> *(the author)*

The first step is truly experiencing my own, personal relationship with the world. This should not be in an egotistical way, but rather experiencing my responsibility and involvement. How does the world affect me and how do I affect the world? What nourishment in the form of beauty, good food, care, and ideas am I asking from it, and what is the world asking from me? What drink am I consuming, physical and mental, and what junk am I dumping in the world?

The social and natural environment weaves images, ideas and feelings into our soul. We are very much creatures of our time and place.

But, in addition to how the world affects us, we also shape our environment, through our soul. The idea, the design and the construction of bull-dozers, bombs, cities, ghettos, skyscrapers, battery farms, filthy skies, polluted rivers, eroded landscapes, gardens, fountains, beautiful homes, porcelain, cathedrals all began their life in the soul. It need hardly be said that not all that

An age of distress: São Paulo has about 35 million inhabitants, many living in slums and high rise apartments with poor water supply

we dream up is good. Humanity has already accumulated a sizeable debt to Mother Earth that will need to be paid off.

For this is an age of distress, with almost intolerable pressures on the environment. There is air and water pollution, degraded, poisoned and processed foods, ugly cities, boxy suburbs, crowded roads, machine-rich working environments, farmland lacking in variety and wild life, and poisons circulating throughout the earth.

Two of the greatest and most insidious problems in my opinion are noise and light pollution. The first surrounds us with a continuous and insidious hum and babble that contributes to the unquiet of the soul. The second means that generations of children grow up with little or no awareness of the sublime, starry heavens because city lights block their view.

All these poisons are absorbed through the senses, breathing and digestion, so contributing greatly to stress. The increasing frequency of allergies in western societies is one well-publicised consequence. Such underlying life pressures make it all the more important to take in hand what we may control.

In addition to the physical environment, the work culture of the West, including job insecurity, very long and competitive hours, and sedentary work with blighting commuter travel also contribute to stress factors. Professor Cooper, who has researched these trends extensively, is deeply worried that the fundamental shift to freelance and impermanent roles may be more than many people can cope with.

A trip through any of the world's great metropolitan centres at rush hour can be alarming and shocking. For example, join the thousands on the crowded London Underground with an open and sensitive eye and you will see all around tension and tiredness, stressed and ill people, you will see obesity or unnatural thinness, grey or blotchy skin, you will see poor posture and apathy, and at more subtle levels the accumulating toxicity that leads to divorce and depression, crime and aggression, and worse, to cancer and heart failure.

The German scientist, Leo A. Nefiodow, coined the term 'salutogenesis' to express a method of promoting social health and well being that is now being adopted by governments and health scientists. According to Nefiodow, psychosocial health is the most important basic innovation for the upcoming decades and he has no doubt that the demand for holistic health will be an economic engine in the twenty-first century. He points out that physical and mental disorders have reached such an extent that quality of life is being challenged. For example 14 per cent of the population of developed countries is estimated to be psychologically ill. Fear and anxiety in Germany costs around €150 billion per annum (nearly 90 per cent of German managers report going to their jobs every day with fear) and the world market place for drugs is estimated at US$ 800 billion. On the whole, social, psychological, mental and ecological disorders and diseases are increasingly hindering positive development in modern societies.

Perhaps even thinking about such ideas creates a mountain of stress? I hope that humanity through societies and governments will adopt ideas such as Nefiodow's and learn to live in harmony with the universe. Fortunately, the process can begin for each of us with simple and modest things. When I improve my self, I already make a difference. When I become less stressed, I become less stressful to others. And the first step is developing awareness.

The mind's role in stress and calm

> There is nothing either good or bad, but thinking makes it so.
>
> *William Shakespeare,* Hamlet *Act II, 2*

The world around us certainly creates potential for distress. But how this world affects us depends on how we perceive it and how we react 'inside' to those perceptions, a fact I could testify to when I was planning to move house.

An example of how the mind determines stress took place while writing this book when my wife and I decided to move house. After some time, we found a house that we wanted to buy and in order to make sure that we did not lose it we offered to take out a bridging loan on our existing house to have the funds available for the new property. This meant that from when we bought the new house until we sold our old one we would have to pay for two mortgages. Various friends warned us against taking such a step, telling us that it would be very stressful and risky.

In our calculations we had worked out that we could comfortably afford this providing we managed to sell our existing property within three months. Looking at the type of property we were selling and the existing market there seemed very little danger that we would not be able to achieve this. So we went ahead.

What happened then? We knew we had three months to sell the property. Having worked out very carefully what the situation was, we should then have been relaxed while we waited for a buyer to turn up. But this is not what happened!

We noticed an immediate tendency to begin worrying. Suppose we did not succeed in selling our house! Suppose it went on and on for months and months, might we end up bankrupted? The principal reason why a bridging loan is so stressful is precisely because of such human tendency to worry. Many other circumstances in personal and work life have the same consequences.

Here, our own wishes and thoughts had created the stress scenario, and the level of stress that we experienced depended almost completely on how we thought about the scenario. Managing the situation and the stress depended on having control over our own minds.

Dorothy Rowe is one of the world's most respected clinical psychologists and an expert in depression to whom thousands turn for help. One commentator described her as the 'guru of gloom'. She says the essence of her understanding and philosophy is: 'What determines our behaviour isn't what happens to us but how we interpret what happens to us.' She gives many examples, including the contrasting reactions of the unemployed, some of whom find it devastating while others see it as an opportunity, whether to pursue leisure activity or to engage in black market trade alongside getting benefit.

This theme is going to appear and reappear in various ways through this book. It is at the heart of the teaching of all great sages and counsellors; some I have already cited and I will cite more. It is wise and it is empowering: instead of being victims of events and people, we may become masters of ourselves, free.

It means that stress and anxiety and fear and depression and anger and hatred and also love and forgiveness and calm and happiness are the consequence of the way that we think, both the quality of our thinking and the thoughts that pass through our minds. Healthy thoughts and healthy thinking lead to positive feeling and behaviour.

Therefore it makes sense to develop awareness of and gradually improve the patterns and behaviour of your mind, and in particular the way that stress shows up in the mind, and I shall describe many ways to do this. It also makes sense to use the mind to notice the physical symptoms of stress and disorder and do something about this.

Becoming aware of stress

The thoughtless man does not care, but the attentive man looks on wakefulness as his greatest treasure.

Buddha, Dhammapada, *26*

A very good way to become conscious of the workings of the mind or soul is to try to become completely quiet inwardly, to think of nothing, but only to rest in inner tranquillity and peacefulness. Not only is this very difficult, but it serves to show the almost independent and uncontrolled nature of the mind, especially when it is 'stressed'. The more you find it difficult to have a calm mind, the more you need to cultivate calmness.

An old Hindu teaching likens the mind to three wild horses harnessed to a chariot and the 'I' as the charioteer who tames them. These wild horses are our thinking, our feeling or emotion, and our will. Training them is the basis for a calm and stress-free life, for they are the images in our soul of the divine nature of the universe. Symptoms of stress can be prompts to you from your friendly coach Ms Stress to work on the taming of your wild horses.

Our body and mind are always ready to let us know our state if we pay proper attention, for the entire body is a sensory instrument and every organ will tell a story to those who sensitively listen. We can use the mind to observe our physical condition and also to observe itself, for example to notice physical tensions and also to notice angry, bitter or defeatist thoughts. Thus the best cure for stress is your own activity and participation.

The importance of the individual's active involvement and self-awareness in diagnosing and curing what is wrong has been known for a long time. Epidauros was an ancient healing site on the eastern side of the Argolid Mountains in Greece where an holistic healing system was practised that could cure all kinds of ills. The Druids appear to have had similar centres, as were the monasteries and nunneries in the European Middle Ages, where herbalists worked with spiritual, psychological and physical healing; and to this day in Lesotho, Southern Africa, there is an ancient centre in Badimong, the Valley of the Ancestors, that interests modern university researchers and drug companies because of the effectiveness of its training and the efficacy of its treatment of ailments as varied as epilepsy and AIDS.

Epidauros was located at a wide, natural mound in the presence of surrounding mountains that still seem to give people a sense of protection today. It was famous for its theatre with its perfect acoustics. In addition to the theatre there was the Temple of Asklepios, the god of healing and the *abaton* or portico where those seeking healing slept the night after making the appropriate preparations.

It was said that during the night the god Asklepios visited them and gave them dreams. When these dreams were recounted to the priest-doctors a curing regime would be prescribed that might include naturopathic treatment with herbs, surgery, listening to poetry and music, attending plays in the theatre, making offerings to particular gods (like those described in Chapter 5), exercise and diet.

Ms Stress and Asklepios are one and the same messenger.

The patient's contribution to healing began with going to the site and committing to its disciplines and continued with dreaming the dreams that indicated ailment. Dreams are still widely experienced as a source of healing inspiration. (See for example Laurens van der Post's book, *About Blady: a Pattern Out of Time.*)

Epidauros also demonstrates the importance of a rich imaginative and creative life, which can cure many imbalances and ills. A regular visit to the theatre or concert, or a walk in the country, may be a much better cure than Valium, or at least an important partner to medicine. Take the example of 'Andy'.

Andy was a busy executive with a life of decision-making rush who began to experience the first symptoms of stress: difficulty in getting to sleep at night through a hyperactive mind and a tense, twitchy body. He practised awareness. Sitting still in a comfortable chair, he closed his eyes and became aware of how he was feeling. He noticed how his mind was racing, but did not follow the thoughts. He became aware of an itch on his arm and went consciously into the itch until his whole world seemed to be itches (and, yes, sometimes he did have to stop and rub them). In this way, he noticed two things. First he realized that he needed to change his lifestyle. He saw the itch was a symptom of the larger unquiet in his life, which was becoming absorbed by his body. It was as though the symptoms themselves had the power to convey their meaning when he listened. Second, he saw that the act of quiet awareness already acted as a cure.

Awareness and acting on that awareness is therefore an essential step in learning to cope with stress. It is a common reaction either to be over-whelmed or to try to run away from the experience of being stressed, because of course we don't like it. But, since stress is our guide and the feeling is a gift, it is better to think of it as a message to notice.

So, when you begin to feel stress, turn your awareness to it, look at it, at the conditions you are feeling, as if it was an interesting object in the world (which in a way it is).

If you notice your shoulders are tight, you can relax them. If you listen to your stress intently, it will speak to you, showing you your condition and needs. It will advise you of changes to make. Only, many people prefer not to hear. Then stress is like the unheard prophet in the wilderness.

Signs of stress

Since feelings and perceptions are reflected in the activity of many of the body's organ systems, individuals can themselves be regarded as 'stressometers', instruments which help to identify factors in the environment that tell hard on their mind and body.

The Oxford Companion to the Mind

Here are a number of common behavioural signs of stress. Do any of them apply to you? If so, it will be helpful to observe your behaviour closely. What changes in your life would be helpful to improve the situation?

BASIC STRESS SIGNALS

- Nervous mannerisms;
- Biting nails, tight shoulders, picking at skin, tapping feet, curling your hair, clenching jaws, drumming your fingers, clenching your fists, twitching eyes, face ticks;
- Moods and behaviour
- Anxiety, depression, irritability, aggression, helplessness, listlessness, impatience, talking or walking too fast, disturbed sleep.

SIGNS OF OVERSTRESS

Lack of concentration

Memory losses

Poor decision-making

Worry, anxiety or fear

Depression

Inconsistency

Not meeting targets or deadlines

Irregular attendance and
   time-keeping

Low self-esteem

Ineffective problem-solving

Lower standards accepted

Over self-critical

Losing business

Customer complaints

Poor long-term planning

Lost orders

No sense of humour

Confusion

Bad mistakes

Regularly working late

Constantly taking work home

Easily disgruntled

Uncooperative relationships

Poor work quality

Emotional outbursts

Unreasonable complaints

Frequent criticism, gossip or
   backbiting

Unpredictability

Tiredness

Cancelling annual leave

Extreme mood swings

Only concern shown is for self

Accidents

Eating difficulties

Greater use of alcohol, caffeine,
   nicotine, drugs

Difficulties with sleep

Low interest in work

No-one wants to work with you

Physical illness

Let the stress speak. Just as you need to pay attention to another person, entering their world with empathy, in order to understand what is happening to him or her, so journey into the sensations of your stress, becoming quietly and calmly aware of them. It might take no more than a moment to hear that it's time to go to bed or have a break, or it may be that you need to let several waves of sensation pass you by.

Remember though: being aware does not mean becoming swamped. In fact, this process should not swamp you, for it is actually a step towards freedom and self-determination, achieving the state known as the philosopher's stone. Carl Jung described how, 'The lapis [stone] signifies the inner man ... which the alchemist sought to set free', and went on to describe it as a transformation taking place within the temple of the head. You begin to take charge and order your own life when you become aware without trying to impose your order on the world; instead listening, noticing and delicately adjusting. Much of the technique proposed in this book derives from this practice, culminating in the meditative practices described in Chapter 11.

As you become aware, you learn to notice your own reactions—how you think, feel and behave. This is the crucial determining factor in changing your life experience.

We don't need to be stressed!

'I am going to have a heart attack as soon as I have time.'

A joke

You might be forgiven for thinking that I am suggesting that it is important to be stressed. Far from it!

We do need to experience challenge, but we don't *need* to be stressed. Indeed our ultimate goal is a condition of dynamic harmony with the development of the cosmos.

I can go further in saying that we don't need to be seriously stressed. In fact I think that there is something slightly obscene about our western stress when I consider the real hardship, poverty, hunger and illness that stalks so much of the world.

Western society cultivates stress as a poison in the same way that it poisons the soil in which it cultivates its foods. By no means is this necessary. It is indeed ironic that the people in most of those poorer countries seem, according to research, to be on the whole happier and less stressed than we are.

How distress develops

> Tom Clavell was a worried man. He was not just worried about one or
> two things at work. He was structurally worried, fundamentally ill at ease,
> because like so many people earning over forty thousand a year he did not
> realise that being permanently anxious was what he was paid for.
>
> *Paul Hoffman,* The Wisdom of Crocodiles

Arthur's history illustrates how stress accumulates.

At 30, Arthur enjoyed the thrill of his career as a salesman: chasing prospects and getting a buzz from every sale. The job included lots of driving in bad traffic, tight deadlines, monthly measurement against targets, and the inherent tension of being involved daily in 'winning' or 'losing' sales. But Arthur enjoyed the social encounters and things were going well. A low salary with high commission meant that he and his family really needed him to be successful, and indeed he was. But the more his successes improved their lifestyle, the more these then needed to be maintained. They moved to a better area with a bigger mortgage and larger overdraft. He got promoted and took on more responsibility. Now he was also partly dependent on other salespeople's performance.

He worked long hours, at least 60 per week with travel, and started waking in the night thinking about something he had to do next day, or should have done. He became increasingly irritable with the children, and he and his wife began to have rows: she didn't see him enough and he couldn't listen when he did get home. By his mid-30s, his leisure energy was reduced to watching TV.

Because he was tired or out late, he reduced his exercise, cutting out the weekly squash match with a friend. To help him up in the morning he needed three coffees by 9.30am and over fifteen mugs of strong coffee a day. Increasing tension made it harder to get to sleep. He began drinking more alcohol. What with entertaining clients, which also meant rich food, drinks with the other salespeople, a drink to relax when he got home, he was soon drinking every day, a total that amounted to at least 20 pints, or equivalent, a week. And he was over-eating. With all the food and drink, he began getting indigestion. When things didn't go so well, the feelings of stress hit him harder, and it began to feel necessary, not just enjoyable, to close a sale. When he lost one particularly big deal he began smoking again after a break of 10 years, two or three a day or a cigar to begin with, and then more.

By 40, he had chronic back problems, made worse by all the driving, and the beginning of an ulcer. By now he was being passed over for promotion. The mid-life crisis made him depressed and he started having an affair with a younger woman. The marriage broke up, creating more trauma and financial problems. At 47 he had his first heart attack. This finally woke him up to the need to change.

The four stages in the 'normal' progress of stress are challenge, distress, disorder and breakdown. They may also be called: no-stress, mind-stress, bio-stress, and organic-stress. All are evident in Arthur's history. First there is fun, then tension, chronic loss of energy and minor illnesses, and finally traumatic physical illness, including damage to the body's organs. At each stage there are plenty of signals that might be listened to. However, people often seem to fail to notice them. The description that follows aims to help you do a self-audit, so you can spot key signals and recognize where you are.

No stress, just challenge

A person with a healthy physical and mental life, whose thinking, feeling and doing are active and balanced, will meet stress first as a *challenge* that encourages creativity and initiative. At this point a bit of challenging stress is enjoyable, as Arthur found. It may even be a thrill. Business can and should be fun. Problem solving is generally exciting, and making a difference is fulfilling and joyful. Furthermore, scientists have found that short periods of stress actually tone up the immune system.

Mind-stress, distress

While we are coping, we feel fine, but the problems may increase. At this point our individual capacities become insufficient to meet the challenge and we experience psychological stress, affecting our inner life (of thinking, feeling and will). This may manifest as jitteriness, irritation, depression, feelings of breathlessness, fear, doubt, panic, uncertainty, mental paralysis and so on. Thinking becomes disordered: problems seem immense and we can't find a space to think through them. The mind may feel scattered, empty or dull. We may begin to feel irritable or bitter. It is common to want to run away from the problem, either physically or by becoming obsessed with something else, usually trivial, like finding a button or fixing a door rather than checking the bank balance. At this point stress has become distress. In Arthur's case, irritation appeared, accompanied by the need to escape into alcohol. If stress becomes sufficiently extreme, a nervous breakdown may follow.

How did it come about that what had been challenge became distress?

Two things normally happen, both connected with the way that we think and respond to the world.

First, we bring about an increase in environmental stress through our own actions. This comes about through the way we think and this in turn affects our emotions and behaviour. I can remember often having to wake up at some unearthly hour to keep an appointment I had gaily booked in my diary some time earlier without properly imagining the consequences. We are always, but usually unconsciously, booking such appointments with stress.

And then, our response to these circumstances becomes degraded. Instead of taking responsibility for the situation and doing something about the problem, we nurture it. Perhaps we get tired and lose energy. Perhaps we start blaming others. Perhaps we begin thinking negatively about our circumstances, seeing them as half-empty glasses rather than as half-full ones. Thus begins a spiralling process of imprisoning the painful experience within a physical and mental framework that itself creates stress, like a canker of the mind.

I remember being told as a teenager, 'You always seem to have an excuse for failure, Angus. Could you ever be the one to blame?' It has taken me many years to understand the truth and implications of this comment. It will no doubt take a long time before I am fully capable of taking responsibility for my own experience, but this is an essential step in development. The pattern of my beliefs weaves the pattern of my life. This too is self-leadership.

> Rachel was a student on a limited grant. Her escape from the stresses of study was to go shopping for clothes. Soon she had run up an overdraft. Every time she got a letter from the bank it threw her into depression. Her only escape from the depression was to go shopping for clothes. The withdrawal of credit facilities became the spur to put her life back in order. Whether it is an outside challenge or personal decision, dealing with stress often requires the conscious resolve to sort out one's life.

Bio-stress, disorder

If the stress then grows even more intense or chronic, we will experience *dis*tress affecting our health and life forces. At this point it is not just the mind that is disturbed but also the rhythms and organization of our biological processes. Our personal biosphere becomes dis-eased. For example, occasional sleeplessness may now become a pattern of insomnia. If you suffer from any of the following symptoms, I suggest you react now if you have not already.

Common symptoms include feeling tired and listless, nervous ticks or any of the illnesses that are disorders of the life-processes like colds, allergies, chronic skin rashes, palpitations, and irritable bowel syndrome. Backache is another potential problem and an important signal of disorder in life. Acute problems lead to a breakdown in the immune system, and can result in illnesses like chronic fatigue syndrome (or ME as it was once called). Sufferers may feel it necessary to take regular doses of one or more of a number of modern drugs such as laxatives, sleeping pills, painkillers, indigestion powders and antihistamines. We may even find ourselves getting stuck with drug addictions to cope with these problems. Coffee and cigarettes first, more serious drugs such as alcohol, tranquillizers, 'speed', cocaine and barbiturates can follow later. In Arthur's case, coffee became necessary to jump-start a tired body each day, but of course only deepened the underlying problem, and his drinking became more serious.

The first symptoms of such illnesses may not be welcome, but they are signals or messages to change, as described in the next chapter. If this doesn't happen and the life forces become too weakened, physical burnout may follow. Stress will only increase and become harmful if we fail to act.

Richard owned and managed a small software company. After eleven years of success, he reached his mid-life crisis and began to question what he was doing and what he wanted to do with his life. He suddenly felt the company and its employees to be a burden rather than a joy. He wanted to sell the company but turned down two offers because they didn't seem large enough. Then it ran into financial difficulties. Always before, he had simply gone out, got some more work and fixed the problem. Now he just felt more and more tired. Suddenly he had a breakdown, like going into a realm of darkness, disorder and nightmare. Richard had to close the company and begin a new career, doing something he felt was contributing to the world, before he could regain his full health.

Organic-stress, breakdown

If the process is not checked, illnesses to the organs, such as heart attacks, liver failure, ulcers, and even cancer may follow. The body itself is physically injured and breaks down—usually from the effects of bad habits developed to cope with psychological and life-stress. Examples of such illness include bronchitis from smoking, liver disease from alcohol and coffee, fatty diseases of the heart from poor diet and insufficient exercise. Degradation of life-style and even death are possible consequences.

How many people have finally realized they need to make serious adjustments only when their doctor has warned them that otherwise they will only have a short time to live? Clearly, it's wiser to begin before then.

The effects of inadequate stress

Thought and character are one ... You are where you are by the law of your being; the thoughts that you have built into your character have brought you there.

James Allen

Distress is not only caused by having too much to do: there can be as much distress, with similar results, through lack of challenge and stimulus in life. The human spirit needs meaningful activity. Too much and too little both cause stress. Boredom, redundancy, unfulfilling work, a couch-potato life-style: all challenge us very deeply for they question our sense of self-worth, identity and the meaning of life.

When we have no outer stimulus, we have to find our own inner energy and order. Solitary confinement is a kind of torture for most people, especially when in a darkened room with few sensory stimuli. Nelson Mandela described how he wanted to make friends with a cockroach during one of his

The couch-potato is a common contemporary image.
Lack of stress is itself stressful.

spells in solitary confinement. Women may find it difficult to go from a busy working life amongst many adults to the solo strain of childcare. Young adults who can't get a job become particularly prey to disaffection and frustration; their creativity may turn to depression and alienation, anti-social or even criminal behaviour. Many people, especially men, who retire, die soon afterwards because there no longer seems any point in living.

The same or similar stages of stress as were described above seem to be possible when there is too little stress.

SIGNS OF UNDERSTRESS

Low self-esteem	Tiredness
Irritability	Critical attitude
Unreliability	Disgruntled manner
Lack of decision making	Simple errors
Irregular attendance	Little interest in work
Confused thinking	Moaning about situation but not changing it
Low energy	Taking extra time to produce work
Lack of enthusiasm	Taking excess of stimulants

Our task is therefore not the ending of stress, but the ending of *being stressed*. Life and development needs a balance of challenge, and is a challenge to balance.

Why it is important to value illness

One way Ms Stress coaches is through illness.

> When I was 40 years old and managing director of a thriving computer company, I was stuck in conflict with a business colleague and increasingly unsure whether this was the job I wanted to do. Whilst on holiday, I got ill. For nearly a week I was very poorly, and during that time I thought deeply about what was happening. I decided to change course, and on my return immediately resigned. I had no idea what I should be doing, but felt certain it would become clear, as it did.
>
> Illness took me out of activity and into a purely selfish regard for myself (my family said so too).

However, sometimes that is just what we need to do. Asking your higher Self questions like: Am I happy with what I am doing? Am I doing the right thing? What should I being doing? is certainly self-oriented, but it can also be necessary. Illness is a time for such questions. It may be a way of being less driven by circumstance and habit and more in self-control.

Illness, bad back pains, knocks on the head, and so on are all, I believe, attempts by the body and subtle mind to trigger self-examination and new courses of action. If you have ever smoked you will almost certainly have experienced how illness can drive the desire to smoke away and give a space to give up if you want to take it.

Illness is often healing too. For example, it forces a break and recuperation. Homeopaths and other alternative medical experts routinely describe illness as a balancing process.

So, I urge you to value your illnesses: ask what they mean and listen to the answers.

Taking responsibility and making a change

> To err and not reform may indeed be called error.
>
> *Confucius*

The purpose or end of stress is therefore to gain personal development, not merely to survive. Reading this is already a positive action (I hope you will agree). The rest of the book is filled with many ways to exercise self-leadership by becoming more conscious and taking action that makes a difference.

The value of becoming aware is not simply that it is the means to reduce stress. It also shows the qualities we need to develop, whether it is courage or presence of mind or tranquillity. Through our human spirit and individuality we can develop these, employing the signals of stress as coach to action. As Confucius also said, 'A man can enlarge his principles. It is not his principles that enlarge the man.' (*Analects* XV-xxviii)

The opportunity for fundamental and systematic self-transformation through learning and transmuting experience has been a goal in all cultures and religions, and has stimulated many different disciplines including the ancient male and female mysteries, cults and temple traditions, shamanism, gnosticism, male and female monastic and other religious rules, military and knightly training, martial arts, 'witchery', alchemy, the guilds, masonry, and others, and this continues in the many self-help practices of today. In most of these, life's trials and pressures play an important role, through the transformative power of awareness and self-responsibility, with exercises and meditation as helpers. Later chapters suggest ways that you can take action, without necessarily belonging to any order or religious belief, and in the Appendix (Resources) there is a self-diagnostic aid you can use at any time.

CHAPTER 3

LIFESTYLE FUNDAMENTALS

'When you suffer an attack of nerves you're being attacked by the nervous
system. What chance has a man got against a system?'
The bookshop owner in The Lion of Boaz-Jachin and Jachin-Boaz
by Russell Hoban

The answer to the bookshop owner is that the human being is also a system, a system of body, soul (or mind) and spirit that has been fashioned by the universe for health and well-being. Health, energy, happiness and fulfilment arise when this whole system is appreciated, engaged and active.

A full and effective response to life therefore needs a holistic and balanced approach, often summed up in the phrase *work-life balance*. All work and no play makes Jack a dull boy. Play here includes 'culture' and fun and physical activity, the enjoyment of nature, the arts and so on.

According to the historian Yannis Andricopoulos, the ancient Greeks subscribed to an idea of wholeness whereby physical, moral and intellectual excellence, all described by the single word *arete*, were considered indivisible. The sharp distinctions that exist today between mind and body, intellect and soul, material and spiritual, nature and culture, individuality and community were alien to the Greek way of thinking. Each element was viewed as an indispensable condition of existence.

For example, the Olympic Games included, alongside the athletic contests, music competitions, prayers and rituals, communal singing, orations by distinguished philosophers and recitals by poets and historians.

Specialization to the detriment of the needs of the whole person was frowned upon; and extremes of any kind, whether in the form of food fads or religious asceticism, were rejected. The person who honoured the virgin Goddess Artemis but not the love Goddess Aphrodite was, according to Euripides, a tragic misfit.

Balance, proportion and symmetry therefore ruled all aspects of life—from health and architecture to prose and mathematics. The Athenian citizen was expected to participate actively in the role of the *polis*, the city state. The *polis*, in turn, was expected not simply to run its business efficiently but in doing so to stimulate the intellect and satisfy the spiritual aspirations of its citizens.

Illness, like health, was viewed holistically, as I described with reference to Epidauros. Hippocrates, the father of medicine, considered that doctors should understand the way a person lived, and his or her physical and social surroundings, even the way the wind was blowing, before intervening. Even then their role was simply to assist the natural healing process.

Health care has lost the holistic view of human beings. Nefiodow (see Chapter 1) now leads the movement for its recovery in a new kind of health sector, more like that of Epidauros, which encourages wellness and improved lifestyle through personal well-being, the feeling for one's own body, and good nutrition. Such an approach would focus on maintaining wellness rather than curing illness. Nefiodow believes this sector and approach includes both environmental and religious or spiritual factors and that it is the powerhouse of the developing economy.

In other words, the complementary needs of the three sub-systems of body, soul and spirit are fundamental to wholeness and health and the driving force of current culture and economy. Together, body, soul and spirit make the human being what spiritual traditions, from the Vedas to Hamlet, and also many physicists, biologists and psychologists, regard as the crown of creation. In our bodies, we are part of the whole world of created nature

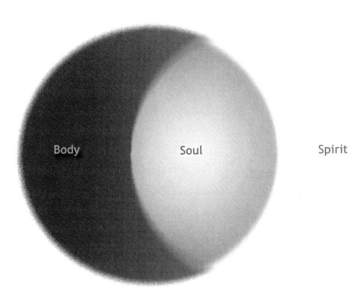

The soul between body and spirit

connected fully and ecologically to the immensity of evolution and material life that sustains us. In our spirit, we belong to the eternal world of being. As Novalis put it: The seat of the soul is there, where the inner world and the outer world touch . . . Thus, in our mind or soul, we bring together spirit and nature in the uniqueness that is you or me, in the world of thoughts, feeling and intentions, which are themselves an image of the divine.

Each of the above sub-systems is also an organ of awareness. Clearly, the soul or mind is an organ of awareness; indeed its very essence is awareness or consciousness. It has the unique capacity within all of created nature known to us to make an inner world that blends and individualizes nature and spirit. It receives and makes its own what is perceived through body and spirit. It is also an ancient paradox that through the spirit we can rise to a higher awareness of nature of the body through scientific and spiritual under-standing, and through the body we can come to awareness of the spirit.

And one of the most important aspects of the spirit is health.

The word *sane* literally means healthy. The link between a healthy body and a healthy mind is very deep, for health affects the very way in which we experience the world. The brilliant and tragic philosopher Nietzsche suffered from increasing insanity that probably derived from syphilis. It radically changed his outlook on life and the nature of his philosophy. As he grew older and sicker, so did his philosophy, in the sense that it became more cynical and life-denying.

The link between health and spirit is not only a mental one. It is a basic principle of the religious view that life is something that derives from a divine source and therefore the experience of life is an experience of an aspect of the divine energy. For example, in ancient traditions that include the Chinese, African Koi, ancient Egyptian and Indian ayurvedic amongst others, Ki or Chi energy is a cosmic spiritual-energy that is also life-energy that can be sensed by any sensitive person or practitioner. Modern Reiki healing uses the same energy.

Hebrew Cabbalism teaches us an important lesson concerning health. In cabbalism, each of the Hebrew language's 22 letters is considered to be a fundamental aspect and principle of God by which the world was created. They therefore have significant meanings, as well as colours, numbers and musical notes, unlike modern letters. The letter *Chet,* which begins the word *chai* (the Hebrew *chi*), is the letter of vibrant health and vitality. It is formed by linking the sigils or forms of two other letters together: *Vov,* which is con-nected to our relationships with others, and *Zayin,* concerned with our inner relationship with time. A healthy, stress-balanced life is therefore, according to this ancient principle, one that is based on a good relationship to time and to other human beings, two themes that are fundamental to this book and to life-wisdom.

The body is a more sophisticated sense organ than most people credit. Not only does it have the conventional five major senses, seeing, hearing, touching, smelling and tasting, but it also possesses a range of other senses, including the senses of balance, warmth and health. Each of these conveys different kinds of message to the soul; for example touch tells us about the hardness, softness and sharpness of things, while warmth informs us about relative temperature.

All of them can convey messages about our health. For example, when we are ill our sense of taste may be affected so that we have a craving to eat certain kinds of food that are good for us and a disgust of others, or we may even be able to taste our own illness; other illnesses may lead to greater sensitivity to smells. Increased stress can lead to giddiness and loss of balance; while the feeling of being hot or cold is also an important symptom of illness.

The body is a complex and brilliantly sophisticated system and modern scientists are still far from understanding it completely. However, they are beginning to discover what has been recognized for millennia, that every part and system of the body has a role in memory and awareness. For example, they have been wondering why patients who have had organ transplants have adopted characteristics that belonged to the person from whom the organ came. They are also exploring the agency of various substances, notably adrenaline, noradrenaline and cortisol, as indicators of the mismatch between the person and the environment.

There is clearly a general sense of well-being or health that tells those tuned in how their life energy and organs are performing. Each of the organs, such as the liver, heart and spleen, will convey noticeable symptoms if they are diseased, although some people are more aware of this than others.

However, a modern lifestyle full of polluting foods and drugs, obesity, hyperactivity and external stimulus will have a tendency to reduce sensitivity to the body's messages. This is important not only because in due course it reduces health, but also for other subtle reasons connected with a differentiated awareness of the world and the capacity to respond to it. It is not possible to go into this in full detail, but such awareness is linked to the seven kinds of qualities outlined in Chapter 5.

Take for example the quality of courage, the French word for which is etymologically linked to *heart*. Since the mists of the past, courage has always been linked to the heart, and this is not simply fantasy. The emotions of fear and courage show up in radically different heart behaviour, while the act of controlling the heart by for example consciously slowing down its beating is able to change our emotional response. Panicky conditions lead to quick, short breathing and a racing pulse. A healthy heart is actually vital to a courageous response to the world.

However, our perception of what is confronting us will be affected by our emotions. When we are frightened, we blow up the source of our fear into a gigantic monster, and when we are calm we reduce it to its proper proportions. This is more than just an idle remark: Through studies by Gestalt psychologists and others we know that the mental pictures we form of what we are experiencing depend on the *frame* through which we look, and if we are afraid, the world ends up actually looking different.

Similarly, I know many consultants who use the subtle sensations in their stomach as a guide to the emotional condition and psychological group dynamics within a meeting they are facilitating.

To keep the three subsystems—body, soul and spirit—tuned up and co-operating well, there are certain basic principles that everyone can follow. Following such practices is a way of achieving self-control and therefore of developing leadership potential. Most are neither clever nor fancy: they just make a difference. For example, getting enough sleep and exercise (and not too much) and eating a healthy balanced diet would probably solve 80 per cent of most people's stress problems, not least because the good disciplines involved would also bring strength and healing.

TIPS TO MASTER STRESS

- Get enough sleep;
- Cut down on coffee and tea, drink much more water;
- Improve your diet, and eat organic;
- Don't use alcohol to deal with stress;
- Exercise!
- Engage in creative work;
- Let wonder and reverence play a part in your life;
- Spend time talking and listening;
- Find times for peace and quiet: try meditation;
- Be moderate;
- Use natural treatments;

- Correct your posture;
- Have a regular massage;
- Wear shoes that are really comfortable;
- Most of all, become more self-aware;
- Don't worry or deny: take regular time out to review progress and priorities calmly.

Get enough sleep

If you are feeling tired, this could be the problem! There are reports that many people are chronically tired. Lack of sleep makes you more irritable as well as reducing your energy to cope with challenges. The amount of sleep a person needs clearly varies according to their personal constitution and life circumstances. I find that when I have a project of great interest and purpose, this seems to give me energy. However, afterwards I may need to get extra sleep to make up the deficit. There seems little doubt that most people in earlier centuries slept longer. Research suggests that people sleep on average 90 minutes less each night than a century ago. Even between 1990 and 1995 we seemed to lose 25 minutes sleep per night. People also slept in seasonal rhythms: more in the winter than in the summer. The light and activity of the summer sustained energy while the sleep bank was re-filled in the winter.

Lack of sleep makes people sluggish, less intelligent and prone to error. All these directly or indirectly increase stress. Sleep is also vital for digesting the experiences of the day. Overnight, people re-process their tasks and learn from them, making it easier the next day. Dreaming is now recognized as a creative, learning activity.

Test how easily you go to sleep when you sit down and close your eyes or otherwise relax. If you drop off quickly, you may be short of sleep. It is estimated that 10 per cent to 30 per cent of people suffer from a sleep disorder.

Unarm, Eros; the long day's task is done,
And we must sleep.
Antony, in Shakespeare's *Antony and Cleopatra*

So, why do many people find it difficult to go to sleep at a good time? In my own case, I think it's because I feel threatened by the thought of the next day, when I will have to rise, tired, to face its difficulties. Instead, I long to hold on to the relative pleasure of the moment, a period when I am without obligations (the day's needs having finished) and can relax and enjoy. I pay the price the next day. If lack of sleep is a problem you share, then I suggest that whatever is your reason, it is important to become aware of it and act.

Good sleep patterns include: quietening down before going to bed (for example by reading), getting to sleep well before midnight, not going to sleep with music or radio on, having fresh air in the room, and a few moments of quiet in the morning. (Avena Sativa comp. is a natural remedy for peaceful relaxation that aids calming down in the evening, available from Weleda—see page 41).

It can also be helpful to have a quick catnap, the so-called power-nap. This is a common habit of the powerful (although they may also just be the folks who don't have enough sleep and so drop off at the drop of a hat). Thomas Edison would have a nap in a chair any time he had a problem he couldn't solve. To keep his nap short he would hold a couple of large ball bearings and wake when they dropped into a tray at his feet. As Edison's example shows, keep your naps short: 15 or 20 minutes maximum. A longer sleep definitely changes the biorhythm and generally seems to leave people sluggish. (The siesta becomes part of the culture and rhythm of the people in some countries, but even in such regions many people only rest rather than going into a long, deep sleep.)

Cut down on coffee and tea

Everyone knows these are bad. Few do much about it. Tea and coffee are diuretics and stimulants. That means they reduce our body fluid while appearing to add to it and they reduce our real energy while appearing to increase it. And they damage our sleep. Still, most people will enjoy, and perhaps not unreasonably, some of these domestic drugs. But, four to six mugs of coffee and/or tea per day are really more than ample. Cut down on the quantity and buy a better quality. Pause and enjoy each cup and use the moment to relax and have a good time.

Drink much more water

When people don't drink enough, which is very common, they actually put on weight, because the body hoards its fluids. Diuretics like tea and coffee make this worse by stimulating loss of fluid, causing the body to fight back and hoard all the harder. Water flushing out of our bodily system cleanses us of impurities. If this does not happen, toxicity increases, reducing energy and health. All stress creates toxicity. So, more water is an immediate help. Very small levels of dehydration drastically reduce energy. So try drinking more. You should find your own level, but a useful guideline is at least two litres per day (four pints). Two glasses first thing in the morning is a good start. When you first start taking more water, you may find out just how thirsty your body is!

Improve your diet

Erratic dieting is another way to impose an irregular pattern on nature and may lead to all kinds of problems. I believe it is widely recognized that dieting can often be physically and mentally unhelpful. Instead, find what your body is comfortable and healthy with, and eat that much. In this way, changes become part of a general development of better life attitudes and a new ecology of life.

I know people who have successfully engaged in radical diets and transformed their physical appearance. This has, however, always seemed successful only to the extent that it was a culmination of an inner maturing and transformation.

Good diet is based on good, fresh, natural food, and it's quite hard to go wrong on this. So, reduce the ratio of things you know you should reduce, like sugar, 'fizzy drinks' and processed foods, and increase the ratio of 'good' foods like whole grains (bread, rice, pasta and so on), fresh fruit and vegetables, and live yoghurt. I don't believe in the faddish foods we now have: calorie free yoghurts, margarine and so on. Butter was once pronounced 'bad for you' and now it's 'good for you'.

Reducing meat and increasing vegetables is helpful for energy and wellbeing. Another good idea is to use plenty of fresh herbs in your cooking. They help with the stresses of life in all kinds of ways. If you don't know much about them then start with the basics like parsley (for iron), tarragon, oregano, garlic, or buy the mixes; then use the ones you like, the taste buds have their own wisdom.[2]

Eat breakfast; it significantly contributes to energy and intellectual capacity.

Finally, make at least one meal a day a social occasion; talk, laugh, share experiences such as best and worst things of the day. Eating together is one of the wonderful institutions of social life. It heals problems and builds community.

Eat organic

Given the level of pollution in the environment, it makes sense to have the benefit of food that is relatively pollution free. A study by David Thomas reported in 2001 that many fruit and vegetables had lost much of their essential nutritional value over the last 50 years. For example, runner beans have lost 100 per cent of their sodium, watercress 90 per cent of its copper and broccoli 75 per cent of its calcium. Other minerals that have suffered include magnesium, iron, phosphorous and potassium.

Generally speaking production farming destroys much of the value of foods and adds poisons. In the case of vegetables it means that we end up eating food that approximates to pulp. The body craves the missing minerals, which probably contributes to over-eating.

In the case of meat, modern factory farming also adds antibiotics, growth hormones and other chemicals to the animal and fish diet. Many animals live indoors all their life, deprived of sunshine. Making the effort and investment in organic and free range produce is therefore really worth while and will be appreciated by your body and mind as well as by the environment. It should taste better too, and improves the immune system. (It is especially valuable and important for children.)

Don't use alcohol (or other drugs) to deal with stress

Alcohol doesn't really work (of course, a little in a social context is fine). The UK government provides guidelines on weekly alcohol limits. If you are approaching these levels on a regular basis it is generally reckoned that you already have a stress problem, or worse. Other drugs, prescribed or otherwise, do not form a permanent solution and may cause dependence and/or health damage.

Exercise

Aim for flexibility, fun and vitality, for a body that feels loose and limber. Obsessive exercise is probably not helpful. However, a good, brisk walk or jog, time in the gym, aerobics, dancing or active sports all help. Exercise helps to maintain general fitness and encourages deep breathing, thereby increasing energy and the capacity to cope. Good breathing is itself an excellent exercise and restorative. Exercise also burns off accumulated poisons such as unused adrenaline. A regular pattern of activity is best.

Loosening up activities, such as stretching, rotating the head and shoulders or shaking the limbs, also help. Stress creates tension and stiffness while relaxing the body helps to relax the mind. A rebounder (a small trampoline) improves the lymph system, heart-lung systems and overall fitness and flexibility. NASA scientists rate it one of the best exercises available.

Here is a really excellent and simple exercise for backache, general health and well being, as well as for gaining a trimmer tummy.

It is an exercise whose roots go back to yoga, but which has been redis-covered recently as a result of research at the University of Queensland. They discovered that most stomach exercises, like sit ups, hardly affect the muscle that lies deepest across the stomach. This muscle is the *traversus abdominus* and it supports breathing, the lower back and acts as an anchor for all the other stomach muscles. With many of us spending so much time sitting down, this muscle gets little exercise, with consequences for health, appearance and back support (we end up using our spine because this muscle is not working).

You may do the exercise in several postures, including sitting and standing, but it has been found that the following way works particularly well. On your hands and knees, with arms and legs vertical (shoulders over arms and hips over legs), pull your tummy button up and in under your ribs. Hold for ten seconds and repeat ten times. It is helpful to synchronize breathing: breathe out as you pull in. This is also a calming exercise and will stimulate digestion.

Engage in creative work

Hobbies are good for you. This might be in any re*creational* field, such as further study (e.g. learning a language or craft), playing with your children, painting, fishing, judo, gardening, cooking, going to the theatre, amateur dramatics, singing, music, poetry, observing nature (or the stars), or whatever hobby takes your fancy.

Singing, for example, helps by improving the breathing, clearing out the poor air that tends to accumulate in under-used lungs. It also involves a great deal of physical energy, many muscles and reconnects the head with the rest of the body. The emotional and soul content of the music helps. The social quality of singing in a choir is enjoyed by many people, but I find even singing in the car or bath is a great remedy.

Reading a good book or listening to (many types of) music is more relaxing than watching television.

Creative activity is incredibly important both for reducing stress and for self-development. Human beings are naturally creative and if there are insufficient opportunities to exercise this, then we suffer badly. Absence of creativity becomes like a drought in the soul, depriving it of freshness and life. (In fact creativity is so important that if a constructive outlet is not available, a destructive one like crime is often the result.) TV is not sufficient, particularly as it is designed to reduce the amount of creative imagination required by the individual. Nor is it enough to say, 'I do lots of creative work at the office, now I need to rest.' Rest may be required (see below), but creative activity that flows from our own free choice is liberating and energizing.

For example, one Saturday I was feeling burdened because my good publisher was waiting for me to finish editing this book. This created a heavy mood which would not have done the book any good, and certainly wasn't good for me.

I sat in a chair and began watching and really looking at the view from the window, and then began writing a poem of which these were the first lines.

A summer morning early, the sun brightening
gorgeous clouds of massy cumulus;
pigeons cooing like soft church bells to worship;
little pied wagtails in yellow-backed jackets
daintily dancing about the lawn,
lightly fanning long tails like guests at a ball;
seeds are floating to and fro like feathers—
a dozen suddenly fly away in a gust
from the wilderness of wild thistle and herbs
at the edge of the neighbouring field . . .

The poem is not brilliant, but writing it was wonderful and let me continue my work in good humour and better creative fettle. Sometimes giving yourself a good time advances what needs to be done.

Spend time talking and listening

Share your troubles and even better listen to another's! Helping others is generally stress-reducing.

Never let the sun go down on your anger. Try to resolve any conflict, with your friends, partner or children, before going to sleep. It is also a good ritual never to go to sleep without having shared something of the day with your partner and any children at home. I believe that doing this helps you sleep better and wake up more positively.

Be moderate

Above all, try to find balance and moderation in your life. Don't worry too much about the food you eat, but don't ignore the issue. Don't be obsessed about exercise, but do some regularly.

Choose natural medicines
Natural medicine is probably less stress-inducing in the long run because it is 'natural'. Clearly there are many useful 'normal' or allopathic medicines, but most have side effects and tend to treat symptoms rather than underlying causes. Homeopathic and anthroposophic medicine work to recover the natural vitality and balance of the body.

There are many different treatments for acute stress and anyone in such a condition should see a qualified doctor or other practitioner. However, there are a number of simple and natural remedies that are often helpful.

I find that camomile tea makes a soothing and delicious drink and is now available from good supermarkets as well as health food shops. Some people like it with a little honey. Camomile is also available as a homeopathic remedy, normally taken in 6x or 3x form. *Rescue Remedy* is good after any kind of shock and is available from homeopathic chemists and health food shops. Arnica is a similar remedy for physical and mental shocks. Lanes have developed *Quiet Life* and *Kalms* herbal tablets. Quiet Life is good to aid sleeping; Kalms is for the day. Weleda, a leading homeopathic and anthroposophic manufacturer, makes the following suggestions (see their website).

- To relieve occasional edginess brought about by everyday stress and strain: Fragador
- Severe emotional and mental stress, panic attacks: Aconite napellus
- Mentally and physically exhausted from over-work: Calcium carbonicum
- Loss of self-confidence with fear of being unable to cope with stress of work: Lycopodium
- Tired, burnt-out executive. Never stops thinking about work, cannot sleep for worry: Nux vomica

The following case illustrates how a combination of medicines and treatment can be used to bring about renewed health and vitality. Here we find an example of a clinic and a range of treatments that is reminiscent of the ancient Greek treatments at Epidauros.

Nick is a professional musician who was diagnosed with ulcerative colitis (a third stage stress condition). A specialist advised him that his only options were to try to control the condition using drugs and if that failed to have a colostomy. Nick then got a shoulder injury that meant he couldn't work. This made him even more frustrated and depressed, so he was sent to Park Attwood Clinic, near Stourbridge in the West Midlands, where they provide a blend of orthodox medicines and complementary therapies. He had a range of treatments that included counselling, sculpture therapy, eurythmy therapy, diet and rhythmic massage. After eurythmy and massage he felt as though the various parts of himself that had been floating around had been consolidated, making him feel very much more whole. Sculpture therapy enabled him to discover and pass through various mental barriers. This was a very liberating experience. After six weeks of treatment he felt changed as a person and much more together physically. He has found more direction in life and significantly reduced his need for drugs to control the colitis.

Here, we see how self-awareness (counselling), creative activity, diet, massage and medical treatment combine to help, the very ingredients described in this chapter.

Correct your posture

Whenever we are under stress, whether from posture or life, there is a tendency to stiffen up, often accompanied by abnormal gestures such as pulling the shoulders towards the ears, contraction of the mouth or tightening of the buttocks. Muscles may even go into cramp. Becoming conscious of this and so relaxing the 'offending' anatomy helps, as can massage treatment. Stretching and loosening exercises are generally very helpful.

Modern sedentary lifestyles can contribute to poor posture as can excessive work in front of computers, especially laptops, which almost invariably cause back strain. When in front of your PC, the top of the screen should be at almost the same level as your forehead. You can get devices that clamp on to your desk or the wall to hold the screen at the right height, or alternatively units that sit under it and lift it to the right height.

Poor posture contributes to stress in many ways. Curled and bent shoulders prevent the lungs from expanding and reduce the supply of fresh air. Poor posture damages the spine. It is also often said that a back problem is a message from the body asking for a radical change in lifestyle.

The Alexander Technique has a wonderful exercise to relax the spine.

- Lie on your back with something under your head to lift it a few inches. A couple of books do the trick.
- Then flatten the small of your back so it touches the ground. (It's good to get someone to check). This may seem odd or difficult at first, but becomes relaxing and soothing.
- Make sure your buttocks and shoulders are relaxed too.

Massage therapy can help

I know several people who go for a monthly massage just to relax knotted muscles, tone up the whole body and unwind quietly. Clearly a life of natural movement with easeful stretching and rhythmic movement will avoid the need for special treatment and serve as a healing impulse, but in contemporary urban society, physical therapy may need to become a natural addition to normal life. For example, as I have got older I have realized how my body has become deformed as a reflection of my increasing stiffness, bad physical habits and occasional physical traumas, many of them reflecting my own lack of consciousness. For example, a moment of daring madness doing a bungy jump was no doubt good for my ego, but the whiplash caused ongoing problems for my neck. Many sports and occupations, even working at a computer, have built in occupational hazards for the body.

Therapeutic massage aims to heal slow, chronic or sudden damage to the spine or other parts of the body and takes many forms, including physiotherapy, osteopathic and chiropractic methods and other specialized systems such as Swedish, Indian head massage, Shiatsu, McTimoney and Hauschka.

I have found cranial osteopathy very helpful. It is the most gentle of all physical massages, yet works at a deep level to help the body to recover its natural form by loosening stuck and distressed physical structures. (If we have a traumatic experience, perhaps as a child, the body holds on to a memory of this in a kind of twisting and distortion of its natural form and organic interrelationships.) It is very useful for children, especially if they have had a difficult birth, the trauma of which can cause long-term physical stress.

As well as 'therapeutic massage', relaxation massage can be given by a partner or friend, and this too can be therapeutic.

Ziad was head of retail banking for a Middle Eastern bank in London. He started to experience classic stress symptoms. He became irritable, stopped sleeping properly and lost interest in his job. He tried a number of traditional ways to relax: more hot baths, classical music, time in the country, acupuncture, a fish tank, decorating the flat (a creative outlet for Ziad, a trauma for others!), yoga, swimming, bicycling, going to the gym. Nothing worked.

Then he discovered a deep massage technique known as Hellerwork. During the course of eleven treatments he first obtained the mental solution that he needed as he went into deep states of relaxation. He then found that the underlying problem was his posture. His weight had been concentrated on his lower back, shoulders and neck, causing him pain. The chronic problems that this had built up were gradually corrected and he adjusted his posture. He also learnt to become aware of stress at an early stage and to respond immediately by taking a ten-minute break and going for a walk outside the office.

Wear good shoes: ones that are truly comfortable

Pleasantly warm feet and comfortable shoes that breathe are a boon to better living. Cramped feet affect the whole body, as any reflexologist will tell you. Discomfort in the feet also prevents us standing firm and erect on the ground, a most necessary condition for dealing with life. High heels usually damage posture, and although they give many women a feeling of confidence, there is a price for this. (I find it curious that so many cultures have adopted practices that damage the feet yet are accepted by women, China being simply the worst with its thousand year tradition of breaking and binding girls' feet, now fortunately ended.)

A good way to help the feet and relax is to lie on your back with a cushion under your head and your feet up on a chair. Your thighs should be vertical to relieve strain.

Let wonder and reverence play a part in your life

> I am positive I have a soul; nor can all the books with which materialists
> have pestered the world ever convince me of the contrary.
> > *Laurence Sterne (1713–68) from* A Sentimental Journey

The skylark is forecast to vanish from Britain in less than 20 years. Think of the country in May without Shelley's 'blithe spirit'! Already we have seen a drastic reduction in wild flowers, butterflies and birdsong, nature's graces that gladdened the heart in times past. Some birds appear to be forgetting their natural songs, replacing them with the sounds of car horns. As already mentioned, the stars have also vanished from much city life. So, not only is there an insidious attack on our health through pollution, but our natural opportunity for wonder, a great reducer of stress, is decreased.

> I or you pocketless of a dime may purchase the pick of the earth.
> Walt Whitman

Rudolf Steiner was already pointing out in the first years of the twentieth century:

> In an age of criticism . . . ideals are degraded. Reverence, awe, adoration, and wonder are replaced by other feelings—they are pushed more and more into the background. As a result, everyday life offers very few opportunities for their development. Anyone seeking higher knowledge must create these feelings inwardly, instilling them in the soul. This cannot be done by studying. It can only be done by living.

He also commented:

> Experience teaches that we know best how to hold our heads high in freedom if we have learned to feel reverence when it is appropriate—and it is appropriate whenever it flows from the depths of the heart.

Fortunately, there is still plenty left to admire, and a society which wonders may be the best hope for the preservation and repair of the environment.

TRY THESE SIMPLE EXERCISES THAT I HAVE FOUND HELPFUL:
- During the day, stop from time to time and look about until you experience something interesting (a pattern on a brick, a sound, the design of a machine, the skin on someone's arm).
- Listen or look more deeply (get close to the object; live into the sound).
- Reflect back on the day and notice something wonderful or beautiful that you have experienced. Every day has such things, but they may be overlooked or forgotten.

Find times for reflection in peace and quiet
Have privacy with yourself. Keep a diary or do some of the exercises and meditations described later, but, really, just making basic quiet time to reflect on your life is a good starter.

Create moments of inner peace for yourself, and in these moments learn to distinguish the essential from the inessential . . . set-aside a brief period of time in daily life in which to focus on things that are quite different from the objects of your daily activity . . . If approached in the right way, such moments give us the full strength for completing our daily tasks... If someone really cannot spare any more time, five minutes a day are sufficient. What matters is how those five minutes are used.

Steiner put it like this:

> In these moments we should tear ourselves completely out of our everyday life. Our thinking and feeling lives should have a quite different colouring than they usually have. We should allow our joys, sorrows, worries, experiences, and actions to pass before our soul. But our attitude towards these should be one of looking at everything we have experienced from a higher point of view. Consider, in ordinary life, how differently we perceive what other people have experienced or done from the way we perceive what we ourselves have experienced or done . . . In the time we have set aside for ourselves, then, we must strive to view and judge our own experiences and actions as though they belonged to another person.[3]

People who do this come to important self-knowledge. They realize how their thoughts and thought patterns shape their lives. They see what kind of people they have become and how they respond to life circumstances as well as how their habits of thought create these circumstances. Out of such self-knowledge it becomes possible to change. Steiner expresses this in the following meditation:

> Take care of your thoughts, because they will become your words.
> Take care of your words, because they will become your deeds.
> Take care of your deeds, because they will become your habits.
> Take care of your habits, because they form your character.
> Take care of your character, because it defines your destiny.

Chapter 6 includes exercises that help, especially the Retrospective, see page 122.

Don't punish yourself—recognize your value

Many of our pressures are caused by negative or blaming self-judgements rather than objective self-awareness. Self-criticism of this sort does not help. Two and a half thousand years before Nelson Mandela, Buddha advised not to belittle your own goodness by thinking, 'I have not deserved this.'

Register your inappropriate pressures and change these, as in the exercises below.

WHAT YOU CAN DO TO CHALLENGE INTERNAL PRESSURES:
- Become aware of them.
- List as many of them as you can. Every time you find yourself thinking or saying 'I must do that' or 'you should do this' consider if it is a pressure you impose on yourself or others and if so put it in the list.
- For each item on your list see if you can replace the belief with another—not too different—which reduces the pressure, e.g. expecting everything done to 200 per-cent perfection could shift to settling for 95 per cent perfection.
- When you find yourself building up the pressures on yourself with your beliefs, pause and reassess the situation and question the belief. Then replace it with a new one.

Help others

> Do good and do it again and again, and gladness and happiness will be the outcome.
>
> *Buddha*, Dhammapada, *118*

Those who make it part of their habit of life to try to be kind and helpful find that stress is reduced, and in times of trouble there are more people who help them. An attitude and practice of helping others changes your fundamental relationship with the world. It is as if all connections have been cleaned and oiled.

Try meditation

Chapter 11 includes descriptions of meditation and how it can help. This Buddhist poem by Li Po translated by David Hinton captures something of the tranquillity and insight which meditation can bring. (Kalpas, in the last verse, are 'great ages' or 'days of Brahma'—each 4.32 billion years long.)

> Alone, searching for blue-lotus roofs,
> I set out from city gates. Soon, frost
> clear, Tung-lin temple bells call out,
> Hu Creek's moon bright in pale water.
> Heaven's fragrance everywhere pure

emptiness, heaven's music endless,
I sit silent. It's still, the entire Buddha-
realm in a hair's-breadth, mind depths
all bottomless clarity, in which vast
Kalpas begin and end out of nowhere.

Meditation can be practised simply to find calm and balance. However, many people have also testified to the possibility of having through medi- tation what psychologist Abraham Maslow called a 'peak experience'. For example, Blaise Pascal, the mathematician and philosopher, kept these words on a scrap of paper wrapped up in his doublet and found after his death:

> From about half past ten in the evening to about half an hour after
>   midnight.
>   Fire.
> God of Abraham, God of Isaac, God of Jacob,
> Not the God of philosophers and scholars.
> Absolute Certainty: Beyond reason. Joy. Peace.
> Forgetfulness of the world and everything but God.
> The world has not known thee, but I have known thee.
>   Joy! Joy! Joy! Tears of joy!

CHAPTER 4

THE TRUE I AND THE EVERYDAY ME

The Self knows all, is not born, does not die, is not the effect of any cause;
is eternal, self-existent, imperishable, ancient.
How can the killing of the body kill Him?

Kena-Upanishad

Have you ever thought or felt that you have unrealized potential? Most people seem to. If so, have you ever felt excited and energized by the possibility of realizing it? Alternatively, have you ever felt depressed because you thought your life was below par? Such experiences and their effects form the backdrop of this chapter. Who am I really? What am I capable of? Is my life like the brief interlude of a bird flying from darkness to darkness through a lighted room, as the Venerable Bede described it, or is each life a portion of eternity? Such deep questions consciously or unconsciously play into our daily striving for fulfilment and meaning.

A starting point for exploring these questions is the nature of personal existence. Common sense tells us that we each have a physical body, and that this physical body is maintained by bio-rhythmic processes such as breathing, blood and lymph circulation, by digestion, nourishment and evacuation, cell formation and so on. Modern ideology assumes the physical body to be all that we are. But inner experience denies this.

The physical body remains after life ends, suggesting that there is a difference between the mere physicality of the organs and their life. Biologists agree that there is still no adequate scientific theory of life. Anyone who has watched a person or an animal die knows the experience of watching something vital drain away or leave the body. Some forms of medicine, including acupuncture, recognize life energy as the second dimension of existence.

Common experience also shows that there is consciousness, an inner, sentient space that is variously called mind or soul. Here we experience thinking (including thoughts, memories and sense perceptions), feelings (also called emotions or affects) and will power (also called intention or conation).

Finally, we also experience a sense of self that we call I. The I experience makes each individual a cosmos, precious and sacred in its eternal uniqueness.

So, if we respect this common experience, it suggests that we have four elements that make up our human existence, and therefore that need to be healthy. These are:

- An 'I', capable of making choices; the source of freedom. When it can no longer meet a challenge with enthusiasm, distress begins. Animals and plants do not appear to have this faculty.
- A mind or soul, a realm of consciousness of the world and its own inner space, where we experience joy and also stress: distress begins with a disturbance of the mind. Animals also have this, but plants do not appear to.
- A life force or energy pattern that forms and grows the body and maintains its life processes. When stress to the mind becomes sufficiently severe it affects the life force and life processes. Plants also have a life force or quality, but stones and minerals do not appear to. As already indicated, the life-principle is found in many traditions, for example as the Chi energy in Chinese science and Chai in Hebrew.
- A body, the only mineral, physical and sense-perceptible part and therefore the only part universally recognized. When life processes are badly enough affected, the marvellous bodily structure and fundamental physical integrity become jeopardized.

These are the origin of the four levels of stress/distress described in the previous chapter. In each case the progressive increase in 'stress' comes about because a further step has taken place in the I's inability to achieve harmony, order and health.

- No Stress: When we experience *challenge* not distress. Here the I is coping.
- Mental stress, including all kinds of anxiety and nervous mannerisms. Here the mind has lost the harmony and well being that it is the responsibility of the I or self to achieve.
- Bio-stress: emerging as illness, including damage to the immune system and life processes. Here the lifestyle effects of psychological problems lead to degradation of health because of a weakening of the life-energy system.
- Bodily and physical organ breakdown. The final Step!

Success in dealing with stress therefore depends on the I. I shall be exploring its nature and working in more detail in this chapter, for who is to bring order to me if it is not I myself?

Although I think it is important to make the distinction between the physical body and its life force, for practical purposes these are so entwined that, should they part, earthly life ends. Together, therefore, they make up the living body.

Thus I can simplify the four elements to the common experience: that I am or have a living body, a mind or soul and a mysterious sense of spirit that comes to expression in the I. Let me describe these and their relationship to stress in more detail.

Body, mind and spirit

> Body, soul and spirit are the elements of the world—as epic, lyric and drama are the elements of poetry.
>
> *Novalis*

Obviously many philosophers and scientists treat the human being as no more than a body, with the mind and I as no more than puzzling epiphenomena—brilliant but ultimately unreal manifestations of the body to itself. This is not the place for a full-blown philosophical argument. Suffice it to say that many other philosophers and scientists as well as billions of human beings have other attitudes.

All the major religious traditions say that the human being is made in the image of the divine. This means, in my view, that we are not just a body, perhaps fat, stiff or tired, and a struggling soul. Each person also has spirit, a greater self or higher I that shines like a beacon encouraging us forward through the trials of life to achieve our potential and destiny. This challenges us into stress but also gives us the ability to cope with that challenge. If friends, family and work colleagues—and we ourselves—notice our imperfections, it is often because the gap between our sensed spirit and potential and our everyday self is causing disappointment.

The human being consists of body, soul and spirit. The body is formed out of the realm of Nature, and spirit out of the realm of Spirit. Soul is the realm of the self-conscious mind that arises in the interplay of these two.

The model or paradigm of body, soul and spirit is particularly helpful because it makes sense of everyday experience. Think of the soul (or mind, although this typically has different connotations) as what arises as activity in the interplay between the body and the spirit (as in the diagram on page 31).

On the one hand I can relate myself to the world of nature. At a very simple level, right now I can observe a hand that is writing things down in the physical world that you will at some point (hopefully) read. This hand has physical presence, as does the pen it holds. Unlike the pen it has life. The biological existence of this hand is described by various natural laws (laws which we are still discovering and refining). We know that there have been factors like evolution of life forms and genetic transmission through the cells and that the maintenance of life and form depends on the continuing health of the body. The hand cannot continue long apart from the body that gives it life. I can observe this body too, from the outside (perhaps with the aid of a mirror) and to some extent from the inside. For example, I have recently eaten and can feel the fullness of my stomach. This reminds me that the body cannot live without the continued support of Nature, through the food and light and warmth and air that maintain existence. Indeed our bodies are an integral part of nature and are thoroughly woven into the physical cosmos.

However, alongside my experience of my body and its belongingness to the realm of nature, I have another experience of a soul (or mind), and within this an I that seeks fulfilment. This is far more ephemeral and yet vital for my mental spirits. As I write this, Mozart's *Magic Flute* is playing in the background. As one of the supreme works of art it is testament to the quest for love and meaning in the world, testament to the human urge to be creative and realize the highest possibility of our individual nature (despite the fiery challenges of life that are indicated in its famous Fire Trial scene, described further in Chapter 10). Our destiny to contribute to the making of meaning and value stimulates us in imaginative play and even, sometimes, to an early sense of destiny. Yehudi Menuhin, having asked for a violin on his fourth birthday, was bitterly disappointed when he received only a child's version and not an adult one like those he had seen played (and was inwardly committed to playing). Thus through the urge of the spirit manifesting in the I each person wants to realize something worthwhile in their life.

It is as impossible to prove or explain the existence of the spirit as to prove the existence of colours to those without sight. Because the difference between the tangibility of nature and the intangibility of spirit is so marked, it is perhaps understandable that the former is generally better recognized. But really, we need only pay attention to and trust what we intuit for the spirit to become reality. As Ralph Waldo Emerson put it: 'A man should learn to detect and watch the gleam of light which flashes across his mind from within, more than the lustre of the firmament of bards and sages. Yet he dismisses without notice his thought, because it is his.'

The soul or psyche or mind (which for my purposes at the moment are interchangeable terms differing only in resonance) is then that part of our awareness that bridges body and spirit. The inner world of the mind or soul is both local and peculiar to us and connected to the universe. Looking up at the stars, we are very tiny and the starry world immense. Yet in our imagination we can include them within our field or body of awareness. (We can also get to Australia in a moment!) Our inside mental world is as unlimited as the outside physical world. It connects to and knows the body and nature through the senses of touch, taste, sight, hearing, smell, balance and the awareness of the body's life. It also experiences the call to attain full potential as an individual human being and in certain special circumstances it experiences Maslow's 'peak experiences'. These include full-blown mystical and spiritual experiences, near death experiences and moments of trans-cendent joy, fulfilment and intuition. He thought that only about 1 per cent of people had such experiences. Later studies have shown however that many more people are familiar with them, indeed up to 40 per cent of the population.[4]

The soul or mind is self-conscious: it experiences and reflects on experience and through this comes towards wisdom.

On the one hand the soul gains wisdom about the world and how to operate in it. For example: don't put your hand in the fire; or, if you drop your cup it will fall towards the floor (accelerating at 32 feet per second). On the other hand, it gains wisdom about higher order, non-material things such as love, the nature of truth, the moral value of honesty and the importance of courage.

As soul I know, more or less, both you and myself. As soul I also experience that the everyday self of my mind or soul is far from perfect. Day by day I notice urges to change this, to achieve what Maslow and other humanist psychologists call self-actualization and even self-transcendence. I sense that my spirit urges realization, urges which I either listen to or ignore.

Here, therefore, is the central idea of the book: When we do acknowledge this aspiring side of our nature, we create a wonderful antidote to the deadening and stressful aspects of life.

Experiencing your soul

And see all sights from pole to pole, And glance, and nod, and bustle by;
And never once possess our soul Before we die.
Matthew Arnold (1822–88) A Southern Night

Becoming aware and mature requires developing a sensitive, qualitative judgement that will help to recognize when we've eaten enough, what type of food we need, when we're tired or need to rest or relax, subtle social signals from others and so on. Artists learn to see things that others don't. So do doctors, car body restorers, trackers and jewellers.

Becoming wise to stress needs self-awareness about the mind or soul, how it experiences the world, its own body, the spirit and so on. Developing healthy—not neurotic—mental self-awareness will equip you to notice how you are reacting to stress and help you to find better strategies. A first step is learning to notice and distinguish the workings of the mind.

This needs to be practised. For example, a good way to become conscious of the body's life forces is to begin with the simple feeling of life, of being alive. You may then extend this awareness to the sense of well-being, or not so well being, as the case may be.

The experiment below is another way to tune awareness. It explores four different kinds of mental experience, at one polarity very tuned to the 'raw nature' of the world and at the other to the decision-making self.

AN EXPERIMENT IN AWARENESS

- Here are four stages in the development of normal human awareness involving a little experiment with the skin. Scratch the upper part of one hand with a nail of the other hand and be aware of your experience. First there will be a simple receptive sensation, the first stage of awareness, provided by the body and its senses. This will give you sensations of movement, a slight rasping touch and so on. This is the basic sentient level of the soul. The animal organism, unlike the plant, is fundamentally organized to have such experiences.

- After a while you will probably find that the experience becomes irritating. At this point you will be experiencing your reaction to these continuing sensations. Reactions are experienced primarily in polarities, especially 'I like—don't like'. Artists, crafts people, sports stars and others through practice and training use this aesthetic sense with an almost instinctive feeling, 'I like this, this is balanced and right (or not)', to make creative judgements. This is the second stage of awareness by which the soul relates itself to the world and thus the senses become differentiated uniquely by the individual soul. This might therefore be called the feeling element of the soul.

- You can then scratch different parts of the skin with different intensities or different parts of the finger and compare the experiences, using memory to help. This is the intellectual faculty at work. The intellect is used to compare experiences, not just to respond to the present one. This extended capacity of intellect or reason most clearly separates us from the animal world.

- Finally, you might consciously decide to stop scratching your skin (probably a good idea!). Or you may decide not to pay attention or to find a positive attitude to the experience. Here, you would be exercising choice and self-determination. At this point the soul becomes home to the free human being, its fourth capacity as the spiritual element of the soul.

As the content of the body is blood and bone and cells and so forth, so there are varied parts of the soul with different functions. In the experiment above (by the way, evidence from other research shows that only about 10 per cent of readers do such exercises, so if you are one, congratulations) you will have noticed a progressive mental movement from 'pure' receptivity to 'pure' decision making and choice. These involve different inner processes and different mental faculties.

The soul operates through human reason on what it observes in nature (trees, our bodies) and within itself, for example memories. Everything it observes is commonly called a percept. Percepts can be of both inner and outer things. As we have seen, both the inner and the outer cosmos appear virtually unlimited. The sensation on the skin is a percept, so is the dislike that comes to awareness.

The invisible is the secret counterpart of the visible.
W. Merleau-Ponty

As I have already discussed, stress arises not simply from *what* we experience but *how* we experience it. Imagine a common occurrence: two people go for a walk and the footpath comes to a field with horses in it. One sees beautiful creatures she wants to walk up to and stroke. The other doesn't want to enter the field. Here the raw perception (or percept) of the horses is united with very different concepts and associations or aspects. One sees playmates, the other dangerous creatures. The phenomenon means different things to each person, indeed this meaning directly affects what is actually perceived by them. This was an important feature of Wittgenstein's late philosophy. He called it aspect-seeing and showed how understanding it resolved fundamental dilemmas and problems of science and philosophy. I will return to this in a later section (see page 115).

As we journey further through the book we will also find various ways in which this process affects our ability to deal with stress, for example:

- in how we see other people;
- in perceptions of tasks;
- in how we view ourselves;
- in how we describe and see nature and natural laws.

As soon as this is recognized it becomes possible to exercise more choice. If I am not simply seeing things 'as they are' but in fact 'as I see them', then I can reflect and change how I see things, if I wish! The more actively and positively self-conscious I become, noticing my own inner processes, my assumptions, mental habits, and mental processes, the more I can do this.

It is important in doing this to avoid negativity, neurosis and so on. Rather, my aim is to bring order and health, positivity and calm into being. I do this through the force of my own I becoming aware of and increasing the regulation and order of my own inner mental activities, and in particular the three fundamental soul activities of thinking, feeling and will.

Thinking, feeling and will are agents of the I that may become unruly (hence the traditional Hindu image of the charioteer with three horses). As a trinity they each have their own quality and yet inter-dependence. It takes will and calm emotion to think. We can only consciously will what we imagine (a power of thinking and feeling). We feel according to our wants and thoughts.

In our *thinking*, a head activity, we come to know the pattern and nature both of ourselves and of all things. In thinking we connect a lion to lion-ness, a triangle to triangle-ness, an oak tree to oak-ness, and so approach the archetypal and living form of things. This means coming to know the essence of things and is traditionally connected to what Christianity calls the Spirit or Holy Spirit. I call it a 'head activity' because that is where it is experienced (and where its principal organ, the brain, is).

In inner *feeling*, a heart activity connected to the rhythms of breathing and blood flow and felt most in the chest, we come into empathic relationship with all beings, we come to know what is outside us through feeling. We come to an awakened sense of individuality through participation in the world. This empathic awareness is traditionally associated with the Christ or Son.

In our inner *will*, an activity brought most strongly to awareness in the activities and sensations of the moving limbs, we enjoy a creative power to bring things into being and fashion the physical world. The will has been regarded by some as stemming from the divine creative power known as the Father.

Just as we can train any other part of our being—for example improving physical fitness and strength—we may train and develop our thinking, feeling and will. When we do this they become more resourceful, effective, and harmonized.

Only when our inner world is in turmoil do we have stress. As we fashion and harmonize our inner self, the space for turbulence reduces. Then self-willed and therefore stress-free thinking arises. Chapters 6 and 11 include exercises and meditation to help do this.

The question then arises: Who or what does these? Who or what develops the thinking, feeling and will that are the basis of leadership, a fulfilling life and human achievement? For this we must once again look to the I and understand it better.

The true I

Two birds, bound one to another in friendship, have made their homes on the same tree. One stares about him, one pecks at the sweet fruit. The personal self, weary of pecking here and there, sinks into dejection; but when he understands through meditation that the other—the impersonal Self—is indeed Spirit, dejection disappears.

He Who Has Found Spirit, Is Spirit.

Mundaka-Upanishad

What *owns* sensations, feelings, thoughts and decisions? What says: '*I* have a skin, *I* have feelings, *I* have thoughts'? Whoever or whatever does so is also responsible for the ability to make free and conscious choices in life, the capacity I am calling self-leadership. Normally, we tend to assume that our mind's thoughts, feelings and intentions are who we are. While there is some truth in this, these are mental impressions and such mental content comes and goes. At ten years old, you were very different from how you are now. Sometimes you are in a good mood, sometimes a bad one. But something persists, waking each morning with the sense of being a continuing person. This experience contributes to the widespread belief that the spiritual Self (as Jung called it) or I (as Steiner generally referred to it) continues after the body dies.

Normally, the closest we can get to the experience of our true I is of the sense of a still centre around which and from which our awareness radiates. This is one reason why it is traditionally represented by the sign ⊙. Just as we can't see ourselves without a mirror, so my experience is that there is a centre to me that *sees* my thoughts and feelings, but does not directly see itself.

Another experience may be noticed immediately at waking, which was documented by Steiner[5] and has been described to me by a person I know well. There may be a first impression of joy and peace, of expansiveness as though filling the universe. This is commonly followed by a sense of desolation, of being compressed and reduced. (In some cases, sadly, only the latter experience is noticed.) The cause is said to be the spirit incarnating into the compactness of the waking body after its freedom during the night.

It is a holy and awe-inspiring experience to meet and experience the true, higher I, the real, eternal Self.

Let us call the everyday content of the mind 'the lower I or lower self', and the part which invisibly observes this content and which persists through the whole of life and beyond 'the higher or true I'. This true I has also had many names, including Greek daemon, Roman genius, guardian angel and spirit-self. It is also the technical meaning in Aramaic of Christ's cryptic phrase, 'Son of Man', the self on the way to becoming a 'Son of God'. It is very different from what Freud called the superego, the controlling I that is actually part of the lower or everyday self.

Through a radical shift in attention it is possible to shift consciousness from the everyday I to the higher I.

In my own experience, it is a holy and awe-inspiring moment to meet and experience the true higher I, the real eternal Self. It is a meeting with a being of timeless wisdom, of purest, unending light and a vision of possibility. For, while the experience often leads to an impression of eternal life, there is often also a feeling: I am on a long journey to transform my present shortcomings in my lower self which is far from the nature of my higher Self. Spiritual self-development or soul development then becomes the process by which our everyday self becomes as our higher Self.

The experience of the higher I that I have described may come by 'accident', or it may be consciously pursued following a path of development or meditation, hence the prevalence of the use of the term 'way' in different religions.

Jung described how the writer Edward Maitland experienced it as a resolution of all opposites, the unmanifest and manifest, love and will, feminine and masculine, mother and father, through an experience of 'the glory of unspeakable whiteness and brightness, and of a lustre so intense as well-nigh to beat me back'.[6] This Pauline experience was achieved through a tremendous effort by Maitland, during which he reflected from one idea to another as they became visible in a long series that seemed to reach back to a source in the divine Spirit. Throughout this intensive process he maintained a hold on both outer, circumferential consciousness as well as the inner, central consciousness to which he was travelling. In other words Maitland used an ascending series of ideas as a ladder to higher consciousness, maintaining the conscious choice to make this inner journey throughout. In this he followed a method pioneered by the German poet and philosopher Novalis (1772–1801), which he called Raising (*Erhebung*). A similar exercise is practised in the initiation art of Eurythmy by maintaining a simultaneous experience of both centre and periphery and thus 'rising above' both. Many other methods have been discovered to suit different individuals.

The result is the experience of the central unity of one's own higher existence in an experience that is classically described as meeting the 'greater guardian of the threshold', the being that is at one and the same time the interweaving presence of one's own highest nature and the presence of the cosmic order, the Logos. Paul's experience of this on the road to Damascus inspired his phrase: 'Christ in me.'

That brings us back to stress and its resolution. Wisdom lies in recognizing a path of development by means of which the true individual rises to the challenges of life by inter-tuning inner and outer, thought and deed, wishes and world condition, capacities and crises: thereby becoming more free, more loving, more wise, less stressed, and less stressful! Failure in this will always be in some measure stressful.

In a letter to a friend, John Keats gave a wonderful description of the world as 'The vale of Soul-making'. He believed the world was created to help the soul to become an individual spark of the divine. This I believe is the true mission or goal of stress.[7]

The I and freedom of choice

> And now the end is near
> And so I face the final curtain,
> My friend, I'll say it clear,
> I'll state my case of which I'm certain.
> I've lived a life that's full, I've travelled each and evr'y high-way
> And more, much more than this, I did it my way.
>
> *Paul Anka (1941–), US singer and songwriter.*
> *Based on the French composition, 'Comme d'habitude'.* My Way

At the heart of the message and quest of this book is the idea of freedom— freedom from stress and freedom to make choices. Novalis, whom I just quoted, also said: 'In all our lives all chance events are materials that we fashion into what we will. He who has much spirit makes much of his life.'

The agent of this freedom, as Novalis makes explicit, is the I. In the most adverse of circumstances, the I is nevertheless capable of deciding how to respond to circumstance. However often we may be storm-tossed, act out of habit and unfreedom or respond with apathy to what life brings, the human being still retains the potential to make a free choice.

Picasso spoke about this in relation to his experience of creative freedom. He contrasted 'seeking', where the individual begins with what is already known, merely to find it in a new situation, with 'finding', which involves the discovery of the completely new. This 'holy adventure' depends on a very special, and perhaps new, human strength to be creatively vulnerable, as Picasso describes it:

> The risks in setting out on such a quest can in fact only be accepted by those who know themselves to be sheltered in their vulnerability—who allow themselves to fall into the unknown and experience no leadership—

who trust themselves to a star in the darkness and direct themselves towards higher aims—instead of allowing their goal to be determined by commonplace hindrances and constraints.

This openness for every new insight and every new experience is essential for being truly human today.

In the face of the fear of letting go, the people of today experience the grace of being carried in the revelation of new opportunities.

This marvellous free strength of the individuality in its vulnerability is noted in quite another context, by Bruno Bettelheim, the Jewish psychologist and SS death camp survivor. Bettelheim put the possibility and importance of freedom at the centre of his 'Orthogenic' therapy. In *The Informed Heart* (p158), he discussed this, based on his observations in the concentration camps of Buchenwald and Dachau:

> Those prisoners who blocked out neither heart nor reason, neither feelings nor perception, but kept informed of their inner attitudes even when they could hardly ever afford to act on them, those prisoners survived and came to understand the conditions they lived under. They also came to realize what they had not perceived before; that they still retained the last, if not the greatest, of the human freedoms: to choose their own attitude in any given circumstance. Prisoners who understood this fully, came to know that this, and only this, formed the crucial difference between retaining one's humanity (and often life itself) and accepting death as a human being (or perhaps physical death): whether one retained the freedom to choose autonomously one's attitude to extreme conditions even when they seemed totally beyond one's ability to influence them.

This is something like the Roman god Janus's head: pointing in two directions at once. While it points towards human freedom and autonomy, it also exposes the dark underworld of the human condition, that which painfully divides human being from human being. Here is the acutely selfish and anti-social side of the self in all its horror. From where does this come?

The I divided

The feeling of separation is bound up with the oldest and vaguest of my memories: the first cry, the first scare. Like every child I built emotional bridges in the imagination to link me to the world and to other people. I lived in a town on the outskirts of Mexico City, in an old dilapidated house that had a jungle-like garden and a great room full of books. First games and first lessons. The garden soon became the centre of my world; the library, an enchanted cave. I used to read and play with my cousins and schoolmates. There was a fig tree, temple of vegetation, four pine trees, three ash trees, a nightshade, a pomegranate tree, wild grass and prickly plants that produced purple grazes. Adobe walls. Time was elastic; space was a spinning wheel. All time, past or future, real or imaginary, was pure presence. Space transformed itself ceaselessly. The beyond was here, all was here: a valley, a mountain, a distant country, the neighbours' patio. Books with pictures, especially history books, eagerly leafed through, supplied images of deserts and jungles, palaces and hovels, warriors and princesses, beggars and kings. We were shipwrecked with Sinbad and with Robinson, we fought with d'Artagnan, we took Valencia with the Cid. How I would have liked to stay forever on the Isle of Calypso! In summer the green branches of the fig tree would sway like the sails of a caravel or a pirate ship. High up on the mast, swept by the wind, I could make out islands and continents, lands that vanished as soon as they became tangible. The world was limitless yet it was always within reach; time was a pliable substance that weaved an unbroken present.

Octavio Paz, Nobel Prize lecture, 1990

Picture a time before the birth of the individual in humanity, a time rather like that of every baby and little child. Imagine a time when the human spirit was undifferentiated, undivided, and integral with the wholeness of the cosmos, a drop in the universal divine ocean.

Then imagine a process of individuation:

Separation into human type and sex and gender;
Into clan and tribe;
Increasing divorce from Mother Nature;
Separation from the Divine;
Loss of innocence;
Increasing awareness of me and less and less awareness of the other until my own individual experience becomes the most real thing I know, the only existential certainty:
I think, therefore I am.

According to most sacred traditions, the first human beings were indeed undivided and part of the divine. This is represented in, for example, Genesis 1, 27, where humanity is made in God's image as '*both* male *and* female'. The Jewish spiritual tradition of Kabbalah has for centuries or even millennia regarded Adam Kadmon, the original cosmic human being, as a whole human, undivided into male and female, just as the first foetal cell is whole and undivided. (This initially totally undifferentiated condition is also found in ancient Greek and eastern thinking. A hymn in the ancient Indian epic, the Rig Veda, describes the first human being as containing not only both male and female, but everything else: all animals and beings are but aspects of the universal human.)

Adam and Eve giving each other the fruit of the tree of the knowledge of good and evil, creating differentiation, freedom and the 'fall of humanity'; from a mediaeval pillar in Lincoln Cathedral

However, Genesis then describes a tragic separation of the sexes, exclusion from Paradise, the denial and murder of a brother and in due course descent to the tower of Babel when folk could no longer understand each other, and the consequent separation of the nations. Since then, blood-clan and nationality have had ever-decreasing power to bind folk together. Now, modern humanity emerges in all its existential pain and post-modern glory, each divided from the other. The Hindu tradition of the four ages of humanity, which also underpins Buddhism, reflects a similar descent.

The poet Octavio Paz described the consequence in his Nobel Prize lecture:

This consciousness of being separate is a constant feature of our spiritual history. Separation is sometimes experienced as a wound that marks an internal division, an anguished awareness that invites self-examination; at other times it appears as a challenge, a spur that incites us to action, to go forth and encounter others and the outside world. It is true that the feeling of separation is universal and not peculiar to Spanish Americans. It is born at the very moment of our birth: as we are wrenched from the Whole we fall into an alien land. This experience becomes a wound that never heals. It is the unfathomable depth of every man; all our ventures and exploits, all our acts and dreams, are bridges designed to overcome the separation and reunite us with the world and our fellow-beings. Each man's life and the collective history of mankind can thus be seen as attempts to reconstruct the original situation. An unfinished and endless cure for our divided condition.

The true I may be glorious, but the everyday I can be lonely, egotistical, abusive and abused. To love truly or appreciate truly anyone or anything, I must struggle to overcome this colossal, one-sided individualism, and the sense of alienation arising from the countless millennia of striving for individuality:

Individualism is the great divorce;
I walk about apart; I am solitary and alone;
To be with others, I impose myself on them;
I strive for my own development against others;
I value in others only what they trigger in me;
Do I really love my loved ones
or do I just like the feelings I have in their company?
I am an egotist and an exile;
I come first.

The greatest of all causes of stress is perhaps this feeling of separation, which by extrapolation sets up the universe as an adversary. Octavio Paz described it as 'rotten masks that divide one man/from another, one man from himself' that lead to the 'iron bars of the banks and jails'.[8] Colin Wilson, in his book, *The Outsider*, described it as the 'sickness of mankind', while the French philosopher Jouffroy described the experience as follows: . . . 'before me another life opened, sombre and unpeopled, where in future I must live alone, alone with my fatal thought that had exiled me there, and which I was tempted to curse.'

Yet, as we shall see, this alienation of person from person is rooted in a deeper alienation.

The universal Cain and Abel

> Cain said to his brother Abel, 'Come let us go into the field,' and when they were in the field, Cain set upon his brother Abel and killed him.
>
> *Genesis 4,8*

The legend of Cain and Abel in Genesis is one of the most potent myths—by which I mean discourses that have powerfully affected culture and spoken to human souls—in the middle eastern and western tradition. For example, it has been an important part of Masonic rituals.

Cain and Abel are the two sons of Adam and Eve, in other words the first human beings created from human sexual union. Cain becomes jealous of his brother because God, Jehovah/YHWH, has accepted the shepherd Abel's sacrifice of livestock, the result of natural generation, while rejecting Cain's offering of grain, the fruit of the art of cultivation. As a result of his jealousy Cain kills Abel—the first murder. God asks him, where is Abel? Cain's famous reply is that he does not know: 'Am I my brother's keeper?' he says.

Statue of Cain and Abel by John Salter

Subsequently, Cain is marked by God with the sign of guilt and condemned to leave his home and become a wanderer.

This primal dynamic of conflict, destruction, alienation and avoidance of personal responsibility remains active today:

Cain slays Abel day by day in cities around the world out of desire and fear;
Cain slays Abel when the rich let children starve every second;
Cain slays Abel when fat tyrants build bombs and bank balances while illness goes untreated;
Cain slays Abel when bitter terrorists hijack planes;
Cain slays Abel when big business cuts and reorganizes headcount, forgetting the souls in those heads;
Cain slays Abel when I blame you and when I ignore you and when I put you down;
And then Cain slays Abel when I say, 'I am not responsible.' When I say, 'I am not my brother's (or sister's) keeper, it is up to governments, chief executives, "them", to fix it.'

The war between the (male) Athenians and the (female) Amazons,
from a frieze in the British Museum

Out of this separateness and alienation and conflict emerges fear, the very fear that forms a barrier to oneness with the universal. Here is the underlying principle, the deeper alienation. Observe the myth closely and recognize that it captures a philosophical and historical principal in story form.

First Cain takes a step away from God and as a result his sacrifice is no longer 'acceptable'. The sacrifice in question symbolically expresses this primary alienation. Cain no longer relies on Nature—the divinely given world—providing, and instead takes responsibility for producing his own output. Whatever that might look like to a modern sensibility, Cain symbolizes modern man and this is a picture of the human who is no longer simply receptive to the God(s) but instead turns to itself for satisfaction. While Abel still belongs in the primal participative consciousness, Cain has moved on. He no longer simply belongs to Nature, but rather works on it, 'improves it'. He represents modernity, in a line that leads directly to plastic and genetically modified crops and cloned sheep.

The analogue for this is the separation of the lower and higher selves.

This frieze from the Parthenon shows a scene from the war with the centaurs
(a half animal image of the lower self)

Remember that the myth tells us that Cain and Abel are made in the image of God, as the lower self is the image or fallen reflection of the higher self. God in the myth rejects Cain only after Cain has rejected God. In my experience (and described in many texts[9]) this shows up in what happens should we try to approach the inner holy of holies that is our own higher self. The result is very simple: the lower self feels uncomfortable—the higher self is too bright, too pure, too loving, too wise to be borne. At the threshold of the higher self I discover by comparison the nature of my own lower self and feel ashamed, unready, impure, afraid. Thus I go into exile from my higher nature, which also means I am divided from the universal in the cosmos. I create or call my own guardian who bars my way to Eden, a guardian who is a projection of my own aghast and agonized self.

At the heart of stress, there is this tension between the lower and the higher self. The higher self brings us to events that we don't welcome. The lower self criticizes, overlooking the value we may come to see in them later. The higher self leads us into challenges that develop us. But the lower self would prefer a comfortable stress-free existence, except that this is impossible because it is fundamentally empty and therefore uncomfortable. The lower human being projects a judgemental and rejecting higher self, in other words it ascribes to the higher self its own lower nature. As Georg Kühlewind put it: 'When the search for fault in ourselves reaches deep enough, we come not only to its immediate and actual cause, but to the basic guilt itself; to the not-willing, not-giving, not-yielding, not-forgiving being in us . . . This threshold has existed since the original sin.'

Just as the guilty person projects personal guilt into judgement by a perceived critical, superior figure, the Bible expresses this archetype in Jehovah's questioning of Cain, Cain's guilty deceit and subsequent rejection.

Thus an inner compulsion to overcome the primary alienation is never far from the surface, and yet frequently leads to a perpetuation of the crisis. Our own demands lead to distress. Instead of a productive acceptance of the true nature of these demands we subvert them into the acquisition of things, as if by ownership we can again belong. Or our distress leads to a projection of fear, disappointment or loneliness on to the other who becomes a hate figure, as Cain kills Abel.

Buddha's great insight that all life is suffering—or distress—caused by unsatisfied desires expresses the Cain and Abel myth in abstract terms. Look at our commercial world and its vast engine unequal to humanity's material desires and needs. Yet, a moment of love or wonder is totally satisfying. Thus discontent arises from the everyday self and soul's failure to experience the blessings of its own higher nature, just as Cain fails to receive God's blessing. The gap between the lower and the higher self is the root cause of all stress.

> The lower self is discontented because it has not achieved its potential, and so experiences stress and suffering;
> The Higher I challenges it to help it achieve this potential;
> The lower self wants results without effort and change and happiness in things. It wants enlightenment in a can and in front of the TV;
> The Higher I continually urges change by its very nature;
> The lower self resists this out of its nature.

The irony in the great gulf of separateness is not knowing our own higher self's responsibility in our destiny, never mind our responsibility for how we react to the world. Our higher, deeper, feeling nature provides an inner stimulus that seeks answers and self-development, and yet we pit ourselves against this with all our might. To update the myth, today we offer as sacrifice to the higher nature our bank accounts and mortgages, branded goods and materialistic sciences, and then are surprised to find the sacrifice rejected, leaving us angry and dissatisfied, unfulfilled, spiritually homeless, living lives deprived of real meaning.

Why this happened, why the Self is so divided, why we are so alienated one from another, why we lost our original participation in the divine and nature, is one of the deep mysteries of human existence. The value and purpose of this otherwise so painful phenomenon I believe lies in the nature, meaning and mystery of the I and individuality.

The meaning of individuality

> To hell with your system. I demand the right to behave as I like. I demand
> the right to regard myself as utterly unique.
> *The protagonist in Dostoevsky's* Notes from the Underground

Erich Fromm, in one of the most important books on human relationships, *The Art of Loving*, agrees that what is essential in the existence of man is that he has emerged from the instinctive nature of the animal kingdom to one that while still part of nature is yet also torn away from it. Thrown out of Paradise, which Fromm calls the original oneness with nature, by Cherubim with flaming swords, he believes that man can only go forward by developing his reason:

> ...by finding a new harmony, a human one, instead of the prehuman harmony which is irretrievably lost... Man is gifted with reason; he is *life being aware of itself*; he has awareness of himself, of his fellow man, of his past, and of the possibilities of his future. This awareness of himself as a separate entity, the awareness of his own short lifespan, of the fact that without his will he is born and against his will he dies, that he will die before those whom he loves, or they before him, the awareness of his aloneness and separateness, of his helplessness before the forces of nature and of society, all this makes his separate, disunited existence an unbearable prison. He would become insane could he not liberate himself from this prison and reach out, unite himself in some form or other with men, with the world outside.

Here is a clue to individuality as a necessary and valuable stage in human development. Humanity in its literature and sacred traditions and on the street tends to honour the unique privilege of individuality, and its associated separateness is seen as a pre-condition for true, conscious love and wisdom: 'I celebrate myself, and sing myself,' said Walt Whitman. Colin Wilson's book, *The Outsider*, documents how it is the great souls who may brave and therefore know the pains of individuality. He ends the book with the comment: 'The individual begins that long effort as an Outsider; he may finish it as a saint.'

The distinction I therefore want to urge is between egotism and the I, between being merely an individual and being an individuality. Egotism is all about me, me, me. Individualism fears loss of face, wants to assert its point of view and stands apart. Individuality, however, celebrates diversity, knows its own and others' value and gives unconditional love.

A passage from a poem by Anne Stevenson entitled 'Poem for my Daughter' describes how a woman through the act and process of becoming a mother is able to make this journey of transformation:[10]

A woman's life is her own
until it is taken away
by a first particular cry.
Then she is not alone
but part of the premises
of everything there is:
a time, a tribe, a war.

Stevenson goes on to say that when through such giving we belong to the world, then we recover something essential, we become in her words 'what we are'.

We recover our true nature.

The higher I, like a beacon, continually draws the lower self up to its side and nature. The everyday practical experience of this is called conscience: and everyone surely knows the feeling of resisting conscience? When the gap between the lower and the higher self is bridged, the human being has progressed from being an unconscious part of the cosmos to a fully conscious one. Without this 'conscious conscience' there can be no true wisdom and no true love. There can also be no true peace, as Shakespeare expresses through the words of Cardinal Wolsey in *Henry VIII*: 'A peace above all earthly dignities,/A still and quiet conscience.'

Separation becomes a path that leads to love and wisdom just as exercise is a path that leads to physical fitness. The opening lines of Whitman's remarkable *Song of Myself* points towards how to reconcile the threshold that divides each individual from his or her fellows and from the universe:

> I celebrate myself, and sing myself.
> And what I assume you shall assume,
> For every atom belonging to me as good belongs to you.

When I begin to see that what I am so are you, and that we are both immeasurable, we lose the fear and neediness that blinds us and kills others. How can anyone with Whitman's view commit Cain's act—killing his brother?

The essence of true individuality and self-leadership is to take personal responsibility for one's own feelings and inner reactions instead of projecting them on to the world. Indeed, this is key to redeeming the condition of separation and isolation in which humanity finds itself.

Then I *am* my brother's keeper! Bob Dylan:

> I ain't lookin' to compete with you,
> Beat or cheat or mistreat you,
> Simplify you, classify you,
> Deny, defy or crucify you.
> All I really want to do
> Is, Baby, be friends with you.

There is a wonderful legend from the Middle Ages that captures the spirit of this: it is the story of Parzival, or Percival in the English tradition of the

Grail legends, immortalized first by Wolfram von Eschenbach and later in the great opera by Wagner.

> Parzival is of the knightly caste but grows up in the woods as an innocent until he meets some of Arthur's knights and joins them. In due course he is led by grace into the Grail Castle where he totally fails to realize his destiny as the new Grail king and healer. All around the land is wasted as a result of the fall of the present king—a poetic image of the human condition.
>
> Parzival could ascend to the throne and heal all if he could only demonstrate compassion for others—in this case the fatally wounded king he should replace. But mired in his own assumptions and lost in his own self-absorption he fails.
>
> Through this failure he comes to a devastating realization of his own naïve and untransformed self and begins a kind of knightly pilgrimage of self-discovery and soul-healing. Eventually after many adventures he returns to the Grail Castle, and crucially he does so (in von Eschenbach) arm in arm with his half-brother Firafiz. Firafiz is half-black, half-white and so represents a kind of everyman. He is also a follower of Islam and so an apparent enemy of the Christian Knight, so representing resolution. Initially he and Parzival fight; the alienation between them dominates. Then the ancient rift is healed, and a mutual discovery and respect emerges.
>
> Parzival then, through an act of empathy, becomes the new Grail King and heals the land. Cain and Abel are thus reconciled.

John Salter's beautiful statue (on page 73) is a partner to his Cain and Abel shown earlier and represents this moment of healing and resolution.

Wisdom and social harmony come about when we learn to take responsibility and develop love. This is the principal task of the higher Self and the one that the lower self most resists. To achieve this inevitably requires that we meet challenges to develop and that we engage with them.

How the I creates destiny

Our destiny, our being's heart and home, is with infinitude.
Wordsworth, Prelude, *Book 6*

James Hillman, the widely respected psychologist and best selling author, has described a so-called acorn theory of development. Just as a great oak grows from the seed that is the acorn, so he suggests that destiny unfolds through a seed principle:

Parzival and Firafiz, by John Salter

Let me put in a nutshell what we may so far cautiously attribute to the
acorn theory. It claims that each life is formed by its unique image, an
image that is the essence of that life and calls it to a destiny. As a force of
fate, this image acts as a personal daemon, an accompanying guide who
remembers your calling.

In his excellent book, *The Soul's Code*, he gives many remarkable examples
of how people find their way to calling and destiny or to recognize each
other. For example, he tells the story of Thomas Wolfe's father and mother:
Julia Westall, a schoolteacher, came into the shop of W.O. Wolfe, who cut
marble tombstones, trying to sell books to supplement her income. They fell
to talking and W.O. lent her a book. When she returned a few days later he
pressed her to stay to lunch and then proposed marriage to her. She protested
that they couldn't possibly get married, as they hardly knew each other.
Then, in what she called 'just a bit of foolishness on my part', she offered to
open the book at random and abide by whatever was in the middle paragraph
on the right hand page. It described a wedding, with the words: 'Till death do
us part.' Their wedding took place three months later.

I can add that my own, now twenty-five year old marriage happened in a
hardly less remarkable manner. I proposed to Sally, whom I had known

merely as a work colleague, after I suddenly thought out of the blue: 'I should marry Sally.' I asked to speak to her with such solemnity that she was rather concerned, and then I proposed. We had never even dated! For some reason she agreed to think about it, and agreed to marry me a few days later. We had our first date *after* engagement and were married within six weeks.

There are no doubt many remarkable stories of this kind, yet it is also fair to say that every life is remarkable and full of wonder. Hillman's theory is that everyone comes with a kind of guiding light or beacon—the image, daemon or guide he describes. During our lives we gradually grow into or enter into our potential or calling through the help of this guide.

The guide he describes is identical to what I am calling the higher Self or higher I. The image he describes normally appears in various imaginative forms, as the idea to be or do this or that, or as ideal self-image. When this image is actually seen, it is the vision of Light that I described earlier.

In *The Soul's Code*, Hillman gives many powerful examples of how circumstantial experiences trigger various people's awareness of who they are or what they need to do, including in childhood. For example, the English philosopher R.G. Collingwood (1889–1943) discovered, aged eight, a book by Kant in his father's bookcase. Although he could read it, it meant absolutely nothing to him—except that he realized at that moment that this was his business. 'I could not define myself except by saying, "I must think."'

There are such big, defining moments that shape lives and destiny. My son at seventeen came across Plato on our bookshelves and in joy remarked, 'This is what I have been looking for all my life.' It changed his attitude and approach, and eighteen months later he was at Oxford University reading philosophy. I knew what I was going to do as a young teenager and despite resisting it in various ways I have come to it.

The so-called traumatic experience is not an accident, but the opportunity for which the child has been patiently waiting—had it not occurred, it would have found another, equally trivial—in order to find a necessity and direction for its existence, in order that life may become a serious matter.

W.H. Auden

It is the experiences and challenges people meet that call forth their full human potential. Not all are huge or traumatic: there are also day-by-day and year-by-year experiences that shape the channel of our lives, that remind or incite or challenge us.

No one is born into anything other than a situation whose imbalance and partiality leads to gaps in experience and character. Everyone starts with natural strengths and weaknesses, given advantages and disadvantages. We can view the experiences that then come to us as unfair, inappropriate or worthless. If we do, we will probably not only make little progress as a person, we will probably decline in character and talent. Or we can see each experience and the very circumstances of our life as a meaningful opportunity, in which case we will progress. Our attitude to life's destiny matters very much.

Imagine that someone possessed of great wisdom and knowledge about you wanted to help you to realize your potential. One way that this could happen would be to design a series of learning opportunities. It is part of my job to design workshops that provide learning experiences for clients, experiences that enable them to develop their leadership qualities such as creative imagination, organization, and social intelligence.

Suppose that life was a workshop designed by an extremely wise trainer. We can test this idea by tuning our awareness. Steiner proposes a kind of thought experiment. Picture an imaginary person who quite deliberately brings about the events that happen in his or her life.

> Steiner suggests imagining someone climbing on to the roof, loosening a roof tile and then running quickly down so that when the tile is quite loose it falls on his or her shoulder. Practise this with different situations until the idea is alive in you. This strange notion is likely to have a curious result, because by doing this you open your mind to the possibility of self-directed destiny. When this happens, you may begin to look at the events in your own life differently. When applied to all kinds of personal life-experience, the idea takes shape that you too have such a part of yourself that brings about these events. If you live with the actual idea for some time and use it to test life experience, this part seems rather fascinating and begins to take on a real significance. The idea then grows that this imaginary person is in fact one's own higher self.

The thought then takes shape that although sorrow and sufferings are misfortunes that we might gladly avoid, we ourselves have brought them about as challenges designed to allow personal growth. As a result, self-leadership now takes on a new and richer meaning.

In the final analysis, we count for something only because of the essential we
embody, and if we do not embody that, life is wasted.

C. G. Jung

The meaning of stress and suffering

What you have experienced no power on earth can take from you.

Nietzsche

Suppose you have had a previous life. If this was the case, then in the present
life you would probably be seeking to improve on what you had achieved in
the past. Whatever deficiencies you had, your wiser self might now want to
find opportunities to put them right and improve.

I think that the idea of past and future human lives is the only thing that
really makes sense of present experience. But, even if you don't believe in a
previous life, we all have a past life; it is whatever life you had before the
present moment. And from this and each moment on, I think that careful
examination shows the human spirit constantly seeking the opportunity to
evolve as a person.[11] Of course sometimes we are more aware and enthusiastic about this. At other times you might want to say, 'Please, I don't want
any more trouble; leave me alone.' Yet, although people get tired of challenges, they never get tired of growth.

This is both at the heart of life and depends on the courage of the heart. As
Joseph Chilton Pearce, the noted child psychologist, observed: 'Adolescents
sense a secret, unique greatness in themselves that seeks expression. They
gesture towards the heart when trying to express any of this, a significant clue
to the whole affair.'

This leads to a curious and at first sight uncomfortable idea: that suffering
and stress has a point. An elementary value of suffering is that it warns us to
avoid the suffering, for example heat tells us to remove ourselves from the
source before we are more badly burnt. As I have already mentioned, stress
symptoms work in this way too—telling us to rest, sleep, relax, eat less (or
more), exercise, calm down and so on.

However, I wonder if suffering—or the extreme stresses—may not act in
the same manner but in a heightened or transcendent fashion as a means of
growth or development. Viktor Frankl commented after his harrowing
experience in Auschwitz and other Nazi camps: 'Suffering had become a task

on which we did not want to turn our backs. We had realized its hidden opportunities for achievement.'

Frankl also commented, as I reported in Chapter 1, that it is precisely in difficult circumstances that the greatest possibility exists for a person to grow beyond himself. Perhaps this is not so surprising. Many athletes in training say, 'No pain, no gain.' Students and scholars know that the more they have to struggle to understand something, the more progress and satisfaction there is when understanding is achieved. Mothers (and fathers) know how the effort of looking after a child is fulfilling. Sales people know that the more effort and challenge there is in winning a major new piece of business, the more elation there is when it is achieved. Scientists know the fulfilment that comes from long and committed effort to achieve scientific breakthrough.

Indeed we all, I think, know that all new learning and true achievement is accompanied by the birth pangs of its delivery. That which is really easy is merely the repetition of what already exists, and represents no real progress.

Rudolf Steiner said that suffering initiates progress:

> In normal life we do not think in this way; we set our face against suf-
> fering. But we can also say that every sorrow, every suffering, every
> obstacle in life should be an indication of the fact that we have within us a
> person who is cleverer than we are. With our ordinary consciousness we
> resist sorrows and suffering, but the cleverer person leads us towards these
> sufferings in defiance of our consciousness, because by overcoming them
> we can strip off something. This may, to begin with, be an oppressive
> thought, but it carries with it no obligation; we can if we wish use it once
> only, as a trial. In this way we are led to the result that many find dis-
> turbing, namely that this cleverer person guides us always towards what
> we do not like. This, then, we will take as an assumption: there is a
> cleverer person within us who guides us to what we do not like, in order
> that we may make progress.

Amongst Frankl's cases after Auschwitz was this one (which I have sum-
marized).

During a therapeutic group discussion, a mother who had recently attempted suicide spoke about her situation. Her eleven-year-old son had just died leaving her with an older son crippled by polio. Frankl then asked another thirty-year-old woman to imagine herself aged eighty on her deathbed after a childless life that was filled with financial and social success.

The woman entered into this imaginative exercise with spirit, and decided that despite all the good times, such a life would have been a failure for her.

The first woman was then asked to do the same exercise. From this vantage she saw how she had made life fuller and better for her crippled son. Then she burst into tears and said, 'I can look back peacefully on my life; for I can say my life was full of meaning. My life was no failure.'

Anyone can do this 'deathbed' exercise with fruitful results.

How to embrace destiny

Everything that happens, happens as it should, and if you observe carefully, you will find this to be so.
Marcus Aurelius (121–180 ACE) Roman emperor

Our journey through the mysteries of individuality shows that human beings suffer from isolation and inter-personal tragedy as a result of their egoism and division. But if, instead of pre-occupation with the ego, we pay attention to the part of our spirit that urges us towards healthy self-development, then we achieve fulfilment. Our higher Self is continually active; by listening to its voice and responding to the challenges life brings we may advance in wisdom, courage and love.

Life does have meaning for human beings and a unique meaning for each, an experience that is the essence of the true I. As Novalis put it, 'To recapture our transcendental Self, to become the central core of our own governing Self, is the supreme purpose of our life on earth.' Embracing this rightly brings us into fellowship with all humanity.

While many live through this unconsciously, at some point we can awake to the ongoing invitation to become conscious and free, the invitation to play an active part in destiny, for example by noticing our own internal mental prejudices and choosing a new way of being.

The following chapters give many examples of how to do this. You may also do this by actively noticing your path through life and the helpful significance of events in your life.

For those who wish to do this, Steiner gave the following daily thought activity as a means of both refreshing and strengthening the spirit. Its regular use is generally healing and helpful. Notice how it embraces challenges as part of life's richness and brilliance. This experience arises most when acceptance of higher wisdom—even in adversity—is embraced and acknowledged.

The best way to do this exercise is to find a few minutes of quiet and to try to accompany the following words with your feeling and with inner pictures. It is not immediately important that they are the 'right' pictures. They will right themselves. Naturally, it is not necessary to begin feeling that you have the experiences it describes; the meditation will lead you to them. You may also replace the word 'fate' with 'destiny' or 'path', and the word 'star' with 'ideal', if you prefer.

> Wishes of the soul bud forth,
> Deeds of the will are thriving,
> Fruits of life are maturing.
>
> I feel my fate: my fate finds me,
> I feel my star: my star finds me,
> I feel my aims: my aims find me.
>
> My soul and the world are one.
>
> Life grows more radiant about me,
> Life grows more arduous for me,
> Life grows richer in me.

CHAPTER 5

HOW STRESS CREATES SELF-LEADERSHIP

*In this world without quiet corners, there can be no easy escapes from
history, from hullabaloo, from terrible, unquiet fuss.*
Salman Rushdie, Outside the Whale

Let us imagine that countless stars are brilliantly patterning a pitch-black night
sky uncontaminated by streetlights, pollution and clouds. Amongst a people
who from childhood recognize these wheeling light patterns as familiar spirits
and the speech of the gods, an ancient group of philosopher-scientists, magi,
whose distant descendants perhaps include the three wise men, are pondering
the mystery of the night. Like every shepherd, they know that amongst the
awesome spectacle of the skies there are seven strange objects. While all the
rest of the astral lights preserve their patterns, and have done so through
generations of oral and written records, these seven appear to 'wander' in
complex dances through the starry world. They will therefore come to be
called the 'planets' or 'wanderers'. The two that are miraculously identical in
size to the eye, the Sun and Moon, are the main lights of the day and the
night. The other five are tiny, but still much brighter than virtually all stars.
Being different and brighter, the wise men see they have special importance.

In the unified science and religion of those magi, the seven planets are
divine objects of holy veneration, tracked for centuries, so that their patterns,
conjunctions and oppositions can be predicted and noted as deeds of gods. The
magi of old were certain that the planets are divine beings: gods and goddesses
who shower their influence upon the Earth. In their divine mythology the
patterns of the sky are echoed on Earth and may be read as an augury of a life
or planned action. Kings and priests will consult them before taking action.

They found in the planets qualities of their own psyches. The most
important variable qualities of the soul or mind were therefore connected to
the seven wanderers that we now call Saturn, Jupiter, Mars, Venus, Mercury,
Moon and Sun.

Those philosopher-priests could have belonged to any one of many
remote epochs. The Maya were making astronomical inscriptions 11,000
years ago; lunar phases were being marked on bone in Ishango (Zaire) 8,500

years ago; the Chaldaens were observing the skies at a similar time and the Egyptians had achieved a calendar based on 365 days over 6000 years ago. (The dates also keep getting pushed back.) At the time of the Babylonians it was known (but later forgotten) that the Earth rotates around the Sun. Through all these remote ages the planets have been revered.

The seven archetypal human qualities that were connected for so long to the seven planets continue to fascinate us and find resonance to this day. At various places and periods, for example, among the Babylonians and Pythagoreans, at Plato's Academy and Ficino's Renaissance centre under the auspices of the Medici, and more recently by Thomas Moore and the archetypal psychologists who take their lead from Jung and Hillman, sophisticated psychological and medical systems were developed based on perceived archetypal correspondences between the human being and these planetary principles or gods.

Joseph Campbell comments in his powerful study of comparative mythology, *Occidental Mythology: the Masks of God*, that:

> ...a fundamental idea of all the pagan religious disciplines, both of the Orient and of the Occident, during the period of which we are writing (first millennium BCE), was that the inward turning of the mind (symbolized by the sunset) should culminate in a realization of an identity *in esse* of the individual (microcosm) and the universe (macrocosm) which, when achieved, would bring together in one order of act and realization the principles of eternity and time, sun and moon, male and female, Hermes and Aphrodite (Hermaphroditus), and the two serpents of the Caduceus.
>
> The image of the 'Meeting of Sun and Moon' is everywhere symbolic of this instant, and the only unsolved questions in relation to its universality are: a) how far back it goes, b) where it first arose, and c) whether from the start it was read both psychologically and cosmologically.

Carl Jung was emphatic about recognizing the importance of such soul forces, which he called autonomous psychic systems. He noted how many of the earlier gods developed from a 'person' into personified ideas and finally into abstract ideas, so that the gods have become nothing more than descriptive attributes (martial, jovial, saturnine, erotic, logical, lunatic, and so on). According to Jung, if we deny the existence of the autonomous systems:

> ...imagining that we have got rid of them by a mere critique of the name, then the effects which they still continue to exert can no longer be understood, nor can they be assimilated to consciousness. They become an

inexplicable source of disturbance which we finally assume must exist somewhere outside ourselves. The resultant projection creates a dangerous situation in that the disturbing effects are now attributed to a wicked will outside ourselves, which is naturally not to be found anywhere but with our neighbour... This leads to collective delusions, 'incidents', revolutions, war—in a word, to destructive mass psychoses... We think we can congratulate ourselves on having already reached such a pinnacle of clarity, imagining that we have left all these phantasmal gods far behind. But what we have left behind are only verbal spectres, not the psychic facts that were responsible for the birth of the gods. We are still as much possessed by autonomous psychic contents as if they were Olympians. Today they are called phobias, obsessions, and so forth... The gods have become diseases.[12]

Today there are few scientists who seriously connect the psyche with the planets, but the psychological aspects are more widely recognized. In a series of workshops around 1990, Coen van Houten, a researcher in adult learning and development, described how these seven fundamental human characteristics, that have for ages been connected to the planets, can also each be associated with a particular kind of stress or challenge. He subsequently kindly passed on his notes to me. This chapter was inspired by these initial suggestions.

It does not require a belief in planetary astrology to find value here. What matters is to recognize that there are archetypal human qualities of character and mind associated with universal stresses and strains and needs of the world. Human beings may have radically changed, but we retain much in common.

Given their ancient history and expressive power I have therefore retained the names of the planetary gods to describe the seven challenges described below—for as the Greeks would have put it, these are the challenges of the gods! It seems to me worthy to recognize and value the best in this venerable psychology. And as long as we do not think that lumps of gas and matter are their origin, why should we not also make a connection between these essentially spiritual capacities or virtues, such as courage and care, and the spiritual qualities, powers or potential in the universe? How else do we come to have these virtues?

Each of the seven stresses is a pattern commonly found in working life and decision-making. Each calls for a different quality of character and inner resourcefulness. Each is stimulating when ability matches the challenge. Each leads to stress when challenge exceeds—or is much less than—the resources of the individual. Each type of stress develops particular qualities of self-leadership and requires a balanced approach.

The seven kinds of stress and the qualities they develop can be summed up in this way:

I. SATURN: A scope and conviction of vision to make choices that affect future destiny

When people face choices with uncertain and significant long-term consequences, the effect can be paralyzing. 'What shall I do? How can I work out the consequences?' Responding to such challenges develops long-term thinking and conviction of vision, never easy to attain, but a wonderful blessing to own.

II. JUPITER: An intelligence to see order and simplicity in complex situations and systems: the insight that separates the essential from the non-essential

The effort of trying to make sense of highly complex situations or systems can lead us to feel overwhelmed. Every idea can lead to another in another direction so that connections are lost and it is hard to see the overall picture. It's like the child's fairy tale fear of being lost in a forest with no way out. Everywhere there are obscuring trees, and nowhere a path. Such bafflement can be stressful, but the challenge can develop insight to separate the essential from the non-essential.

III. MARS: A forcefulness and initiative that makes things happen

Perhaps you have experienced challenges that loom large and imposing, or even dangerous. 'That's beyond me,' we might think. Deep down you might even admit that you are scared. Bosses, big institutions, formidable people and difficult tasks can all do this to us. In such cases, taking appropriate and proportional action, making things happen, or opposing the 'enemy' develops initiative and assertiveness.

IV. VENUS: A bounteous capacity to nurture potential, caring for, renewing, and re-energizing people, organizations, processes and places

Nurturing or caring for people, organizations, processes and places can be wonderful, giving a real feeling of having done something worthwhile. But the ever-ongoing process of pouring one's energies out can become exhausting. To be able to perceive and nourish potential, to ceaselessly repair,

renew or re-energize people or a place in the world develops inner boun-
teousness and the ability to give.

V.   MERCURY: Flexibility in blocked or continually emerging circumstances
Ever experienced a challenge to your creativity? Finding a creative solution is
a delight, and typically a source of real self-satisfaction and fulfilment. But
what about continually new circumstances that throw up unexpected results
and difficulties that generate the 'not again' factor? Many companies have
been through such continuous and relentless change that their employees are
weary. And then there are situations where there does not appear to be any
creative solution. Instead, it feels as though only a wall faces you. Such
challenges develop resourceful and optimistic flexibility.

VI.   MOON: Evaluation, feedback and control in a busy world
'Busyness', anxiety-generating activity as this originally meant, is one of the
most frequent causes of stress. The whirl and range of activity that many
people face is both tiring and can lead to a feeling of bewilderment and lack
of focus. Nerves become frayed and the things that need to be done seem to
loom larger and larger with less and less will to do them. The ability to select
priorities declines and instead we find ourselves opting for the easy jobs,
while the undone tasks grow ever larger like phantoms in the mind.
Furthermore, the greater the potential risk of failure or difficulty the more we
fear being judged a failure. In all such cases our image of the task threatens us
with loss of control, or failure, whether the judgement is another's, our own,
or our fear of another's. Mastering such stressful situations develops balance,
control and orientation through increased inner awareness. Those who have
learnt objective judgement and awareness of all that is happening while
maintaining and following their priorities have gained a great prize.

VII.   SUN, APOLLO: Courage and moral maturity in the moral maze
Finally, what about life situations that call for moral judgement, perhaps in
conflict with apparent self-interest? We have all seen the movies where the
hero has to choose between advancement and integrity. They happen in
your life and mine too, I think. Such challenges can be hard to face, especially
when there is some ambiguity. Then we might be able to rationalize how, 'It
is really OK, to do this,' while inwardly knowing the exact opposite. The
challenges of such moral mazes are certainly stressful, but dealing with them
develops our moral maturity.

I hope you will recognize these stresses and strengths, whatever you may decide to call them. My experience is that each type or pattern becomes a real and useful idea, by which I mean that it moves from being an empty idea to one that makes real sense. As you become familiar with the idea, test it out in your own experience. In this way you get to know yourself better as well as the patterns to look out for. Learn to recognize the type of stress that you are experiencing. This helps you to find a solution in the form of an inner or outer response.

When you start to feel some kind of stress, ask yourself what kind it is. Is it challenging your Mars capacity or your Mercury capacity? Are you being asked to show more of Venus quality, or is it being stretched and needs a rest?

Perhaps one of the greatest changes between the past and present is that few people now assume that their destiny is governed by the gods. Instead, we increasingly believe that we are responsible for our own lives. The gods are now internalized. Instead of thinking of Mars as a force out there that rules over me, as say the Greeks did, I may think of it (or any of the other types) as an inner resource which I 'own' as part of me but which I need to develop.

So I invite you to use the understanding of these mythic figures as symbols to help you in your life. In time, it is my experience that these 'planetary gods' can become more than just names, or a theoretical psychological system, or a myth, or horoscope superstition. They become recognized as real aspects of the mind and therefore the world. Ancient ways of knowing belong to ancient mindsets, and human beings have greatly changed, yet these archetypal qualities can have a new resonance and meaning should you recognize these stresses and the qualities they develop, and feel that the knowledge can help. I hope so.

In addition to characterizing the basic stresses, I shall also be describing in each case the balance that has to be achieved between two polar responses, what might be called the 'too positive' and the 'too negative'. In each case I will emphasize just one response most likely to lead to that immediate stress. However, the alternative way of reacting also tends to lead to stressful consequences, often for others first and for you afterwards.

I. Saturn: when uncertainty challenges

We need a scope and conviction of vision to make choices that affect
future destiny.

The unknown is always stressful.

Many problems call on us to find vision and take responsibility in a
situation of uncertainty about the future. This is even more difficult when
combined with feeling comfortable about the past or present. Such questions
tackle the issue of who we are.

People want to know where they have come from and where they are
going. This is commonly central to the sense of self. There is a need for a
sense of history and meaning in life, a plan. Absence of this is stressful. Yet,
often, we only find the answer to this when facing exactly those questions
that call for a real sense of what is enduringly important to us.

When my wife and I were considering moving somewhere more rural and
quiet (as described earlier in Chapter 2), I noticed anxiety in myself. 'Where
should we go, what will it be like, do I want to have to travel more in order
to have a quieter location and better house or would it be better to stay in an
area (or even house) we know?' and so on. The uncertainty caused me
worry. Other questions people face include: Which school do we choose for
our child? Should I change jobs or career, or move on to another company
(where it might be safer and more comfortable to stay)? Is it safe to make this
major investment in new machinery or employees, or do we stick to the old?
Which alternative machine will be best?

When faced by uncertainty there are two rival ways to respond that are
each unhelpful and may lead to problems or even evils. One is to go madly
forward making wild and naïve decisions that can lead to great harm. Many
business, political and military leaders have done this. The other is to become
stuck and irresolute. It is this that most often leads to anxious stress. After all it
is in the *consequences* of irresponsibility that stress usually arises.

The historian in us grows comfortably rooted in the past, reminiscing
about the good old days and finding it difficult to change. How many leaders
and politicians have found it difficult to change a corporate or society culture
because of fear of change?

The greater the future uncertainty, the greater the potential stress. For
example, stress is typically greater when there is a long time between the
moment of decision and knowing the consequences.

In February 2000, Ken Livingstone, the charismatic British Labour politician, had to make a decision between two mutually exclusive alternatives that tested his values and destiny. He had to decide whether to stay in the Labour Party, to which he had belonged for decades, or whether to fight to be Mayor of London, a position he felt he owned and for which many Londoners would support him, on an Independent ticket. If he chose the former, he might never be Mayor. In the latter case, he would be thrown out of the Party, and might not even win as Mayor. Such a question must have challenged him very deeply, calling for an answer to what had priority and meaning in his life. (He answered it by standing for mayor and winning.)

The danger is avoidance and short-term decision-making—Nero fiddling while Rome burns—or else playing it safe when long term decisions are really required. This is actually very tiring. It often means doing much more work too: implementing temporary solutions that later get replaced.

Such challenges call on our *Saturn* qualities. Saturn is the Roman name for the Greek Chronos, the god of time and death who is often pictured with a sickle (see his sign or sigil).

The Saturn Sigil

Every decision kills other alternatives; every new thing kills or changes the past. It has been found for example that major organization change induces the same process of grieving that Elisabeth Kubler-Ross identified amongst those bereaved (see page 212).

Saturn was always associated with the forces of death. To the mediaeval mind, Saturn with his sickle was the grim reaper, an animated skeleton. However, there is another way to look at this. Saturn or Death was always shown as a skeleton. Why? The skeleton obviously survives death longest. It is also already the 'deadest' part of the body, the most fixed and unchanging. Yet its marrow is the source of renewed life—it is where new cells and blood are created—and its rigidity is vital to life on the Earth.

Just as the cells in their life-cycle are embodied in more enduring organs that need to be fashioned around the architectural permanence of the skeleton, so do good plans need to be fashioned around values in a strong and permanent framework of vision linked to self-knowledge and identity. Just as cells are born within the marrow of the bones, so good day-to-day plans arise from a living centre of vision.

Developing our Saturn character means being able to respond when tough questions come that will impact upon the future. It calls for vision, rather than shying away from the discomfort and risk, holding on to the past, or making wild, uncaring or thoughtless decisions. Hitler, for example, had a vision that was uncaring and irresponsible to the point of being evil. Chief executives have sometimes thoughtlessly bet the future of their companies, causing pain to hundreds or thousands of 'merged' or 'reorganized' or 'let go' employees. Uncaring conviction is no answer, but nor is sentimental fear.

Personal growth means developing the energy, vision and realistic self-confidence required for making long-term decisions well. The more I can develop clear ideas about what I want to bring about—or who I want to become in the future— the easier it becomes to assess options. The choice becomes murky when I lack a vision of what I really need. Having a larger aim in mind is one of the essential characteristics of the human over the animal.

Another example of clip art capturing a contemporary issue.
Peering into an uncertain future is worrying!

Saturn is regarded as the historian of the soul, the part that gives permanence to the past by remembering and valuing all that we have experienced, while still calling on us to fulfil our potential and destiny. Saturn's sickle harvested all that humans had made of life.

While too strong an adherence to the past becomes a barrier to change, and lack of concern becomes a recipe for disaster, what helps is honouring the past without being stuck in it: letting the past die while drawing from it values that are important for the future.

At other times, the problem may not be deciding on the future, but wondering what will be the consequences of different ways of trying to get there. I may know exactly what I want to achieve, but don't know which option will achieve it. What will actually be unfolded by each option? Growth then means developing the courage to make the best decision I can, and living calmly with the consequences. Alternatively, if I am not yet in a position to decide, I should quietly postpone the decision while developing a plan to become better equipped.

As the Saturn quality develops, people become more and more capable of visionary and strategic leadership, as though they feel the future in their bones.

Saturn stress is very common among organizations, among leaders who have to take decisions and among employees who find they face uncertain consequences from decisions that others have made. Success comes most to those who keep their long-term vision clearly in mind and ensure that each thing they tackle leads usefully towards it. 'Eat the elephant in bite sized chunks,' by all means, but don't forget there's an elephant to eat.

> Judith was running a company with two offices a hundred miles apart. The geographical separation created all kinds of inefficiencies, but both offices employed people who were valuable to the company and would probably not relocate if the two offices were merged. People in both centres liked being where they were and associated the location with good things from the past. A decision was required, but it was nearly impossible to know what was right in advance or what might happen. Once one office was closed there would be no way of reversing the decision, so it kept getting postponed. At the same time, no firm decision to remain as two offices was taken and, because of the continuing awkwardness and inconvenience, for several years the question kept coming up. For Judith, this meant living with uncertainty and an unanswered question, an uncertainty that also sapped the morale of the company.

Some organizations have started to use ceremonies to help them let go of the past, for example having a celebratory funeral for an old product line as a step towards accepting the new line. Effective change projects in organizations often begin by drawing on the mythology and history of the company's past to reconnect to the fundamental aims and aspirations that still need to be as much a part of the future as the past. For the strength of the Saturn quality is that it helps to give permanence and persistence to the core vision.

> Pythagoras is famous for both the musical scale and for his studies of the 'planets' and he saw a connection between them. I believe an interesting way to experience the nature of the Saturn challenge is to listen to the

interval of the seventh in a musical scale. (This is the prime or tonic note in
the scale and the seventh, the one just before the octave, played together.)
It is a sound with edge, awakening but also uncomfortable. It draws one
on towards the new octave, yet at the same time it heralds a return to old
values, now raised to a higher power.

II. Jupiter: when you need insight into complexity

The intelligence to see order and simplicity in complex situations and
systems: the insight that separates the essential from the non-essential.

People are often challenged to make sense of a complex situation.

It could be something very obvious, like the design for a computer
application or a chief executive trying to understand everything that's happening in a very large organization. There is also, however, the complexity of
human relationships and ethics. If I give to one child all the time and
resources that she wants (perhaps because she is chronically sick), what will be
the effect on the others? Jack Straw, the British Home Secretary, faced a series
of such stressful questions in 1999, including how to respond to the various
arguments around General Pinochet, and others around refugees. The
challenge here was not the moral dilemma itself (that comes later!) but the
complexity of understanding the issues themselves. Once these are understood the moral solution is typically easier to reach.

Sometimes, one's head doesn't feel big enough to hold the picture.

Complexity clearly takes many forms.

Typically, people find themselves facing challenges they have already
developed capacities to meet; then suddenly something comes along a little
more complex than they are used to! It may happen to anyone. Every day,
juries need to make sense of a mass of conflicting data. A teacher needs to take
into account a wide range of behaviour, attitudes and intellectual performance in order to come to a real picture of a pupil. Every time I *really* want to
understand anything, I need to take into account a range of different factors,
such as personal, social, technical, economic, short term and long term
effects, and so on. Balancing many conflicting demands, relating the parts to
the whole, mediating between many different alternatives, assessing the

impact on the complex whole of any change in some part, are all examples of this challenge.

The stresses that meet us here are challenges that help us to grow a wonderful human capacity: really to become a *homo sapiens*: a wise human.

The skill that life develops is an intelligent imagination that forms judgements that take into account the inter-relatedness of things, separating what is essential from what is not essential. We learn to see the parts in the context of the whole; to be able to pass through and connect a mass of data in order to get the whole picture, to be able to see the wood formed by the trees.

Notice, this is neither simply abstract generalization that ignores details, nor is it being occupied with and hence overwhelmed by details. Both over simplification and over complication ultimately lead to stress for oneself, or others, or both. Rather, it is the ability to understand the relatedness of the particular and the whole that is required. This is, for example, important when you want to understand how one action, person, sub-assembly or change will affect the entire pattern.

♃

The Jupiter Sigil

In the past, this intelligent imagination was called the *Jupiter* quality or capacity. Jupiter was the king of the Roman and Hellenic Gods (the Greek name being Zeus). Jupiter brings the wisdom we also associate with Solomon. Jupiter sees the entire pattern and understands how one change will change the whole pattern—as in a single click of a kaleidoscope, or a single flash of his lightning bolt that illuminates everything.

A wise king or queen (or mum or manager or analyst) needs to sit upright on his or her throne (see the Jupiter sign or sigil for an abstract expression that also contains both this and the lightning bolt) with the ability to survey the whole realm or domain. Every part should be treated fairly with ideas and policies that have the best possible effects for both the whole realm and each part of it. An uncomfortable task! Parents, managers, knowledge workers, planners, designers and so on must find such wisdom every day.

This capacity needs an exact imagination inspired by the creative spirit. That which can take in the immensity of the stars is admirably equipped to know the world around in both universal and particular. Hence, in some spiritual traditions, this imaginative capacity is called the 'astral body' and is linked to the Sophia, the spirit of Wisdom in Gnostic and Platonic philosophy (philosophy = love of wisdom). However, its essential usefulness for everyday life makes it far more than just a mystical or academic wonder.

Zeus' spear or lightening bolt (to be imagined in this statue) symbolizes creative intelligence

Every day, every one of us needs to be able to make sense of the complex pattern of the world that we meet.

Such a challenge can be very enjoyable. We love the stimulation of being *homo sapiens*. Work without such challenge really can be extremely depressing, another kind of stress. We ache for something to tackle, work that actually stretches our mind. There are millions of people who every day work to order and who could with the right conditions take on much more.

> On the musical scale, I believe the interval for Systemic Wisdom is the sixth. It seems to express aspiration to embrace diversity as dynamic inter-relatedness. In the Indian raga modes, it is associated with the horse, in esoteric tradition the animal connected to thinking.

III. Mars: empowering yourself

> The forcefulness, courage and initiative that make things happen.

Empowerment and assertiveness are fashionable words. Both relate to the power of the individual to take the initiative and confront a challenge. It might be asking for your money back on a faulty pair of shoes or it might be deciding on a marketing plan for 10 million customers (and it's just possible that the person who can do the latter might have a problem with the former).

Initiative is a capacity for courage, imagination and action, sometimes in unpredictable and unplanned situations. It is a test of both our freedom and our resourcefulness. Aristotle believed that courage is the basis of all virtue. I believe initiative is closely related to our spiritual essence and how we appear in the world and to others. As St Gregory Palmas said: 'God is called Light not with reference to His essence but to His energy.' In the same way, Christ urged human beings not to hide their light under a bushel (or bundle of hay).

Great examples of leaders with courage during the last century include Nelson Mandela, Gandhi and Winston Churchill. Then there are the less well-known figures like Vernon Dahmer who was killed in Mississippi in 1996 by the Ku Klux Klan, and of course uncounted thousands of men and women known only in their own circles. True courage arises from an upsurge of human spirit: when we act out of the power of our higher Ego or I. Many spiritual traditions point to awe of God (a sublime form of fear) as the fear that allows us to transcend all other fear, while Martin Luther King pointed to the power of a cause or purpose to override all selfish fears when he, rather challengingly, said: 'If a man hasn't discovered something that he will die for, he isn't fit to live.'

On the other hand, there are times when we either meet a too forceful person or are told that that is how we appear. Initiative can become aggressive: when a powerful person or authority forces themselves on to the situation or other people. Such people rarely feel (immediate) stress; often they enjoy the power. For others though this can be extremely stressful. In time of course there are likely to be highly stressful consequences for the individual. What we need is therefore a balanced, aware, respectful initiative and assertiveness.

The Mars Sigil

Such courage and initiative has traditionally been associated with the god *Mars* whose sign also symbolizes male energy. Depending on your philosophy of life, you may be uncomfortable with the idea of developing martial qualities, but as indicated above there is no suggestion that one should become belligerent or a bully. Christ more than once demonstrated the courage to assert his convictions and this is the pure Mars quality (see also page 7). As Georg Kühlewind put it: 'He who does not wish to conquer is unconquerable.' Rather this is a question of developing our genius, the inspiring part of the soul for the Roman male, and here considered the masculine or *yang* spirit for everyone, whether male or female.

The conquest of oneself is better than the conquest of all others.
Buddha, *Dhammapada*, 104

Does this seem too far away from our everyday lives? In fact, the need for courage and purposefulness is everywhere. Many organizations are riddled with fear. Challenging a proposal by a boss or taking a decision that affects him or her could be our measure. Making an ambitious plan (often called an 'aggressive' plan) and going for it requires forcefulness and spirit. They are qualities we traditionally associate, quite rightly, with leadership. (Increasingly, of course, it is not one rather autocratic leader but groups of people individually committing to a team goal who make such plans and so exhibit leadership.)

Thoughts of doubt and fear never accomplished anything, and never can.
James Allen

Life seems to bring us challenging situations according to the strength of character we have already developed. (Mind you, it might sometimes seem as if we are faced with rather too many situations just above the scale of our preference.)

The experience of Mars stress *is a challenge to develop the courage necessary to overcome fear and stick to convictions and the truthful way.* Difficult decisions, frozen will, the feeling of powerlessness or fear are, I suggest, teachers calling forth from us our sleeping courage to be human.

In David Whyte's moving poem, 'The Old Interior Angel',[13] he describes the point of fearfulness when even a hero (such as you or me) sits down, momentarily afraid to take another step until finding inner inspiration. ('Namaste', in the text, means 'greetings'.)

One day the hero
sits down,
afraid to take
another step,
and the old interior angel

limps slowly in
with her no-nonsense
compassion
and her old secret
and goes ahead.

'Namaste'
you say
and follow.

The 'interior angel's' compassion, her secret and her leadership belong, I believe, to the same assurance in vulnerability that Picasso spoke of: when the human being, with no external leadership, but trusting and following the inner star in the darkness, feels sheltered even in acute vulnerability by knowing and pursuing higher or true aims (see page 60).

Inner trust and courage form the assertiveness that enables us to pursue and achieve our goals, even in the face of opposition and difficulty. True assertiveness is not aggression, nor is it just confronting people, nor is it a social mannerism and polite language formula. The courage required to start a new business, to change job, or even to face a rebuff and ask a girl for a date are each an example of assertiveness. If I do not have enough of this strength of mind, what happens? People and situations tend to push me around and I lack the ability to achieve what I really value. Little progress takes place without human beings asserting their deep inner wishes shining from Picasso's star or Whyte's interior angel.

Instead of being defeated by what seems too much for me to face, I grow when I can confront it. As the poet Rilke put it:

Winning does not tempt that man.
This is how he grows: by being defeated, decisively
By constantly greater beings.

We may not wish to be defeated, but nearly all sportsmen and women know the thrill and importance of playing against better opponents. Yet is it not all too uncommon for people to be afraid of real challenge, or to feel that they are too impotent to make a difference?

Marie worked for the administration director of a small production company. She was gradually becoming slightly neurotic, imagining that her boss disapproved of the work she was doing and was overlooking her for promotion. She had a one-to-one session with a counsellor who suggested that she should go and ask her boss what she really thought. The experience was enlightening. In fact most of the problems had been imaginary.

Anthony was a divisional manager of an information technology company responsible for managing a Europe-wide business unit. When the company began to experience financial difficulties, the top management team made one of his managers redundant without consultation. Anthony was furious and at the same time panicky. Together we agreed that the issue was that Anthony had to have the power to manage without unnecessary interference if he was going to be expected to achieve the company results. As a result, Anthony decided to go and visit the chief executive both to complain and to assert certain minimum conditions needed in the future if he was going to do a good job. The meeting went very well. In fact, the chief executive came out of the meeting with a better understanding of the situation Anthony was in, and with more respect for him as a leader.

Life experience gradually teaches us assertive technique and courage. As this grows, we become able to take on greater and greater challenges.

Normally, we learn that lack of assertiveness does not work. For example, when we fail to communicate our mind to a boss (or a partner), we find that they just don't know what we want. And if we don't strive to achieve a difficult goal when we have one, the chances are that we end up drifting through life. When Edmund Hillary was asked why he climbed Mount Everest, he said that it was because it was there. In fact, Mount Everest was there for many other people too, but not all of them wanted to climb it! We all have our own metaphorical Mount Everest waiting to be climbed.

Courage may arise from stupidity. For example, a millionaire once said that an entrepreneur is a person too stupid to know that his or her idea will not work. This is not the courage I am referring to. Wagner's opera *Siegfried* tells a story from the Edda of a hero who wants to understand the meaning of fear and therefore goes to fight a dragon. Dragons usually symbolize hidden resources and wisdom. The wisdom in this tale, for all old legends contain wisdom, lies in the fact that in the experience of fear overcome, we grow in character and maturity. As the title of the best selling book by Susan Jeffers goes: *Feel The Fear and Do It Anyway*.

> On the musical scale, the interval for Courage is the fifth, the sound of the awakening call to action. In the ancient Indian raga scales, this interval is called Pa and is linked with the elephant-headed warrior-god, Hanuman.

IV. Venus: the call of care

A bounteous capacity to nurture potential, caring for, renewing, and re-energizing people, organizations, processes and places.

One of the most memorable scenes in the Gospels concerns the visit of Christ to the home of Lazarus and his two sisters, Martha and Mary (probably Mary Magdalene). Mary, in an act of loving devotion takes some expensive oil and anoints Christ as if he were a King or Emperor. This irritates Martha. She has so many things to take care of and wishes that Mary would help her. Western civilization sees the difference between the contemplative and practical spiritual paths dramatized in this scene. It illustrates that although joy can come from caring for another person, animal or situation, this can become distressful if there are so many demands on the caregiver that she or he feels unable to cope. I am sure that this is an experience that has been had by

The generous beauty of the Venus de Milo in the Louvre famously demonstrates the Venus equation: whatever makes us feel good is beautiful and desirable. Venus de Milo speaks to this yearning with her bountiful beauty

almost everyone in the caring professions: teachers, nurses, doctors, social workers and so on. It is perhaps not surprising that so many professionals feel they have to nurture a kind of neutral coldness, a professional distance to those whom they are looking after.

But an excess of needs in others is an experience just as easily had by a mother (or father), a businessperson with many employees reporting to her or him or even just with a lot of things to take care of.

It is a pleasure to check into your hotel room on holiday and find that it is not just clean and efficiently provided for, but also has some little touches that show that someone has cared about making it a place in which to enjoy a visit. It may be an interesting picture on the wall, a bowl of fruit, some flowers, the gardens, or some other welcoming and homemaking touch. Hence we associate this quality with the caregiver who meets our needs and desire for joy and beauty, traditionally associated with goddesses such as Venus, Aphrodite, Freyja, Artemis and Mother Kali (in one of her guises anyway).

Such caregivers can make the wretchedly sick feel comfortable, can turn the desolate meeting room into a welcoming workspace, the house into a home, and can make a lonely and shy young person feel significant. Or they can ensure that the visiting client feels personally welcomed, fêted, and cared for. In fact, it is the quality of personal service given to customers and clients that is typically most significant in shaping their future attitudes and loyalty.

While we might associate such care with women in general and professions

The Venus Sigil

like secretaries or nurses in particular, it is a feature in every life, for everyone needs to experience caring, if only of pigeons or a stamp collection. For as the *Venus* sign suggests, the quality of care comes from strength in the depths, not necessarily in outer show like Mars. It is like the well that never runs dry but nourishes the thirsty; thus fruitful power is drawn up to serve the circle of humanity (as symbolized in the Venus sign or sigil).

At one end of the spectrum there's the challenge of finding sufficient inner resources genuinely to care for others' needs. At the other end lies the interfering carer, the person who imposes their care and concerns upon you. Every teenager normally goes through the moment of revolt when he or she says 'Enough!' to parental care. This example (often a painful experience for the carers) shows how care has to be appropriate to the needs and indi-viduality of those cared for and therefore wanted. This is achieved through genuine empathy rather than habit or a selfish desire to be 'wanted'.

Once again, therefore, life brings us the opportunity to develop an

important, human capacity. If there is any-thing the Earth and human society needs, it is an abundance of people with more and more capacity to care. *The call of care aims to develop a love of reality, life and people, of human situations and of details that develops an ever more abundant fountain of generous spirit equal to needs.*

What happens if the number of things to care for exceeds the span of care, like the performer spinning more and more plates who has to run faster and faster from one plate to another to keep them all up in motion? Mothers (or fathers) with several small children—as in this reworked con-temporary image—understand this well. In such circumstances, people start to feel not only that their forces are being exhausted, but also that they are no longer even doing a good job of caring. The task becomes a chore. The generous fountain of goodness runs dry or turns sour.

Of course, forces *are* being exhausted. These may include physical strength and energy, but very often the real problem lies in more subtle energies: in the psychological and, especially, emotional energy and life forces. Whenever we genuinely care for something, it is as if it is bathed in a glow of warmth and attention. We put something of ourselves into the world. However, what we put into the world needs replenishing if we are not to become empty.

One valuable remedy is often to ensure that the caregiver is receiving care. On this principle, every company should look to see who is caring for the carers. Organizational resources both emotional and practical need to be mustered in the support of front line service personnel. Another remedy is that we take the time to look after ourselves. Have a good night's sleep; take a walk in the refreshing beauty of nature; do some painting or go to a concert. The more a company can make space for and encourage such activities, the more likely that it will have an enlivened workforce. The more the individual acts responsibly towards himself or herself the more they equip themselves.

Here, therefore, is the fourth quality that life itself can bring about as a life-giving quality in us. Conscious awareness and exercise will, however, speed and strengthen the process. The exercises described in the next chapter are helpful. As a general principle, the more we develop our interest in what is around us, our keenness of observation and our sense of wonder, the more we refresh ourselves and encourage empathy. Interest enlivens the soul as air does the body and wonder the spirit.

> I believe Care is found in the musical scale in the lovely interval of the fourth. It evokes the warm and generous strength of the Mother goddess. In the ancient Indian raga scales, it is called Ma, her ancient name.

V. Mercury: the call of flexibility

Flexibility in blocked or continually emerging circumstances.

Have you ever had the experience of being driven down a road you know well only to find at one corner, when you fully expect to be turning one way, that the driver goes another? It can be as if your whole body has actually made the turning inwardly, and now has to be wrenched back to join the actual motion of the vehicle. This is an example of how we can become stuck in a pattern, in fact in a rut, which prevents us responding flexibly to the situation in hand. When such a jolt happens, the inner experience is of a type of stress and, at the same time, an awakening reminder that we have got stuck in a habit. A pattern (the 'rut') has been moulded into our personal body of patterns. This imaginal body or field is a source of life, imagination and creativity. We use it, for example, to anticipate an activity, such as making a movement or gesture or trying to sing a particular note. Craftsmen and musicians learn the patterns of techniques and musical pieces. We drive and walk and speak and read from such learnt patterning. And to do the simplest thing, such as pick up a glass, it must first be imagined as an action or pattern of movement. With repetition these become ingrained.

Patterns in our flow of life, in our personal biosphere, or life-forming nature, are very necessary, for example in breathing, but if they become too set they don't respond flexibly to new circumstances. The heart needs to respond quickly to the entire dynamic range of its potential for real health and fitness. Our conscious mind can also become set, accustomed to particular thoughts and situations to patterns of thinking.

As we get older, the danger increases that we lose the openness and creativity to respond with situational imagination. It is said that as we approach middle age the slim waist and broad mind of our youth exchange places! When this happens, our stress levels increase. Psychologists at the University of Maryland argue that conservatism is a set of neuroses rooted in 'fear and aggression, dogmatism and the intolerance of ambiguity'. Our response can therefore be to seek out the safety of past practice, conformity, habits and known environments: or we can relish the challenge to stay young and creative.

> Dick had become obsessed about a training workshop that he was due to deliver. First he tried to lock himself away to find the time to work on it, but was constantly interrupted. In the time that he managed to grab, he became fixated and produced more and more teaching and lecture material and less and less experiential exercises for the participants. He had become too stressed in his attitudes and this was impacting upon the quality of his work.
>
> The breakthrough came when he had a meeting with a colleague who asked him what he was doing and if there were any alternative ways that he could approach the task. 'If you have so little time, is there some way that you could create a lot of material with very little work for yourself?' This simple question had Dick immediately looking flexibly at alternatives. He could design large chunks of the day around exercises that would be more fruitful for the participants and would take him a lot less time to develop.

In mediaeval courts, kings would licence the court jester to poke fun at proceedings or otherwise insert levity and imagination into court life. Without this, there was a real danger that the grave business of making policy would have become too formal and stodgy. In short, it prevented the court from becoming too serious and inflexible.

At the opposite extreme, there is the individual who is so flexible and inventive that he or she is continually inventing new possibilities, revising plans and seeing new opportunities. In a manager, this can become impossible for staff who never have time to implement and never know how long anything will be a real plan. In such circumstances, their response to the stress is often to ignore each new idea or imperative until there is sufficient evidence that it will 'fix'.

Similarly, I see in companies a regular problem of so many (and often conflicting) change processes that it is extremely stressful for staff. Typically most change projects in such an environment end up failing. The inventor may find it fun, but it is unproductive.

Nevertheless, one of the challenges that working life brings us—whether working at home with the family or in the office—is the need to be imaginative and flexible in the face of an array of problems. Whereas Jupiter asks us to have the ability to overview the complexity of what meets us and

Mars demands of us the incisive ability to cut through problems, we also need the imagination to be able to view the world from a different perspective. While Jupiter notices that there is a wall surrounding the space we want to enter, and Mars tries to bludgeon through it, sometimes a smart person is the one who is figuring out how to go over or under or around the wall.

Too much rigidity, in time, rules and planning, in changing circumstances eventually leads to stress. Entering the office each day to get some work done can be a hazardous business. Work interruptions, telephone calls, email, and visitors can seriously derail your plans. Amidst the diversity of action in the office, the most serious problem may be that we need continually to adjust our attention between people and from one subject to another, one mood to another, one suggestion to another. The inner challenge this brings us is to be able to be completely present, in the right frame of mind and on our toes, from moment to moment.

When we are unable to switch quickly enough from one activity to another totally different one, we gradually become more and more over-loaded and stressed.

The Mercury Sigil

On the other hand, if we can bring sufficient situational imagination into our tasks, we become lively and creative. It is probably no accident that the court jester was usually also an acrobat and skilled juggler. These are skills that require balance and dexterity, the ability to flow from one posture to another without losing balance, the quickness of wit to respond instantly to circumstance. Perhaps it is also no accident that the English word quickness means both speed and aliveness.

The marvellous human capacity of quickened flexibility was traditionally associated with *Mercury*. The Mercury quality was related to everything connected with flow, movement and transformation, for example in imaginative thinking, as in Mercury's winged feet. Mercury's rod, known as the Caduceus rod, symbolizes the lively energy that flows up the spine through the nervous system to give wings to the soaring mind (and the sigil is an abstracted image of this). The silver metal, mercury, or quicksilver, quickly forms moving globules and is the most liquid and flowing of metals at normal temperatures, as well as being highly responsive to temperature changes (as its use in thermometers shows).

A juggler learns to juggle by juggling. An acrobat learns to roll and tumble by rolling and tumbling. So do we all. The stresses that call for flexibility develop flexibility. The mother creatively juggling with the demands of the day, the businessman rolling with the problems of the market, the inventor approaching the problem from a new angle, all are practising the Mercury art. Only sometimes the juggler has too many balls to juggle and the acrobat too many twists to perform before landing. Any juggler must learn to accept that he or she will drop balls and any acrobat that he or she will sometimes fall. The experience can be painful. But when we view it as part of a process of developing situational wisdom, then this lightness of attitude already helps us to develop just the quality needed to progress.

The difference between the Venus juggler described above and the Mercury juggler helps to illuminate both. Venus stress arises when, exhausted by the caring tasks I have to accomplish, I cannot keep up. Mercury stress arises when I lack the flexibility to adjust imaginatively to the new or to the speed or range of things coming to me. Moon stress (see below) has yet another quality.

When you develop such quick, imaginative reflexes, in responsible and responsive ways, I believe you will bring into your work situations the valued quality of being a healer, for Mercury is also connected to the healing arts. All healing involves transformation. According to many systems of medicine, illness only comes about through an imbalance in the body's systems. Healing is therefore the process of restoring balance. Problem solving always needs flexibility to bring resolution.

> Mercury's interval in the musical scale is I believe the third. It feels lively, but unfinished, as if striving to become something else. In fact, it becomes very satisfying to play a fourth immediately after the third: to move, to pass on to the more comfortable joy of the care-giving mother.

VI. Moon: judgement and control in a world of activity

Evaluation, feedback and control in a busy world.

The sixth capacity affects our ability to evaluate both the world and ourselves accurately and objectively. It is concerned with whether we feel at ease—with what we are doing, how we expect to manage and how we think others evaluate us. Opinion—our own and others'—may be the toughest stress to cope with.

At a purely physical level, the moon reflects the cosmos, and especially the sun. Thus *Moon* became associated with the ability to reflect on the world and to reproduce ideas and life. The moon was naturally regarded by most pagan peoples as one of the most important elements of the cosmos. Each of the ancient peoples had at least one goddess associated with the moon, including Juno for the Romans, Artemis or Diana amongst the Greeks and Near Eastern peoples, Ishtar for the Babylonian and Chaldean peoples and Isis amongst the Egyptians.

Similarly, the capacities that we associate with the moon are amongst the most important for the human being because of their association with self-image and reflection on the world. Each Roman woman had a 'juno', a part of her soul that corresponded to the male 'genius' and was connected to her fundamental identity. While this inner reflexiveness belongs conventionally to the female polarity, its yin quality belongs to members of both sexes.

The Moon Sigil

As we have been discovering, the two factors of self-image and reflection are closely related. The opinions we form about our experiences, in other words how we judge them, are affected by the filters that we put on experience and these are largely shaped by our self-image or identity and attitudes.

Evaluation requires the ability to make a clear mental image of what you want to evaluate. You then form impressions of this image. It is this aspect of reproduction—analogous to 'man being made in the image of God'—that explains why Juno, Diana and others were rulers of reproduction and childbirth.

It is interesting that photography, a process of capturing an image of the world and reproducing it, was developed using silver, a metal alchemically associated with the moon. Photography is a technique that reflects a common human desire to control and capture the world, as well as to fix images of it. In the same way, the sixth self-leadership skill depends on how we see ourselves managing.

Life constantly requires the ability to be aware of all that we are responsible for, even when in a rush or amidst many activities. This applies as much to a parent as in our jobs. We need to be able to maintain an objective overview of all that is happening as well as detailed information on whatever is important. Unlike the Mercury challenge, which required creative responses, the challenge here is simply awareness and prioritization. At the same time we are constantly deciding whether all is well (in which case we can be at ease) or whether things are or will soon be fraying at the edges (in which case we become anxious).

Take these four common causes of stress:

- You have a wide range of tasks ongoing that you are responsible for. It becomes hard to make a picture of everything that is happening;
- You start to feel out of control. Or you start to fear that the project you are managing doesn't look as if it is on course;
- You are preparing for some major undertaking when other people will be judging you or your work. This could be an exam or a business pre-sentation or a meeting. You start to form a picture of how you might be seen and so you worry;
- You get some feedback—perhaps from the kind of event just mentioned, perhaps by surprise. It gives you someone else's picture of you and at least for a while it is unwelcome because it differs from your picture of yourself in a way you don't like. It challenges your self-image.

All are frequent causes of stress and all are concerned with self-knowledge and the way that we evaluate both the world and ourselves. Mastering the capacity to see things accurately provides great strength and the basis of serenity.

Amongst the most common causes of stress is the anxious way that we evaluate the world and ourselves. Seeing things objectively yet positively strengthens you for life.

The personal mastery that comes from developing a healthy moon capacity includes:

1. Time and work management;
2. Energy to handle unpleasant tasks;
3. Openness to learning from others—especially about yourself;
4. Self-knowledge.

'Too much to do!'

This classic Moon stress is probably the area of work life that is the most common source of stress. Who does not know the experience of a long 'To Do' list and not enough time to do it? Who hasn't felt the panic of too many things to control? One of the stress signs is starting to forget details, like people's names, appointments and required actions. I also find myself losing things, a common problem. Life may become a rush from thing to thing, or an unrelenting treadmill. At first the rush may be exciting (level one stress as described in Chapter 2), then more stressful. We may reach a stage of pushing papers around unable to do a thing. When I become too stressed by such a life, I become irritable and lacking in awareness of others. If the stressfulness becomes too extreme, it often leads to skin irritation. (Perhaps by now it is no surprise to learn that traditional medicine linked the moon to our skin and nervous system.) Eventually, burnout or a nervous breakdown may follow. These stages correspond with the levels of stress and illness described earlier.

The first recorded meaning of *business*, in the Lindisfarne Gospels, was anxiety or worry. It was not until the twentieth century that *business* acquired its modern meaning. Nevertheless, the association between *business* as anxiety and as economic activity remains profound and perhaps not co-incidental. After all, Genesis associates the fall of humanity with the distress of needing to live by the 'sweat of the brow'.

'It's impossible to keep track'

Many people have the related experience of being responsible for activities that they have no hope of closely monitoring. Work and activity has to be trusted to others. Perhaps you know the experience of how you need to remain in touch with events whether or not you know the details and indeed whether or not you can even maintain a real overview of all that is happening? The capacity to keep control in such a situation sometimes seems to need a sixth sense! I can remember a series of managers who seemed to have the uncanny ability to cut through whatever had been prepared in a presentation and ask the one question for which I was not prepared.

The bustle and demands of working life can lead to a nervous breakdown, but more typically they develop in us an important life mastery: the facility to maintain awareness of the progress of all that is important. To get off the treadmill and take charge, hence to develop the capacity to know what is really needed, mastering clock time, maintaining momentum, dealing with priorities.

Of course, the more you develop this ability the more you are shunted into situations that demand ever more of you. Perhaps you know the saying: if you want something done, give it to a busy person. After all, another way of describing the 'Moon skill' is the ability to manage. Promotion tends to follow those who have it.

In the intervals of the octave, this challenge corresponds with the second. This is an uncomfortable sound. For what are we aware of if it is not all the unfinished business that needs to be transformed? To achieve this, we have to proceed right through the scale until we reach the bright sunshine of the octave.

'I hate doing this'

Have you ever, like this lovely clip art nurse, found yourself with something to do which you would rather not? At this point, people normally find all sorts of other jobs, usually trivial, that take up their time. The job to be done weighs heavily on the mind, but does not get done. This burden is moon stress. The longer it sits there, the more exhausting it is and the less we want to start it.

Unfinished tasks actually create an aversion to their own completion, leading us to loss of control of our lives. Finished tasks on the other hand give us satisfaction. This is an interesting phenomenon. A little thought shows us that this is in fact a weakness of character (although such phrases are not very 'PC' today). It is in fact very important to our sense of self and self-satisfaction and inner serenity that we feel able to tackle even unpleasant jobs and that we have the strength of will to do so. So this rather frustrating experience actually takes us, eventually, in a direction that we can applaud.

The effect of avoiding issues is a little like getting drunk: it might seem pleasant at the time, but the hangover the following morning brings its own educational material. So in the same way postponing what is important might seem like the best thing at the time but time shows the importance of tackling priorities.

Ann was an Open University mature student. Every time an essay was due, the house would get spring-cleaned, the garden tidied and lawn mown. With each essay, Ann would avoid the difficult task and instead turn to others, creating an alternative list of priorities. Interestingly, the deadlines became both a cause of stress and the means to force herself to face the issue. Achieving each essay successfully became an accomplishment that gradually led to an increase in confidence.

'I'm worried about how others judge me'

So far I have focused on the ability to master the world, recognize the status of things and take appropriate action. What happens, however, when the bit of the world under examination is *me*? What happens when we expect to be assessed by others? And what is the effect of our own self-critical judgements. In time, these lead to the final gift of moon stress: self-knowledge.

Many of the causes of 'unpleasant tasks' are connected with nervous anxiety about whether others will perceive that it has been done well. Consider exams, presentations, reports, or any assignment. We may postpone or be anxious about the work because we anticipate the evaluation. This is most likely to be the case when we are ourselves unsure of the outcome. *In other words, we are anxious when our present reflection on our ability, however unconscious, leads to the fear that it will be below standard.* It is called worry.

This is connected to what Jung called the shadow or what other traditions call the 'double'—our half-conscious awareness of our imperfect nature, which alchemy and other esoteric traditions also describe as our moon nature. Put together an instinctive feeling of imperfection—however it may have come about—and a wish to 'do well' and there is a perfect recipe for anxiety and worry.

Mix self-doubt and the desire to do well; bake until thoroughly anxious!

In most cases fear does not flow from a conscious and objective picture of reality. It flows from the murky world of emotional conditioning and suppressed awareness. Those who think clearly about what they want to do and look at this objectively in conjunction with their abilities are much less likely to be worried and distressed. Doing this also removes the sting of anxiety about someone else's judgement and lets you respond to such judgement more coolly. Viktor Frankl commented that 'Emotion, which is suffering, ceases to be suffering as soon as we form a clear and precise picture of it.'

I know for myself that one of the worst causes of my own stress comes when I have a big presentation or workshop to prepare and I worry about how my client or the public will take it. In my anticipation I brew up worry based on half-suppressed images of failure.

Supremely and positively confident people anticipate with enthusiasm. They know they will do well. Such reactions *may* be as unbalanced as the hopeless worrier's. They may, for example, get very angry if they get

Diana is often shown with bow and arrows, as in this statue from the Louvre. In an important classical myth, Diana uses them to kill a young man who sees her and her maidens in their privacy. This myth captures (amongst other things) the essential fear of exposure that lurks in the human soul

negative feedback. Or they may quickly bubble up with enthusiasm again and so never gain self-knowledge. (The stresses of these personality types are described in Chapter 7).

The more openly and truthfully we picture ourselves, the more aware we are of what is imperfect, without being despondent, miserable or angry, the easier it is to face and receive feedback. It becomes easier to judge its accuracy and easier to accept. This is why the daily practice of objectively reviewing the day is so powerful in reducing stress and developing self-leadership. (This is described in more detail in Chapter 6).

The judgement and awareness that grow out of moon stress contribute to an understanding that reduces silly anxiety and worry. One proverb calls worry an interest paid on trouble before it falls due. Aristotle said, 'There is either a solution to the problem, in which case it is pointless to worry; or there is no solution, in which case it is pointless to worry.' Worry gains us little or nothing. Self-knowledge gains us strength and serenity.

Be Here Now!
A traditional meditation, popular in the 1960s.

In conclusion, moon stress proves to be the most common: it is our all too familiar companion. However, with time, it can help us to develop wisdom, powerful resources and mature character.

VII. Sun: the need for moral maturity to confront the moral maze

Our path is to become heroic.

The seventh and last of these stress patterns stems from the challenge of maintaining moral balance in a complex world. Day to day work and life experience regularly brings situations that require an ethical or moral response. We might see a fellow employee being bullied or unfairly treated by a manager. The company we are working for and which pays us might be producing products or selling them in a way that gives us a dilemma: do we risk the result of a confrontation, or stay quiet? Or we might see someone taking the credit for what another has done. (It could be that *we* are praised when someone else was really responsible for the success.) Poorly tested solutions, shoddy research, products that you only *hope* you can deliver: tensions, dangers, prestige, threats: this is the environment of the moral maze.

Some jobs carry inherent problems. Sales and advertising people, for example, are often asked to sell products that may not be the best in the market, or where the real human need is somewhat questionable. Western companies are promoting cigarettes to young people in Africa and expensive branded products in third world countries. Hundreds of thousands of people are employed in the West in the armaments industry. Sunday newspaper colour supplements often describe some social or environmental iniquity in an article that faces an advertisement for the pampered lifestyle.

But although these are the most obvious cases, they are by no means the only or the most common ethical challenges. Most people make decisions quite early on about what they find acceptable and so avoid facing these extreme dilemmas. The challenge to be fair and honest and have integrity in day to day dealings is more typical. Which person should be promoted? How much should staff be paid? Does this person need to be fired? Do we stay with our old supplier who has served us well, or go with the new cheaper one? How much do we increase the pay this year? Can I use the phone or the photocopier for private use? Shall we tell the boss the truth? How do we communicate these results in a 'more positive' way? The list goes on.

Living in the complexity of lies and misinformation and truth, deeds and misdeeds, trustworthy and untrustworthy people, is certainly a challenge. Leaders and companies try to create trust amongst employees, customers and suppliers, a task certainly not easy and often not achieved. After all it can take years to create trust and only a day to lose it.

Nor are these issues simple. Suppose your company is going through a poor financial period. Do you frankly and honestly tell everyone about this? The consequence might well be that suppliers call in their debts, customers stop making commitments to buy, and key employees make plans to leave. So announcing such news can make the matter worse. On the other hand, covering up the situation means living with a lie.

The stress of such situations arises not only in the challenge to integrity but in deciding what *is* integrity. The stakes can be very high. *The common thread of this challenge is that failure leads to loss, either outward or inward loss.* For example, we may be afraid that by speaking out we will lose our job, that the company will go bust, that we will lose someone's favour or friendship, or a client's business, while silence can lead to keeping a friend you no longer admire, a job you feel uneasy about, a career that later you may regret.

We may be faced then with an agonizing decision to sweat over. The stress in this situation will probably be quite obvious. But, if we try to pretend that all is well, in other words if we choose to ignore the issue, we may find ourselves living with a secret, undiagnosed, psychological cancer (and it has been suggested that this may be a cause of physical cancer).

It is of course a curious phenomenon that the more our conscience troubles us the more uncomfortable we are. The morally insensible appear to suffer less! Arguably, though, the effect of living with a dormant conscience is a mind that gradually grows greyer. Dream life may become less vivid and colourful, the ability to think and make pictures may deteriorate and the imagination becomes less rich and more cunning. The real trouble with the cunning imagination is that it is one-dimensional and fixated. It is a form of obsession that we might welcome because it appears to bring success, but like any addiction it kills the quality of life.

If we are going to avoid wandering into these shady dimensions then we need to develop maturity and encourage our creative resolution and self esteem. Not only will this help us with the moral challenge but it will also give energy and purpose in dealing with the other six challenges described in this chapter.

Maturity, and especially moral maturity, is the great prize of life. Those who have genuinely developed it bring a courage and fairness to life that is deeply appreciated.

Innumerable works of the imagination portray the drama of the moral dilemma and the triumph of the right. *King Lear*, the great Shakespeare play, confronts us with the evil Edmund and his half-brother Edgar. While Edmund enjoys sexual favours and power, Edgar is reduced to playing a half-naked madman, but his are literally the last words. From here to the simpler world but similar code of the Hollywood Western there is a direct connection. When Shane, mysterious hero of possibly the best Western, turns back to rescue a town because of a boy's belief and hope. He also discovers his higher nature.

True maturity is a quality traditionally linked to the harmonious *Sun* that shines equally on all. Amongst gods, the sun god was typically pre-eminent or most loved: Marduk amongst the Babylonians, Ahura Mazda for the Zarathustrians, Apollo for the Greeks, Baldur for the Norse, Lugh for the Celts, Ra, Horus and Aten amongst the Egyptians, Michael for Jews and Christians as the leading angel, Vishnu in the Hindu tradition, and Christ are all linked with the Sun. The Sun symbol was the most important in megalithic culture.

The Sun Sigil

When the sun is shining it brings joy and life and growth into the world. When it grows faint or is obscured then gloomy winter comes and life goes underground. Ancient societies the world over honoured the radiating sun and its cycle of fertility (shown in the sigil).

The sun hero was the leader in each community. For example, commentators have associated King Arthur, Charlemagne, King David, Alexander the Great and other legendary and real figures as sun heroes to their people. As these legends suggest, our path is to become heroic too.

Christ, the 'Light of the World', is sometimes called the Sol Invicta, the unconquerable sun, and His death and resurrection echoed a common theme in the ancient Mysteries. These Mysteries were a vital part of the civilizations of Egypt, Greece, Rome, Carthage, Troy and Persia. It was a high honour to be initiated into these mysteries—for example the Roman Emperors insisted that they were initiated—and those who were, were considered fortunate.

> Blessed is he among men on earth who has beheld this. Never will he who has not been initiated into these ceremonies, who has had no part in them, share in such things. He will be as a dead man in sultry darkness.
>
> From the Hymn to Demeter, 480–2. This Homeric hymn composed in the seventh century BCE is the canonical hymn of the Eleusinian Mystery. (Translation by Care Kerényi.)

The Mystery ceremony involved some (mysterious) event so that participants received a sudden certainty about the nature of human life and death and an understanding of the cosmos. According to a leading modern scholar, Walter Otto, 'There can be no doubt of the miraculous nature of the event.'

To the classical mind, death meant entering the world of the shades, Hades, darkness. But, in the life and death of the Sun or sun hero, or of grain and plants, they saw a symbol of hope that gave courage for life and right conduct. For example, Adonis (or Thammuz) was central in the ancient initiation mysteries of the Near East and Greece during classical and pre-classical periods. Adonis spent six months with Aphrodite above the earth, amongst the sunlight, and six months below with Persephone. The Hymn of Demeter tells of how Persephone was carried off by the god of Hades, but was rescued for part of the year through the action of her mother Demeter, goddess of fertility. Well, life is an initiation path that brings us, too, an ongoing challenge: to go the way of light or the way of greyness, the sunny or the shady mind, or more particularly to be willing to experience both with equanimity.

Life's path often involves being willing to face the darkness, both our own inner darkness and the shadiness around, and then to shine into it.

The immense Indian saga, the Mahabharata by Vyasa dating from before 1500 BCE, describes the epic struggle of the Pandava brothers. At the heart of the tale there are a series of challenges to their *dharma*—exactly the quality of moral maturity described here. For example, the eldest brother, Yudhistira, is required by his understanding of right conduct to take part twice in rigged dice games. He loses everything he owns and he and his brothers are forced to go into exile for twelve years. Eventually this loss is fully recompensed.

Like Yudhistira, sometimes we too are challenged to risk our all to protect and sustain what is really important to us. In Christian legends, Christ accomplished this in the 'harrowing of hell' during his Easter period of death and resurrection. It means strengthening our Ego while reducing our egotism: developing our self-esteem through awareness of our conscience and our own higher Ego or I. Shakespeare's wonderful psychological portrayal of Macbeth shows us what happens when this does not take place. By contrast, his late plays like *The Tempest* and *The Winters Tale* show us the healing power of self-awareness and atonement. Organizations that are struggling to keep their customers and employees loyal could do well to recognize this.

It might appear from this that moral maturity is associated with tragedy or death. Far from it! It does require us to find our way down the narrow path of integrity rather than fear or self-interest. Yet those who live in this way are those who ultimately bask in the sun. As the Greek philosopher Epicurus (341–270 BCE) put it: It is impossible to live pleasantly without living prudently, honourably and justly, and impossible to live prudently, honourably and justly without living pleasantly.

> This experience is reflected in the interval of the octave, the soaring experience of rising from the lower note to the same note an octave higher. Doing this on an instrument like the piano opens us to the movement and quality, but really to experience the epiphany—and the effort involved—it needs to be sung.

CHAPTER 6

EXERCISES FOR INNER DEVELOPMENT

*Achievement, of whatever kind, is the crown of effort, the diadem of
thought . . . We are limited only by the thoughts that we choose.*

James Allen

If we are beaten by stress we find ourselves increasingly gripped with helplessness to control events or take long-term decisions. But, as we conquer
stress we develop the powers to meet inner and outer challenges. This
chapter provides exercises that can help to develop these powers. We are
used to the idea of going to school and university to train our minds. We are
used to the idea of going to a gym throughout life to exercise the body for
well-being. But we are perhaps less used to the idea that we can develop
health and well being of the mind through ongoing exercises. In the stress of
our times it becomes increasingly important to have a regular mental
workout—a gym for the mind.

The good news is that—unlike our school experience perhaps—it is a
satisfying and wholesome experience. And the results radiate into our general
health and well-being.

Many of the exercises in this chapter were suggested by Rudolf Steiner,
others originate in older traditions. I have found that they develop essential
strengths to cope more effectively—although I am not suggesting that I have
mastered them. They include ways to improve memory, empathy, listening,
courage, self-discipline, reliability, and imagination. Most of these exercises
take hardly any time, but work through continual practice.

Observation and sensitivity exercises

*Every living being that you bestow your love upon reveals itself to you;
lack of love is a veil overlaying the things of the world and shrouding them
from view. Inasmuch as you send out love you will receive knowledge in
like measure.*

Rudolf Steiner

Certain sensitivity and observation exercises amount to a basic preparation for schooling in spiritual development, whilst helping to deal with stress.

Sensitivity through accurate observation of our own inner responses to things is helpful in becoming aware of feeling stressed. It also helps us to become aware of the inner processes of our mind by which we generate our own stresses. I shall also explain in a later chapter (on the trial by fire) how they may school us in the most profound awareness of our circumstances and world.

Krishnamurti described observation without prejudice or opinion as one of the highest types of human intelligence. Indeed, from early times, philosophers have observed that how a person sees the world is a measure of their self-development.

Aristotle comments in his *Metaphysics*: 'Man is the measure of all things', implying that that which seems to exist for each man assuredly does so. If this is so, it follows that the same thing both is and is not, and is bad and good, and that the contents of all other opposite statements are true, because often some particular thing appears beautiful to some and ugly to others, and that which appears to each man is the measure.

(Take a look at the picture below. What do you see? It is discussed on the next page.)

What do you see?

The importance of this appears in every branch of life. Chapter 10 explores the risk of conflict that arises when observation is poor and riddled with prejudice. I have been frequently asked to perform audits for client organizations because I am expected to be able to observe closely, freshly and accurately and therefore to draw better conclusions about their company.

This indicates the close relationship between observation and thought. Often, these are almost undivided. The danger is that instead of discovering healthy meaning, we only confirm prejudice. Early Gestalt psychologists report how the mental frame that we bring into observation then conditions what is seen. Take for example the image on p. 116. What did you see?

Most people find it difficult to see anything meaningful until they are told that it is a picture of a giraffe, at which point it becomes obvious. The importance of this is that it demonstrates how the process of seeing is routinely also and simultaneously a process of meaning making. We see things meaningfully and cannot see until it is meaningful. We can explore the way by which this happens and its implications further. For example, you will see that the picture below is clearly a caricature of a rabbit.

A caricature picture of a rabbit: we recognize it because it is familiar

Let us consider this rabbit. First, it is important to be able to observe freshly, with an open-hearted intelligence. When observing things generally, try to eliminate prejudices and assumptions. It is very different to say, 'He spoke for seventeen minutes of the thirty-minute meeting' compared with 'He spoke too much'. One describes facts, the other opinion.

Peer pressure and other cultural influences also encourage the adoption of the point of view of others, especially when they are respected. Then prejudice provides a kind of mask that filters how others also see things.

Hence those who feel themselves in danger of being imprisoned behind this mask will resist it, and so the mask induces conflict.

Perhaps you have by now noticed that the picture of the rabbit is also a picture of a duck? The same image with not a jot or tittle changed can be two things. This ambiguous aspect-seeing (seeing according to different aspects) fascinated Wittgenstein who saw it as a paradigmatic phenomenon. What looks at first sight like a little fun demonstrates the ubiquitous tendency of human beings to experience different worlds or phenomena according to the aspect from which they view.

What happened when you read my commentary and caption? If you did see a rabbit first, perhaps it is because I influenced you? Notice how it requires motivation and inner effort to be able to see the image freshly in different ways. A similar effort is required to become free of fixed opinions or points of view.

As I have noted, observations and life experiences are coloured by feelings and preferences. For example, research shows that while a majority of cola drinkers select the leading brand as their preferred drink when testing labelled bottles, this is reversed on unlabelled bottles. This means that it is prejudice that is forming the preference, not 'true judgement'. Notice that seeing differently in this way becomes more than merely a trivial example (as in the duck and rabbit) but something a little more serious.

Indeed, it can become even more serious and important. Prejudice is behind many of the opinions that people have of the world, each other and even of themselves. The Klu Klux Klan lynched blacks because KKK members saw with a nasty culturally-conditioned aspect. Scientists who view the biological world as determined by competitive drives are, I believe, similarly biased in their view (and this will be explored in the final chapter). Developing open-mindedness and equanimity is an important virtue:

- To ourselves;
- To colleagues, family and friends;
- To people we meet and serve or who give us services;
- To life experiences that come along;
- To the creatures of nature;
- To new ideas and changes.

I believe that learning to observe how you describe things will genuinely help to reduce stress for both yourself and others around you. In particular, it will reduce conflict. Every fact and observation-based statement is inherently calming, for it brings order and understanding and rationality. Every pseudo-observation filled with opinion, emotion and negative judgement increases stress.

> Amaryllis was an enthusiastic new recruit to the management team of a pro-
> fessional service company. With an outgoing, sparkly, social personality she made
> a great effort to get on with everyone in her new team, but did so by forcefully
> expressing her social and political opinions as if they were facts everyone naturally
> agreed with. Of course, they did not, sometimes being 'too polite' to say so, and
> sometimes disagreeing. Amaryllis was unconsciously creating conflict with those
> who didn't fit 'her set'.

Good observation is the means to recover beauty and wonder in the world. For example, I noticed that I tended to walk through the world without really looking, far too occupied with my own thoughts. Taking up painting and photography revitalized my eagerness of looking. My daughter and son, both artistically active, have trained themselves through practice to see what others often miss.

At its most potent, observation becomes the power to rediscover the magical–divine:

> To see the world in a grain of sand,
> And heaven in a wild flower.

Or, as Whitman put it, 'A leaf of grass is no less than the journey work of the stars.' Such observation sees the instance of the divine and the universal in each particular. Steiner described a way of knowing or realizing that depends on thinking with heart. It is an 'instantaneous cognition—not a previously acquired view' and it cannot depend on memory or norms or past acknowledgements or habits. It enables a true realization, the 'making real' of something.

Zen practises this kind of thinking. For example, Zen poetry such as the Haiku is amongst the most sublime and yet simple achievements of the human spirit precisely because it requires long training in pure observation to capture the spirit of a moment, as in these three examples by Bashô:

> On the mushroom
>   Is stuck the leaf
>   Of some unknown tree.

> Just washed,
>   How chill,
>   The white leeks.

The snow having melted,
 The village,
  Is full of children.

Here, something real is 'realized', and the trick of the poet is to be able to re-evoke that in us. We too can practise observation. For example, simply take any old object, a part of a wall, a leaf, a patch of pond, a portion of the office and observe it, practising this regularly.

> Try what Goethe demonstrated in marvellous studies, in which he became able to see in a precisely scientific and yet artistic and wonder-filled way the life of a natural phenomenon. Begin with exact interest, precisely observing and experiencing any natural phenomenon through its stages using the senses. For example, you might observe the stages in growth of a plant or the transitions of a sunset. Although you cannot easily see a plant grow, you can observe several plants, for example different older and younger silver birches, and so begin to see exactly how the plant develops, what has grown this year and what in previous years (there is always a ring around the stem of the trunk or branch, at least for recent years, that denotes a new year's growth). Then bring what you have seen into exact life, seeing the various developmental phases as one process through exact imagination. It is not too difficult to be able to 'see' a plant grow from seed to full growth in this way. Goethe and others have been able to use this to see how all the myriad forms of plants emerge from the archetypal leaf form or how the endless potential of plants emerge 'like a fountain' from the archetypal plant.

In his book *The Wholeness of Nature*, Henri Bortoft describes Goethe's way of observing. See the Resources section for more information.

Observing means opening yourself up to what is there, paying attention until the invisible appears. The attitude that needs to accompany this should be as close as possible to wonder and love. Without feeling devotion to what is being observed, it is impossible to be truly open, or to find the beauty and wonder that is always present and whose discovery is a sign of true observation. Those who enjoy the spirit of wonder and devotion create, in the language of Gestalt psychology, a mental frame that illumines the living reality of things.

Tuning observation reveals a magical creation.

Here are some more exercises. They also have the effect of integrating the pure process of perception with the kind of healthy imagination that is needed to translate what is seen into what is understood in ways that add up to meaning without prejudice.

Observing living processes

In the first exercise, take every opportunity to observe plants, how on the one side they grow and flourish, blooming with health and vitality, and then how they decay, droop and die. This observation should be as accurate and active as possible, paying close attention to the actual phenomena, such as colour and form of the plant, suspending thoughts but paying close attention to inner response and the inner imagery that arise.

Life is a series of increases and decreases, of increasing energy and decreasing energy, of increasing stress and decreasing stress. In time all things come right. Becoming sensitive to this flow helps us to tune ourselves to what is needed in the moment.

Awareness of sounds

> It flashed up lightning-wise during a performance of Beethoven's 7th Symphony at the Queens Hall, in the triumphant first movement when 'the morning stars sang together and all the sons of God shouted for joy'. The swiftly flowing continuity of the music was not interrupted, so that what T.S. Eliot fairly calls 'the intersection of the timeless moment' must have slipped in between two demi-semi-quavers.
>
> *Warner Allen,* The Timeless Moment

A second exercise involves us in immersing ourselves in the experience of sound, in the inner world of sound, and indeed into the whole world of listening. Here are three examples:

- Set aside time to listen to the opinions of others, even the most contrary of opinions, without taking sides inwardly or outwardly. The aim is to be able to withdraw from any feelings of approval or disapproval. In this way, unite with the other person not on the basis of sympathy but out of a direct and pure experience of who he or she is. This will also be very helpful in dealing with conflicts (see also Chapter 9).
- Listen to someone speaking so that you are able separately to distinguish their thinking, feeling and their will (or intention). For example, some-

one may say, 'I am not angry'; but you may be able to hear how angry they really are and become aware of their intention to do harm. Or a person may be talking about their plans: become aware of their enthusiasm and determination, or otherwise.

- Listen to the difference between the sound of the object and the sound of an animal. For example, suppose you drop a stone on the ground and compare the quality of the sound with that of your cat meowing. One of them has only a kind of dull, compacted or heavy sound, while the other is filled with emotion or soul. The more sensitively we notice this, the closer we are to appreciating the soul world of the other.

Observing and understanding people

> Patience and tolerance means that you will do no harm to another.
>
> *Buddha,* Dhammapada, *184*

Here is a good exercise for observing people:

Very carefully, watch someone doing something and then guess what they will do tomorrow. Then compare what happens with the prediction, without any prejudice. You may also observe the present and try to work out the cause and find out if you are right. It depends on very close observation, not just random guessing.

At first, this exercise is likely to reveal the number of errors you are making, but gradually it enables you to get to know people better. People do have habits and characteristics: seeing them is not at all the same as prejudice.

Gaining self-knowledge through daily or life-retrospectives

> That true self-love and social are the same;
> That virtue only makes our bliss below;
> And all our knowledge is, ourselves to know.
>
> *Alexander Pope*

All self-development requires self-knowledge, and as I have commented on a number of occasions already, the art of dealing with stress is to develop self-awareness. Furthermore, as Pope reminds us, true self-knowledge is not a selfish but a social deed.

There is one invaluable exercise that will help with many areas of self-development, including equanimity, memory, meditation and others. This exercise is the Retrospective. The idea is simple: look back over your day, in reverse order, observing all that you have done and all your interactions with the world and other people in an absolutely neutral way, without judgement, as if you were looking at somebody else's life in whom you were interested, with no emotional baggage.

Let me explain the elements here in a little more detail. First, the retrospective exercise is based on reviewing the day backwards, i.e. it is an exercise for the evening and you do it by remembering the day, finishing with the morning. Do not worry if you fall asleep when you first begin this practice. In time, you will be able to remember your day as if you were watching a video backwards, but when you first begin you may find it easier to remember it in terms of a series of incidents, each of which you might remember forwards, proceeding back through them until morning comes.

There are several reasons for remembering it backwards. One of these connects with the next point I will discuss, the need to develop an objective outlook. Most people find that by remembering in reverse order they improve their ability to disengage their emotions from what has happened and view their day more objectively. Another reason is connected to the way that human beings establish and make sense of memories during the night, when of course everything that has happened in the day is taken more deeply into the soul. Remembering backwards helps with this.

You may find when you first do the exercise that it takes a tremendously long time to remember your day. After what seems like an hour you find you have only remembered the last fifteen minutes. Obviously if you carry on like this you will never be able to remember the whole day. In fact, your aim should be to be able to remember the whole day in only a few minutes, perhaps five to fifteen. The probable reason why you are taking so long is because you are being waylaid by emotion and interpretation, factors that are not only not needed but positively get in the way of the exercise. Another reason is that you might not be practised in the basic process of observing yourself.

Your aim is to be able to look at what you have done as a kind of moving tableau or film, observing yourself as the actor in the film while remaining a spectator. As soon as you are doing this, you can then move the image as fast as you can while still remembering what has happened. Thus a whole day can be compressed into a few minutes.

If you do have one particular part of the day that was particularly significant, then you can choose to do your Retrospective focusing on just that part.

There is an alternative form of this exercise. This takes the form of remembering your *life* backwards. Obviously you will probably need to remember your life in less detail than a day, but it is important sometimes to see the shape and character of your life history and so the character of your personality and patterns of your behaviour and destiny.

The second key aspect of this exercise is to observe your experiences as if you were looking at another person, and therefore to develop equanimity, objectivity and neutrality. If you remember what you have done and become angry, disappointed or pleased with yourself then this emotion is a barrier to true knowledge. Most people are better at noticing the qualities of others than they are of themselves. The reason for this is that emotions of satisfaction and dissatisfaction act as a distorting mirror; it is much better to look at yourself objectively and simply notice what you did without passing any judgement on it at all. People who blame and accuse themselves are more likely to blame and accuse others, so it is good to learn how to avoid this trait. People who are self-satisfied and pleased with themselves are more likely to become egotistical; another quality you might wish to rid yourself of. What happens when you practise simple observation, accepting that *this* is what you have done for better or worse, is that you truly get to know yourself.

And then something wonderful takes place: during the night this self-knowledge is turned into positive impulses for change. During dreams and deep sleep we take what we have seen and transform it into images of what we might have done, into actions that would have been more effective, and these become impulses for the future. It does not happen in one night, nor are you likely to achieve mastery of the retrospective exercise in one day, but steadily the combination of your conscious awareness and your subconscious working will have an effect on your character.

Furthermore, there are other positive benefits, including the fact that there will be times when you realize that there is something you have not done or that you need to put right and then you can make a decision to follow up in the morning. For example, I have reviewed a conversation I have had with someone and realized that I didn't thank him or her for something they had done. However, it is important to realize that the aim of the exercise is not to decide what you need to do but simply to see what you have done.

Other benefits include:

- Improvements in memory;
- The ability to form mental pictures;

- Equanimity;
- Presence of mind.

Finally, I think there is a wonderful and healing paradox embedded into this exercise: that you practise self-acceptance and self-development at the same time. Self-acceptance is a pre-requisite for serenity. We all need to be able to live comfortably with ourselves in order to reduce stress, remembering that if we don't we are most likely not only to damage ourselves but to create waves of repercussion for those around us. People who are driven, neurotic, paranoid and the like are not easy to live with. At the same time, it is clearly important not to be self-satisfied, but instead to look at ways to improve. The cultivation of an objective, non-judgemental view is a tremendous help in this and you will find that not only does it apply to the way that you look at yourself but also your ability to view the behaviour of others.

I believe it is important for human beings to acknowledge that fallibility is a fundamental aspect of our present-day nature and through this acknowledgement to develop tolerance combined with determination. Any exercise that can do this should surely be part of an everyday routine. One of Jung's patients sent him a letter which demonstrates most of the principles of this exercise, in which she described how her healing was brought about:

> Out of evil, much good has come to me. By keeping quiet, repressing nothing, remaining attentive, and by accepting reality—taking things as they are, and not as I wanted them to be—by doing all this, unusual knowledge has come to me, and unusual powers as well, such as I could never have imagined before. I always thought that when we accepted things they overpowered us in some way or other. This turns out not to be true at all, and it is only by accepting them that one can assume an attitude towards them. So now I intend to play the game of life, being receptive to whatever comes to me, good and bad, sun and shadow forever alternating, and, in this way, also accepting my own nature with its positive and negative sides. Thus everything becomes more alive to me.

Thinking exercises

> A wandering mind is weak and unsteady, attracted here, there and everywhere. How good it is to control it and know the happiness of freedom.
>
> *Buddha,* Dhammapada, *35*

The old image of the mind as three half-tamed horses drawing a chariot has already been mentioned. Each of us, as the 'charioteer', needs thinking, feeling and will trained to be at our command. In particular, chaotic thinking leads to chaotic life, and ordered thinking to an ordered life. (Ordered is not the same as dull. It really means being in charge, being free, not a slave.) Thinking that flits about indicates unquiet, disorder and nervousness rather than a calm manner and centred consciousness.

A way to improve thinking is simply to decide to do so and then find regular times to think about some subject you decide. For example, you could think about a childhood holiday, a friend or some subject you discover by opening a book at random. Spend at least five minutes—or even half-an-hour—thinking only about the chosen subject. Repeat this regularly and it will help to bring order into your thinking.

And here's a bonus; it will help you to have the idea you need at the right time. How many times have you kicked yourself because you thought of something too late. Well, here is an exercise that helps. If you regularly devote yourself to one thought for a time, the time will come when the one thought you need will come.

The following is an even more rigorous way to train your thinking:

Take some simple object like a pencil or pin and spend five minutes a day thinking about nothing except what is relevant to the object: its shape, how it was made, how it is used and so on. You will notice that your mind tends to wander. Each time bring it back. The first days are often easier because the object is new, but you need to persevere for some weeks even when it seems boring and you have thought everything that is to be thought. Stay concentrated and find it fresh and interesting each time.

Suppose that you are thinking about a light bulb, beginning by actually observing one. A useful sequence of thought is as follows:

- Describe to yourself everything to do with outer physical appearance, materials and form;
- Consider the manufacturing and distribution processes by which it was created and brought to you
- Review the qualitative aspects, like design, function, ergonomics;
- Who invented it, what is the source?
- Why do we need it?
- The family and history of such objects (candles, lanterns, lighthouses);
- The different forms that all fit the concept 'light bulb'.

When you can repeatedly focus on a simple object and stay on your subject, you have developed enormous power for life. By the way, you will probably discover many gaps in your knowledge of how the world works. Filling those gaps also gives strength. (One place to look on the Internet is www.howstuffworks.com.)

I recommend that you supplement this exercise by regularly observing *how* you think, trying to make all your thinking more ordered. At various times observe what you are saying or thinking. Do you put your thoughts together in a sensible, logical way or are they haphazard and casual. Do you, for example, say 'blah, blah, blah' to save yourself completing a thought properly? Do you leap to conclusions with no justification? Instead, try to make your thinking processes sound. The more sloppy your thinking, the more likely that the world will overwhelm it.

Strengthening the will

> You are the master and you are the way. Where else can you look? As a
> merchant breaks in a noble horse, so you should master yourself.
> *Buddha,* Dhammapada, *380*

In life we are continually met with the challenge to do things. How many times have you heard (or said):

- I always meant to...
- I never get round to...
- I forgot...
- I haven't got time...

Such thoughts have a tendency to be damaging, because they weaken the will and encourage us to be more helpless.

The following exercise helps you to eliminate all such problems. It gives control of time and builds self-confidence and strength to achieve your plans. It makes you reliable and trustworthy. It gives certainty. It is indeed a powerful exercise:

Each day, at any time you previously choose, do something with no value except that you decided to do it! Make it something easy to do in any circumstance. For example, you might move a coin from one pocket to another, scratch your nose or wave a finger about. Each morning, decide a couple of times in the day (e.g. 10.08 a.m. and 3.42 p.m.) when you will do your deed and what you will do. If you miss, say the 10.08 a.m. act, schedule another immediately for a little later. (You can do this once or twice.) Consult your watch *after* doing the act.

The aim is to achieve a 100 per cent record 30 days in a row. At first, you may allow yourself some margin of error. Don't be upset if you don't manage this for quite a while. It is the practice and effort that makes the difference. Even when you miss, you become stronger.

Finding emotional balance: equanimity

Identifying oneself with all, one pervades the entire universe with thoughts of equanimity, with heart grown great, wide, deep, boundless, purified of all ill will.

One of the four sublime states of Buddhism

Most people are more swayed by emotion than they realize. Feelings of pleasure and disappointment are like waves on the ocean. One measure of maturity is finding balance and serenity, learning to live with disappointment and success. Through this, feelings become richer, not weaker. Joy becomes more secure. Our heart forces can respond to the world in a less selfish and insecure way.

In *Zen Flesh, Zen Bones*, compiled by Paul Reps, we can read of neighbours praising the Zen master Hakuin for living a pure life:

> A beautiful Japanese girl whose parents owned a food store lived near him. Suddenly, without warning, her parents discovered she was with child. This made her parents angry. She would not confess who the man was, but after much harassment at last named Hakuin. In great anger the parents went to the master. 'Is that so?' was all he would say. After the child was born it was brought to Hakuin. By this time he had lost his reputation, which did not trouble him, but he took very good care of the child. He obtained milk from his neighbours and everything else the little one needed. A year later the girl-mother could stand it no longer. She told her parents the truth—that the real father of the child was a young man who worked in the fish market. The mother and father of the girl at once went to Hakuin to ask his forgiveness, to apologize at length, and to get the child back again. Hakuin was willing. In yielding the child, all he said was: 'Is that so?'

Viewing both others and ourselves without blame, accusation or anger is important, as Marshall Rosenberg, indicates when he says: 'If we are going to make an enemy of ourselves, what chance is there that we make peace with others?'

The following exercises or practices are all extremely helpful:

- If you can learn to look at your feelings, becoming aware of them, in an interested way, it will help you not to be swept off your feet. Think: whether of good or bad fortune. Think: This too will pass.

- If someone or something upsets you, rather than assuming that you deserve to feel upset, look at the *feeling* of being upset, and find balance. Practise thinking objectively about a person or situation that is upsetting, learning to look with calmness at your feeling.

- Use good observation to help separate what actually happened from what you assume is happening.

- Consider the thoughts you have that determine your emotional reactions. The cause of emotional stress is less what the other person has done than how you react to it. For example, how I translate the actions of others into thoughts determines what I think has happened and this in turn affects my emotions. If I react with understanding, tolerance, openness, if I have an open mind as to what is happening or the motives, if I suspend judgement, then I reduce the incidence of experience that generates negative emotion.

The exercise of the *Retrospective* or review (see page 122) is especially helpful because it aims to see our days and our selves objectively rather than emotionally.

If you notice a bad emotional habit, like always getting upset by some person or event or a habitual negative response to things, work to change this. One person I know kept saying, 'I hate . . .'. When she noticed this, she became calmer. When something challenged me, I found myself using the phrase, 'I don't need this'—a definite stress-inducing response. Changing these habits improves equanimity while increasing your creativity, as it means you are less habit prone.

Blaming others for my reactions creates stress and conflict and destroys trust and teamwork.

When we perceive events through the filter of what we personally like or don't like—avoiding what might upset us—we can never see the world objectively and fully. Similarly, if I listen with touchiness and sensitivity so that I easily become hurt by what others say and do, I lose the power to listen to the needs of others. Instead, we need to transform personal vulnerability into equanimity and empathy for others.

As long as we feel threatened and therefore inclined to react aggressively to the world, we block our own higher nature and purpose as loving beings. As long as human beings do violence to each other, they are cut off from their own higher nature. We need to cultivate the compassion and concern of the heart, ensuring that our footsteps through the world reflect a desire to do good and see the good in others. Thus we encourage our will to action and activity through awakened compassion and concern.

There is a very effective meditation to develop this equanimity, inner peace and concern for others that I have adapted from Mabel Collins' influential nineteenth-century manual of spiritual development, *Light on the Path*. Each line should form the substance of meditation for at least five minutes a day (by your impression rather than by a clock) for a month. So, in the first month you dwell on the first line; in the second month on the second line, and so on.

> Before the eyes can see they must be incapable of tears.
> Before the ear can hear it must have lost its touchiness.
> Before the voice can speak in the presence of the higher self, it must have lost the power to wound.
> Unless the feet are washed with the blood of the heart, you cannot hear the voice of your higher nature.

A first, superficial, impression might lead to questioning these thoughts. Is Collins suggesting that we become incapable of empathic sorrow, for example? However, this is clearly not the case. These images help to shift a person from selfish to unselfish emotion and thus to love. However, there is no need to speculate on the meaning of these lines during meditation—simply let them fill your mind.

Positivity

> My road it might be rocky,/The stones might cut my face,/But as some folks ain't got no road at all/They gotta stand in the same old place,/Hey, hey, so I guess I'm doin' fine.
>
> *Bob Dylan,* Guess I'm Doin' Fine

Finding positivity is like switching on your sun.

It improves everything for you and others. It seems that just the act of trying to smile changes the body's chemical balance positively—and can certainly help others.

As we have already seen, how people think is significant for their level of stress and performance. Forstater and Radin, in their book, *The Spiritual Teachings of Seneca*, include this account by the great Roman philosopher:

> I arrived at my house in Alba completely exhausted by the journey, which was thoroughly uncomfortable for an old man like me, thrashed about in that heaving carriage. And what do you know? Nothing was ready for my arrival, apart from myself. So I am writing to you from my old man's bed (which is of course unmade), resting, and unbathed (for there's no water) and so tired that I'm not all that sorry that the baker and cook (now that we've located them!) are slower than snails.
>
> All these difficulties have made me aware again of how calm life is if you don't take its inconveniences to heart, and how we wear ourselves out by magnifying them.
>
> It is indeed true that my baker has no bread—but perhaps the farm manager will have some, or a tenant, or the steward. 'Not very nice bread, though,' you will say. But wait a minute: it will soon transform itself by hunger into food fit for a king. So I'll wait to eat until I have my own bread, or hunger makes me less picky.
>
> We must teach ourselves to bear things... None of us can have everything we want, but we can refrain from wanting what we haven't got and cheerfully make the best of what is to hand... Perhaps freedom consists of a stomach that knows when to be quiet.
>
> Think of your troubles as training. Take in good part whatever happens, and turn it to your advantage. It is not what you endure, but how you endure that matters.
>
> To be always happy and pass through life without suffering is to be ignorant of the condition of being human.
>
> You have sailed through life without an enemy and no one will ever know what you are capable of, least of all yourself. Good luck never made a fool wise. Before all else, learn how to feel joy. Hurry to live. And measure life in each day. It takes the whole of a life to learn how to live.

Seneca outlines truths echoed by thinkers of all times and cultures. With a positive mental attitude, a person can find contentment or joy in (almost) any circumstance. Furthermore, our attitudes determine our outcomes. Those who are 'picky' will find that life appears to pick on them. Those with a positive and open attitude will find that life opens doors to positive experience.

In this, it matters not only how we view outer circumstances, but how we see ourselves and the expectations that we place upon ourselves. Those with confidence and modest self-esteem have an easier life. Those with reasonable but positive expectations will be less likely to be depressed or angry about under achievement. Those who recognize that sometimes there are diffi-culties in life, and that these can be of great value, will not be resentful with every difficult moment or experience.

How you think transforms you and affects others. Being around positive people is a refreshing experience. And so they become leaders. Those with authority, such as managers, will significantly affect the culture and environment over which they have responsibility according to their beliefs. It is therefore an act of both personal and social responsibility to develop a sane and positive mental attitude to life and to try to make that part of your surrounding family or work culture.

Most people have to practise this and here are some simple exercises that work wonders if you have the determination to do them:

- If there is someone you have difficulty with, think of one positive thing per day about that person. You can do the same thing about a job, institution or life situation.
- Before you allow yourself to make any criticism, public or private, remember that the flip side of any fault is typically some virtue. In other words, the fault is the shadow side of a positive quality that the individual also has. Perhaps he or she seems rude? Is it a by-product of honesty? Does he or she take a long time? Perhaps it is the desire to do a good job? (See also Chapter 9).

The more we think negatively or fearfully the more we trap our head in a vice. So, whenever you come across a negative or unpleasant thought (or object or situation), think of at least one positive aspect. 'Having done it today, at least I won't have to do it tomorrow.' 'Even if they did wake me up, at least they're having fun.' 'Being sick is a good rest.' You can say, 'Find the positive twist in everything: every cloud has a silver lining.'

Look back on your day and find at least one wonderful thing that happened.

Look back on your life and at circumstances that at the time seemed quite awful. Ask yourself if in fact positive things have not come from this, even if it is only the wisdom to avoid such things in future and the possession of a richer character through the experience. Then learn from this: make it a habit to remember how positive things come in surprising ways.

Remember during hard, painful or stressful times that in fact this too will pass. One day it will make dinner time conversation, or good advice, or compassion for another's trouble.

Memory exercises

A sound practical memory—not so much for facts, but for life details—brings incredible order to life and strengthens life processes.

How do you train memory? It is by giving yourself simple things to practise remembering. The following exercises are extremely helpful:

- Put one of your everyday objects like your keys in a different place each night. Make a picture in your mind of its location. Think to yourself: 'I have put this here.' In other words, instead of making yourself lazy by having a routine, deliberately exercise your mind.
- Do you forget people's names (I do)? Make an extra effort by connecting the name to a picture or impression (Paul, 'not the prophet'; Emily, 'a dancer').
- Try to remember some situation from the previous day, for example the chairperson of a meeting. Where was he/she sitting? What was she wearing? What posture? Who sat on either side? What was the temperature? Skin colour? Of course, you may find this hard. You may find blanks in your memory. Never mind. Just fill them in with your imagination! Supply a shirt colour and a tie or dress pattern. This will stimulate better observation in the future. 'A reliable memory,' said Steiner, 'is the child of exact observation.'

The retrospective exercise mentioned earlier also helps with memory.

Decisions and decision making

In a nutshell: to live is to know (living is effective action in existence as a living being).
Maturana and Varela, The Tree of Knowledge

Being able to make your own decisions out of your own choice is truly human and the path to freedom. Many decisions are made for us by rules, upbringing, and other strong people. We need to find the force and freedom to choose some things for ourselves. So practise actively making choices by looking at two or more sides of any question.

- Imagine all the good reasons and all the bad reasons for doing something.
- Let these be like two people who give conflicting advice (but both have come from yourself).
- Now choose between them. (It is most important to choose, and not just to do nothing.) Even if your decision is wrong, *you* have made it. That is important. We all make bad decisions and we can learn from them. (Even if you end up asking for advice, you can consciously decide between the benefits of asking or not asking for advice.)
- Try also to leave out your feelings of what you might like or not like and concentrate on whichever will lead to the best results (the better decision).

Generally speaking, the more we can deliberately find alternatives the more we reduce stress and improve decision making, for we take control of our lives. (This is not the same as endlessly oscillating amongst a sea of possibilities. The secret is to *look* for alternatives, then genuinely choose.) An excellent way to do this is to consider two or more alternative possibilities and review what their outcomes may be. Then sleep on it, and in the morning your ability to make a good decision will be enhanced. Three nights sleep is even better. The result is a positive, no-stress, calm approach to the decision.

Becoming more flexible

Most of us are easily caught into habits. All habits mean loss of freedom. Some cause us stress and some make it hard to change in the way we want. It is not that we should change all habits, but that we should be able to change when we want to. It is much better to have conscious and chosen routines or practices than unconscious habits. The former represents a free and masterful life. The latter is the behaviour of an unconscious slave.

It is easy to become more flexible, and it will help at work too. It will also keep you feeling younger and more creative.

Try to change a habit regularly. For example, wear your watch on a different arm. Put your toothbrush in a different place. Drive to work by a different route. More profoundly, change your handwriting, or look at some gesture you have (such as how you sit or walk) or some other behaviour, for example a way of speaking or interrupting, and change it. (The review of the day already mentioned is a good way to notice habits.)

At first, just practise a new behaviour for a few minutes a day. The ability, once achieved, to change in one area becomes a general ability to change and so those who practise become more flexible people.

Meditation

At that moment what do they lack?
As the truth eternally calm reveals itself to them . . .
A Zen meditation

Meditation is an important aid in dealing with stress and developing serenity, and is therefore described in Chapter 11. Meditation may play an important role in many lives in the future because it is a tremendous inner activity, a working of the mind and spirit of the individual that has great results. As James Allen puts it, 'You cannot travel *within* and stand still *without.*'

Each of the exercises I have described in this chapter is also a kind of meditation. They work through the combination of inner attitude and repetition. Gradually, conscious repetition has the effect of internalizing change and you become anew according to your intentions. Dainin Katagiri, who is a Zen practitioner, describes this in *You have to say something* in a way that would be familiar to many other traditions:

> The changes that occur through spiritual practice are not really your business. If you make them your business, you will try to change your life directly. If you try to change your life directly, no matter how long you work at it, you will not satisfy yourself. So, if you truly want to change your life, you should just form the routine of doing small things, day by day. Then your life will be changed beyond your expectations. If you

practice continuously, day after day, you will become a peaceful, gentle and harmonious person. There is no explanation for this.

I have heard an interesting story about how a famous psychologist in Japan cured a young girl after she suffered a nervous breakdown. The girl was from a wealthy family, and the psychologist met her regularly. But he didn't do or say anything. He just sat with her. One day, as he was sitting with her, the girl peed on the floor right in front of him. He was a very neat gentleman, and he was dressed in a very fine suit. But the moment she did this, he immediately took the beautiful handkerchief from his breast pocket and, without comment, cleaned up after her.

In time she completely recovered. She later recalled this incident, because she was very impressed by the psychologist's actions that day. Without any hesitation, he just mopped the floor with his fresh, neat handkerchief. There is no way to explain why she recovered. He didn't do anything. He only cleaned up after her during this one incident. But she could feel something very soft, gentle, and magnanimous coming from each pore of his body. She really respected him.

Have you ever met such a person? The moment you meet such people you feel relief just by their presence or their smile. Such people actually do exist in the world. How can we cultivate and nurture this kind of character in ourselves? It is not done through any intellectual process. This kind of change only comes about through living in vow, through taking care of your life. If you just practise the little things, day by day, without attempting to satisfy any of your individual desires—you just do this continuously—your magnanimous personality will become manifest.

Living in vow is like taking a trip down the Mississippi River. If you go to the centre of the river, there is no need for any extra effort. If you go to the centre of your life, the river of your life will carry you. If you practise in this way, you will find a natural rhythm to your life. Start with taking care of the little things in your life on an everyday basis, and eventually you will get to the middle of the river.

Before you reach the middle of the stream, practice feels hard. Most people give up. But they give up only because they don't see their life in the long range. They want results, right now. Life is very hard on us if we take this attitude. We become nervous, irritable, and cold-hearted.

If you learn to take a long-range view of life, you will continue to practise routinely, and you will get to the middle of the stream. Then, without any extra effort, your body and mind will move along in peace and harmony. A sense of gentleness, generosity, and magnanimity will come forth from each pore of your body. Your vow will have become your life.[14]

The idea of 'living in vow' to which Katagiri refers is both a Zen and a Jewish term. In effect, this is a vow to your own higher purpose. Meditation—meaning 'getting centred', or 'in the middle'—is equivalent to what Katagiri calls 'getting into the centre of the river's flow'. The meditations I will be suggesting (in Chapter 11) can help you to correct any imbalance and so centre your life. In this way, instead of life being an illness-inducing path of stress, it becomes more of a flow of fulfilment.

> Flowers every night
> Blossom in the sky;
> Peace in the Infinite;
> At peace am I.
>
> Rumi

CHAPTER 7

STRESSES OF TEMPERAMENT

I am for people. I can't help it.

Charlie Chaplin

This chapter focuses on the second of the three primary causes of stress outlined in Chapter 1: being out of tune with other people. The cause is often not understanding the other person and his or her values, especially when they are constitutionally at odds with our own.

The story is told that when Christopher Columbus set off on his epic journey to discover the New World there were four kinds of people who joined his crew. Those of the first type were very enthusiastic, rushing all over the ship exploring, climbing the rigging, looking in the holds and getting to know everyone else very quickly. Many of them were open-faced, good-looking and fair-haired. They were looking forward with bubbly excitement to all sorts of good things; their minds darting from one possibility to another like squirrels or birds.

But there was another, very different type: they were more serious in appearance and quite a few seemed to have droopy faces and sloping shoulders. Their minds were filled with foreboding: would the ship be sunk in a storm or sail off the end of the earth? Would their fellow crewmen like them? Many of them thought of beautiful things that might happen, such as discovering rare fish or lovely islands, but on the whole they found it unlikely that they would be fortunate enough to enjoy such pleasures.

There was a third group that was different from both the others. They tended to go about the business of getting the ship ready in a slow unhurried way; in fact when they were asked to speed things up they did nothing different at all. Very little bothered them, indeed they were generally very comfortable with life, and good humoured. But while they were working one worry did keep returning: weevils. Would the weevils get into the hard tack and damage it, and in fact would there be enough food to last out the journey? Loving food as much as they did, they tended to be a little bit rounder in the waist than most of the rest of the crew and this generally gave them a very comfortable, untroubled manner. Very little upset them.

The fourth group was quite different: they were often strongly built with squarer faces and jaws and included several of the officers. All of them seemed to be active in telling the others what to do. And whenever they didn't get their way, they were inclined to get irritated and bossy. Yet, all the time their minds were filled with the hope of heroic deeds and new worlds to conquer.

Whether there is any truth in the story I do not know, but I am pretty sure that Columbus did in fact have these four types amongst his crew. The reason is quite simple; the four temperaments that I have caricatured here have been recognized as basal building blocks of personality for millennia. Although the six billion or so people on Earth are truly six billion individuals, these four personality types form an underlying pattern of tendencies amongst them. Getting to know how they function helps in the understanding of basic stress typology.

Psychologists traditionally knew such types as sanguines (the quick explorers), melancholics (the doubters), phlegmatics (comfortable foodies) and cholerics (the bossy ones) respectively. They may also be known respectively as the Responsive, Sensitive, Receptive and Active types.[15] Most people will find that one or two of these types or aspects are more significant in their personality. Each of the four types brings good qualities but has weaknesses that come from its one-sidedness. For example, the sanguine is the classic life and soul of the party, but may be scatty. Each type causes stress and reacts to stress differently. The table below will help you to decide where you and those close to you might fit.

The effect of the temperaments

The more intelligence one has the more people one finds original.
Commonplace people see no difference between men.

Blaise Pascal

What do my temperaments mean for me and for how I get stressed and how does this affect those around me? As we shall see, each of the types has a one-sided tendency that leads to both advantages and disadvantages for both the individual and others, as well as to characteristic types of stress, whether caused or felt.

Cholerics are active personalities who are frequently in leadership positions because, being very goal-oriented, they are impatient to have their own way. They are also the most irritable when they don't get it. But the great advantage of a choleric is that their anger blows over almost as quickly as it arises. It can be frightening to work with someone who gets hot and bothered and angry at the touch of trouble but there is a simple strategy that the wise adopt in dealing with the choleric: don't take the reaction too seriously, simply keep out of their way for a short while and wait for calm to return. The choleric is also impatient. When the Duke of Wellington was asked by a vicar what he would like the sermon to be about, his answer was 'Ten minutes.'

Cholerics are active personalities who are frequently in leadership positions, as for example President J. F. Kennedy and Winston Churchill

If you are an active choleric you will have many fine qualities. Cholerics like helping others (providing it meets their objectives) and are generally the natural movers and shakers of the world. However, if you are choleric you do need to work actively on controlling your impatience and temper, for just as it is not very safe to have an untrained driver on the road, so it is unsafe to have an uncontrolled choleric at large.

The action-oriented choleric will commonly like to excel, so they can find great benefit in taking Goethe's words to heart: 'It is in self-limitation that a master first shows himself.' The choleric can usefully set him or herself the goal of being 'the most tolerant person around'. The exercises for equanimity and for will that are described above will be helpful in this. A typical choleric will set to with impatience to achieve this goal (so it may be important to resolve on persistence).

The seas are quiet, when the winds give o'er;
So calm are we, when passions are no more.
Edmund Waller

Someone with a more brooding temperament is a *melancholic*, who may also be called the sensitive type. On the positive side, melancholics are common among poets and artists, for they normally have a great love of beauty. However their sensitivity means they are the most likely to get depressed and miserable. They tend to feel criticism deeply and not only do they feel wounded, they nurse the pain, and sometimes a grudge. In this respect they are almost the opposite of the choleric. Whereas the choleric explodes into anger in a moment and then becomes sweetness and light within a few minutes, the melancholic seems to turn little anger or violence upon the outer world but may remain distant and difficult for days, brewing their pain. They visit their disappointment on themselves rather than others. However, their feeling of being deeply upset may cause considerable stress to

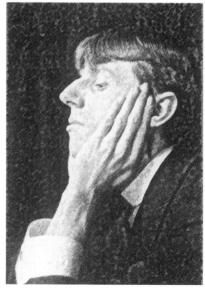

Melancholics are typically brooding personalities and common among poets and artists, as in dancer Nina Rambert and artist Aubrey Beardsley

others and especially to the person who may have, perhaps even inad-
vertently, triggered the upset. Melancholics could do well to note that this is
not so beautiful!

How should you deal with a sensitive melancholic? The worst approach is
insisting that they cheer up or that the world is not so bad, a common
choleric strategy. Melancholics need to be led out of their brooding isolation
with kindness and humour. It is not very helpful to be too sympathetic,
agreeing with the melancholic about how hard life is (for then they sink
deeper[16]). Instead show gentle kindness, for sensitive types love beauty and
most of them find kindness the most beautiful of human qualities. Gentle
good humour can also help to draw them out of their misery. When
appropriate, it can be helpful to remind the melancholic that others might be
in an even worse situation, for example refugees or the homeless. In this way,
they turn their strong sympathy qualities, which up till now have been
directed inwards (sympathizing with themselves), upon the plight of others.

And what if you are a sensitive melancholic yourself? Perhaps you
recognize in yourself a tendency to disappointment and the feeling of being
misunderstood or unappreciated? To be lost in the sway of such moods will
not only be difficult for others, it is excruciating to experience in oneself and
so there is good incentive to try and find ways to reduce the tendency to
depression. While the choleric has to learn to control his or her temper, the
melancholic should learn to become less depressed, which is not easy.

As with the choleric, I believe the first step is self-knowledge, becoming
aware of the nature of your behaviour (the review of the day or Retrospective is helpful for this). Remember, ultimately, the cause of stress is not
what the other person has done so much as how you react to it.

The *sanguine* or responsive personality might at first seem to be the least
stressful, for this seems to be a popular, happy and sunny personality. In that
mood they are often exceedingly welcome, especially in social gatherings
where they seem to like and know everyone and are good at connecting
people together. Their quick and wide-ranging interests mean that they have
something to say to everybody.

A further advantage of the sanguine nature is that they don't remain upset
for long. How can they, since they don't remain with anything for long?
There is a restlessness that underlies the sanguine's nature, leading them to flit
like a bird or butterfly from one experience to another and one person to
another because very little is ever sufficiently deeply satisfying. This restlessness may in turn be disturbing for others (especially to teachers in school).

As a generalization, I suggest that the sanguine needs to be able to enter more deeply into experience to find the value that lies at its heart.

At the heart of all disciplines, from playing cricket to selling to meditation, the ability to concentrate deeply is greatly valued. This is the particular challenge for the sanguine nature whose inclination is to pass on from thought to thought and experience to experience in order to find satisfaction. This very restlessness may be a source of stress. So once again, if you recognize a strong sanguine side in your nature, Goethe's maxim proves of value: 'It is in self-limitation that a master first shows himself.' The 'control of thinking' and observation exercises described above will be useful aids.

The sanguine personality is a popular, happy and graceful personality, as in the actress Meg Ryan and the mythical Hermes, messenger of the Greek gods. Hermes the Roman Mercury, patron of the fluid metal (and of thieves whose activities keep properties restlessly moving), illustrates the fluid side of this temperament. Sanguine personalities do well to remember the proverb: Still waters run deep

The *phlegmatic* or receptive person has the capacity to be a miracle of calm, for it is their nature not to be upset (although once roused they can be like an erupting volcano). I have had the pleasure of working with several such friends, and I can tell you that it is indeed easy to work with someone who does not get annoyed when they have every right to get extremely hot under the collar. Furthermore, their calm temperament can be an excellent basis for careful thinking and consideration: many philosophers have had a phlegmatic side, and it can also make for sound business thinking.

The receptive phlegmatic has a miracle of calm and happy personality that can be a basis for deep thinking, as in the poet John Betjeman. A love of food may lead to a characteristic roundness

The developed *phlegmatic* has a wonderfully receptive capacity to respond to the full set of life circumstances with an energy that is calm, purposeful and persistent. The melancholic may be so aware of the multitude of the world's problems and their interconnection that a mountain of impossible gloom frustrates any attempt at change or action. The sanguine will take up one cause today and another tomorrow, while the choleric is easily frustrated because he cannot immediately change the world. By contrast, the phlegmatic, once roused to a cause, is likely to stick with it to the bitter and probably successful end.

So if such wonderful qualities are part of their nature, how do phlegmatics ever cause offence to others? The answer lies in the unruffled, even pace that is the characteristic of someone who lets life just roll by him or her. Little annoys the choleric or sanguine in a rush more than a person who can't be rushed! Phlegmatics are excellent at work that requires patience; I remember one individual who was the supreme analyst of details—literally millions of them—but he only had one pace at which he could work. While that was necessary for that kind of work, it can be frustrating in circumstances when you want an urgent result. If allied to a bureaucratic nature, it can also become tiresome to others.

The phlegmatic also has to beware a tendency towards the enjoyment of ease, comfort and good food that can lead to him or her becoming over-weight and unfit.

The challenge for the phlegmatic is to allow a little stress. If Ms Stress is the guide who helps to develop full potential and human gifts, to become a whole person, it is important to be stirred into reflection, emotion and action so that these may empower new growth in personality. For example, I might need the flexibility to respond quickly and creatively to changes in circumstances, or I might need to be roused by an injustice or lack of quality to challenge the status quo.

All four temperamental types respond differently to the same experience. The active choleric will get hot and bothered and try to fix the problem. The responsive sanguine may get upset briefly but is also the most likely to be trying to cheer everyone else up. The receptive phlegmatic, as the name implies, is the least likely to become upset, for this is a most easy-going temperament. The sensitive melancholic will however take trouble to heart, and unlike the choleric's quick, hot anger, is much more likely to develop a slow, cold anger, fuelled by hurt. Yet, since the phlegmatic is not hurt, then it is not the experience in itself that has the power to upset so much as the person who reacts. What I *think* about the event is what determines the experience. If I can recognize this aspect of myself, and also how it creates difficulties for others, then I have an incentive to begin to work on myself. However, unless I act, nothing changes. The exercises for equanimity and positivity described in the last chapter are helpful here.

As you think, so you are;
As you continue to think, so you remain.
James Allen

Exercise: recognizing your temperament

His life was gentle; and the elements
So mix'd in him that Nature might stand up
And say to all the world 'This was a man!'
William Shakespeare, Julius Caesar

First, identify the type or types that most closely resemble you (remember, you have all four characteristics to some extent). Then look below to see how stress affects you and what you might do.

An overview of the four temperaments

Type	Personality	Appearance
Sanguine—the Responsive person	A quickly roving personality and intelligence. May be scatty. Easy with people, with a wide network of friends. A popular 'party animal'. Too quickly bored to stay committed to one thing for long, but therefore quickly responsive to new ideas and influences.	Often physically balanced and well-proportioned. Lively. In Caucasians, there is a tendency to be fair in complexion.
Melancholic—the Sensitive person	A serious person who takes experiences much to heart and can nurse criticism or bad fortune. A worrier. Sensitive, can be artistic and concerned about words and beauty. Usually has a few very close friends. Responds to being listened to with empathy.	Physically can appear a little drooping—e.g. sloping shoulders or facial features, and commonly a slimmer build. Caucasians have a tendency to dark or brown hair.
Phlegmatic—the Receptive person	A calm person who routinely lets things flow by that would disturb others. This calm can contribute to very sound if not always innovative thinking. Also excellent at completing tasks. Rarely angry, the phlegmatic if riled has a powerful force. Commonly loves food and may be physically lazy. Gets on well with everyone—but others may be frustrated by their 'one-paced' way of life.	Relaxed in appearance. A tendency to be over-weight.
Choleric—the Active person	Physically energetic and robust, and wanting to have his or her own way. Gets quickly irritated and almost as quickly forgets all about it. Often found in positions of leadership. May be very insensitive to others and have few friends. Responds well to challenge.	Often barrel-chested, strong, with bold facial features.

How stress comes and what to do	
If you are a responsive-sanguine person	You will create stress for yourself by the variety of things in your life. Mostly this will be fun, but you may find yourself saddled with commitments you are no longer interested in. Your lack of sustained commitment may also hold you back. But your roving mind and wide network are great aids to life and you turn things quickly into positives. Beware you don't miss what really matters.
If you are a sensitive-melancholic person	You will create stress for yourself by taking things more seriously than is needed. Instead of being affected, look on experience as the opportunity to learn. Your penetrating mind can help you here. The power to see what can go wrong is helpful, but remember that what you can imagine won't always happen. Indeed use anticipation to avoid the downside for yourself and others. And that hurt that was done to you—it probably wasn't meant and has almost certainly been forgotten by the person who 'did it to you'.
If you are a receptive-phlegmatic person	Make sure that you have a sufficiently active life to stay physically healthy and achieve the immense potential that your calm purpose allows. Try also to adjust your dynamic range so that you can respond with appropriate speed and energy to challenges. Not everyone is blessed with your calm, so be responsive to their needs.
If you are an active-choleric person	You probably have the most frequent fits of irritation as you continually plunge into challenges, trying to frame the world to your pattern. Remember that this is not only stressful for you but also for others. Try to flow creatively towards your objectives, opening the doors instead of walking through them.

CHAPTER 8

LIFE AND WORK TECHNIQUES

If a man is himself controlled, he will be able to control others. When he comes to know himself, he will be able to teach others.

Buddha, Dhammapada*, 159*

This chapter focuses on the first of the three primary causes of stress outlined in Chapter 1: being out of tune with our environment. However, it also makes suggestions connected to the other two factors, helping to connect us to other people and to the spirit.

It includes a number of practical ideas concerned with reducing distress, many of which are akin to feng shui. They include time management, desk and work organization, preparing for meetings, work rhythms, positive personal stress codes, work boundaries and steps for management to reduce office or factory stress. Generally, they help with 'Moon stress' (see Chapter 5) by helping to create order and priority. If you have management responsibility, I think you can use them to influence a lower stress/higher performance culture for the organization and people.

Creating positive mental and cultural attitudes

Ask and it shall be given you; seek and you will find; knock and it will be opened to you.

Jesus Christ, Matthew 7,7

In Chapter 6 I described some personal development practices to encourage positivity, or positive mental attitudes. Here I want to discuss some ideas on how to apply these in the workplace.

Create a positive personal and/or organization stress code

How you think forms your character and habits and affects how others think about you. Consider the following beliefs; which ones do you or your organization subscribe to? Are you always able to subscribe to these, or only sometimes (say with some people or some work or personal circumstances)?

You could either reflect on them individually or discuss them in a group or with another person.

CULTURE AND ATTITUDE REVIEW
- I am worth being treated with respect;
- I do not always have to be the most important person;
- I deserve to be listened to and taken seriously, but don't need to force my opinions;
- I do not need to prove myself all the time;
- I recognize that anyone might have the good idea we need;
- I can express views that are different from other people's and accept the consequences;
- I am able to express feelings and accept the consequences;
- I can say 'no' when I feel it is justified, without feeling guilty;
- It is all right for me to ask for what I want, although I accept that I might not get it;
- I can make mistakes, try to correct them and learn from them;
- I can admit ignorance and, if appropriate, will be prepared to learn;
- It is always my choice whether I work longer hours or not;
- I can act as I believe is right;
- I can choose not to act on any of these beliefs (rather than just finding excuses for not acting on them).

Alternative beliefs tend towards increased distress and poorer performance, for they are more likely to be negative mental attitudes. Everyone deserves respect, everyone has valuable life experience, everyone has the right to say both no and yes, everyone makes mistakes. Including you!

As an organization leader, you can influence the culture of your organization by example and policy by making such principles part of the organizational ethos, leading by example.

Setting limits and boundaries for work
Often distress arises because people and organizations don't set boundaries on work. In an environment where work ever expands the result is all too often like the endless sprawling encroachment of urban development into the country.

> John was working very long hours at a professional firm. 'I have to do this,' he said. 'Everyone does it, it is expected of me. It is how long you have to work to get through what is needed.'
>
> Then he recognized that it was his own choice at root. He chose to work in demanding conditions; he chose to try to excel; he wanted to keep up with others.

When he started to say, 'I work long hours by my choice because I want to further my career,' he also became conscious of having choices and his ongoing freedom to change his mind.

When you say 'can't', remember that you probably mean 'won't'.

Boundaries and limits require that you make choices and stick to them. This is a way of taking charge of your life, strengthening your will and purpose. It will help with your practical and spiritual life. Without these, there is a tendency to become disempowered as tasks—Just one more! And one more!—take charge of your life. Instead, enable yourself to have expectations such as these:

- I can come and go at reasonable hours using flexitime;
- I can take my breaks and holiday;
- I can ask the reason and give reasons for a task or assignment;
- I can delegate work;
- I do not have to absorb another's unhealthy stress;
- I can take time to reflect and take stock and allow others to do this;
- I can ask for help and give it when needed;
- I should thank and be thanked, appreciate and be appreciated, although I am not wholly dependent on others' perceptions for my feelings of self-worth;
- I can challenge others' perceptions of me and be prepared to listen to others' views;
- I can be wrong, and will be often;
- I can maturely express my dissatisfaction or disagreement;
- I can admit my vulnerable points to my boss or family;
- I have a responsibility to manage my time and resources;
- I have a responsibility to monitor my own well-being and build my stress fitness;

● I have a responsibility to encourage the well-being of any staff I manage while recognizing the autonomy of their lives and selves.

Discuss good things together

> I tell you that to let no day pass without discussing goodness and all other subjects about which you hear me talking and examining both myself and others is really the very best thing a man can do, and that life without this sort of examination is not worth living...
>
> *Socrates at his trial, according to Plato*

Continuing with the theme of creating a positive culture, I would recommend that you try to instil regular practice of discussing good things together.

In our family we have by some combination of good fortune and good management been able to enjoy many excellent conversations over the years at the dinner table. The review of 'best things' (in the day or holiday) and conversation about what makes a good life or a good person (whether we are talking about good restaurants, or good wine or good parenting or good education or good games or good films and books...) have made a great contribution to our life.

It is so also at work. Discussion about positive values, vision, what people want to see happen and so on are central to organizational meaning, well-being and success. For example, there is a very good consulting technique called Appreciative Inquiry that is used to help organizations and communities reflect and develop. Its exciting quality is that it is concerned only with what people find to be good in what is happening or has happened. It then asks how to gain more of the same.

I believe that when social communities—families or giant organizations or countries—discuss in a positive spirit what is good (rather than bad) and seek to bring it about we get close to what it means to be human.

Since we identified in Chapter 1 that relationships with people are a fundamental cause of anxiety and stress, and since problems of conflict about opposing values can be so significant, Chapter 9 will look further at conflict. However, conflict rarely comes when we look at what is Good but rather from what we see as Bad! Pay attention to what you find good, and goodness follows.

Time management

> Time is but the stream I go a-fishing in.
> *Henry David Thoreau*

There are innumerable books as well as workshops on the subject of time management. Yet, time management is rarely a problem of managing time, it is a problem of managing the mind. Our mind tells us that we have to do the work and that it cannot be delegated. Our mind drives us to fit one more item into the crowded schedule. Our mind causes and suffers the stresses described in Chapter 5, in particular the Moon stress such as the time-wasters listed below, through which one ends up feeling unable to control all the events of one's life.

It is the mind that dislikes some difficult task and leads us to waste time on trivial items. It is our mind that drives us into lifestyles such as the Dasher or Stroller (shown in the table on page 154–5 below). That is why time management advisers focus on helping us to become clear about our priorities and goals and why they encourage us to develop good habits of thought.

THE TOP TWENTY-ONE TIME-WASTERS ARE TYPICALLY CONNECTED TO 'MOON STRESS' (see page 84)

1. Constant interruptions—telephone or other;
2. Indecision;
3. Meetings—too long;
4. Switching priorities;
5. Lack of objectives, priorities or daily plan;
6. Personal disorganization;
7. Cluttered desk or work area;
8. Ineffective delegation;
9. Shuffling paper work;
10. Limited access to required equipment or materials;
11. Trying to find or track down people;
12. Attempting too much—inability to say 'No';
13. 'Butterflying' from job to job, leaving tasks unfinished;

14. Inadequate, inaccurate delayed information or communication;
15. Unnecessary socializing;
16. Office procedures not clearly established;
17. Confused line of responsibility or authority, or the need to get decisions approved;
18. Constant checking up on others and their work;
19. Plunging into a task without planning;
20. Lack of self-discipline;
21. Exhaustion!

Given the importance of time, it could be said that the whole of this book is a course on time management, for ultimately our life and our time amount to the same thing. To be born is to move from the realm of the eternal to the realm of time. Death reverses this. Time, as expressed beautifully in Ecclesiastes, is the resource into which all life fits as, moment by moment, the sands of time flow by:

> To every thing there is a season, and a time to every purpose under the heaven:
> A time to be born, and a time to die; a time to plant, and a time to pluck up that which is planted;
> A time to kill, and a time to heal; a time to break down, and a time to build up;
> A time to weep, and a time to laugh; a time to mourn, and a time to dance;
> A time to cast away stones, and a time to gather stones together; a time to embrace, and a time to refrain from embracing;
> A time to get, and a time to lose; a time to keep, and a time to cast away;
> A time to rend, and a time to sew; a time to keep silence, and a time to speak;
> A time to love, and a time to hate; a time of war, and a time of peace.

On the other hand, we do not live truly with the realm of time, but rather under the rule of the clock. As E. E. Cummings described it:

> there are so many tictoc
> clocks everywhere telling people
> what toctic time it is...
>
> spring is not regulated and does
> not get out of order, nor do
> its hands a little jerking move
> over numbers slowly

The exercises given in Chapter 6 such as the following are therefore invaluable in becoming a better manager of time:

- The will exercise by which you decide to do something at a particular time of day helps to give mastery over all the realm of time and the power to do whatever you determine (see page 127);
- The review of the day or Retrospective develops awareness of how you actually spent time and where it has been meaningfully used and where wasted (see page 122);
- Taking time to review life helps to determine priorities and goals (see page 243);
- Memory exercises help to remember what is needed (see page 133);
- Exercises that develop flexibility, such as changing habits, help to deal with the confusion of the day and sudden changes in time demands (see page 134);
- Thinking exercises develop more ordered ways of working; they also help to see what is essential, so avoiding wasted time (see page 125);
- Much time is wasted through emotional mismanagement. For example, when I get upset I waste time on my upset or I find that I don't like something and avoid doing it; worst of all I may find it difficult to work with a particular individual and this can be a terrible drain of time and energy. Such problems can be helped by the exercises that develop equanimity and emotional maturity (see page 128).

Two Lifestyles: which are you? Or have you found the middle path?

Dasher	Balanced	Stroller
Last minute	Never late	Casual about time
Very competitive	Co-operative	Not competitive
Anticipates what others are going to say and finishes it for them	Listens well	Listens without really engaging
Always feels rushed	Never feels rushed even under pressure	Never rushes
Impatient about waiting	Everywhere is interesting	Enjoys idleness
Tries to do too many things at once	Focuses on priorities	Takes things as they come; mañana will do
Speaks emphatically and fast	Speaks consciously	Speaks slowly and deliberately

Contd.

Contd.

Dasher	Balanced	Stroller
Wants public recognition at work	Does what is really needed	Personal satisfaction more important than what others think
Walks and eats fast	Calm	Does things slowly
Drives self and others hard	Purposeful	Easy going, casual
Hides feelings or explodes	Manages feelings	Shows feelings or is unbothered
Too occupied with work for outside interests or has too many things to manage	Rich life	Couch potato
Ambitious	Confident	Unambitious

Plan your weekends too

I have an Israeli colleague and friend, Shmuel Merhav, who gave me a great insight into time management. This is to recognize the importance of scheduling the weekend. He puts the idea like this:

> Probably you think that the weekend is the last time that should be scheduled. Surely the weekend is for relaxation, not for schedules? But how many times have you come to the end of the weekend and felt dissatisfied because you have not done what you had planned? Each time this happens, it is demoralizing, and you did not actually get the things done that you wanted. So your weekend is probably the most important time to schedule of all. Plan it: what you want to do, and when, whether it is going to a play or party, doing necessary chores, working on a hobby, walking, exercising, reading. You can even plan that you will leave space to follow your mood—then you won't feel guilty. Do not plan to do things that are unrealistic. By the same token, try very hard to make sure that you achieve what you had planned.

It is good advice, for I know to my cost how weekends can vanish leaving a trail of undone things and disappointment.

Make appointments with yourself

There can be few pieces of advice that I have found more helpful to managing my time than to make appointments with myself. An appointment with yourself is a space you are making in your diary when you will meet yourself, and only yourself, to do some essential reflection or planning. It can also be used to schedule time for things like reading important technical or professional development material. But its principal purpose is to ensure that you have the time to reflect, plan and prioritize.

A similar idea is to make appointments with projects by scheduling in your diary when you will work on a particular project. When you make these appointments, they should be as important as appointments that you make with anyone else. Why would you think otherwise? (And if your appointments with others are not important to you, I would suggest that this may not be helping you to gain the respect that I expect you would like to have.) Once your appointments are scheduled, you can relax, and you also see what time you really have free.

Use your email system to flag items to be dealt with at specific times and switch it off for periods when engaged in thinking and writing rather than being at the mercy of every email.

Finally, schedule free time, for example some space every day. You know that things will come up. Perhaps someone wants to see you. Perhaps a task comes up. Have a space to be flexible.

Desk and work organization

What is character but the determination of incident? What is incident but the illustration of character?

Henry James

Amongst those who have one, I believe you can tell a lot about people from their desks.

More and more people are working via a work-flow system on their computer, in many cases with no physical paper. These are systems designed to order their work processes, and can be very helpful. The email system is also a primary task manager today, with hours being spent responding to emails.

What matters with electronic office work is that we don't become sucked into the routine and imperative of computer-driven tasks. This means prioritizing, taking space out from the computer and retaining self-awareness and autonomy. It is easy to be lost in a computer screen.

With more conventional environments, the physical evidence of work style is more obvious. I know that the more I lose control, the more my desk becomes disordered. There is considerable evidence that the way we manage our desk makes a difference both to our effectiveness and to our stress levels. The more things there are on the desk, the more potential distractions. The distracted mind is less effective and more stressed. It makes sense to reflect the effort of improved and more ordered thinking in the working environment. Indeed, the more ordered our thinking, the more likely our desk will become ordered. There is a symbiotic relationship between mind and environment, for they grow together.

So how can you make your workspace, if you have one, a well-space?

Over the years, I have found one piece of advice from Time Management Inc. very helpful. It was to maintain six hanging files in your desk drawer. The equivalent is to have 6 folders in your email or electronic management system. Label them: *Today, Soon, Awaiting response, Read, Out, File.* Working in this format is both a practical and spiritual discipline, respecting yourself, your work, your colleagues and their work. It will develop qualities such as maintaining the larger perspective, distinguishing the essential from the non-essential, applying due energy and forcefulness to achieve real goals, building trust and reliability, nurturing and caring for responsibilities, having the poise to respond to new and immediate necessities, and developing self-awareness: qualities that I earlier associated with Saturn, Jupiter, Mars, Sun, Venus, Mercury and Luna/Moon.

The first principle is that everything that should be done today goes into the *Today* file, while other items go elsewhere, such as the *Soon* file. Your plan should be not to go home until the *Today* file is completed. (However, because you will be disciplined and want to go home at a reasonable time to meet your other life obligations, you will also be disciplined about what goes into it.) Each day, sort through new items and those in the *Soon* file and decide what to bring into the *Today* file. Items that hang around in the *Soon* file should either be disposed of or transferred to a project file.

Where possible, deal with each item only once to avoid wasting time and mental energy after making a quick scan to sort incoming electronic or physical material. (One of the major inefficiencies of email is the difficulty of doing this along with the continual arrival of new mail.)

Aim to have only the item on which you are working on the top of the desk or electronic desktop. If anything else must be on the desk, keep it in the minimum number of neat piles possible. It is preferable, however, to have a deep file drawer in your desk and to use this to keep all pending paperwork using the six file types mentioned above.

The challenge of the physical desktop is the scattered mind dancing between the objects that litter the space. The challenge of the electronic desktop is the mind-on-a-lead, drawn from item to item as they appear in the electronic frame.

Suppose there is a piece of work that depends on some input from another person. Perhaps you have sent a recommendation and are awaiting a response. This should be put in the *Awaiting response* file, with a note saying the date by which you expect the response. (You can do the same thing with good email systems by flagging emails with a 'date due or reminder'.) Each day, you should check if there are any items for which you should have a response. If this has not happened, aim to contact those involved immediately to indicate that the schedule is being affected. Many software packages will remind you automatically.

Remarkable things happen if this becomes a discipline: other people will come to believe that your requests are serious and will treat them (and you) more seriously. Most of us are used to people who appear to be in a panic or who ask for things but have no intention of following up. I have found over the years that many people have an effective strategy of waiting to see if they are asked twice to do a piece of work. This is useful in preventing unnecessary work, but otherwise a very wasteful practice. It means that both parties use up mental energy and time to achieve nothing. So, I believe, it would be more helpful for others and for yourself if you became known as a person who only asks for things that are really needed and who, in that case, will always follow-up.

Good working disciplines are also spiritual disciplines.

How you follow-up is also important. Your purpose is not to act as someone else's minder or diary. They are adults and shouldn't need this. Your aim is to convey your professional expectation that the input would be received today. One more thing therefore becomes very important. Dates you schedule should not be unilateral: they should be negotiated and genuine requirements. Your aim is that your colleague has committed to giving you what you really need by the date you really need it. This means that you will either have emailed, phoned or spoken to the individual, or individuals, and have secured this agreement. Alternatively, the first date that you put down on the pending document is only the date by which you have *requested* an acceptable schedule. There is a profound morality and spiritual discipline in such seemingly simple human connections.

The *Read* file, whether electronic or physical, is for items that you would like to read, that is items you *really* intend to read at a more appropriate time. One option is to pull these out and read them when you get the time. This is a nice idea that in practice tends not to be very effective. I would recommend that you schedule spaces either during work or privately to read what is important for your personal, professional development.

The *Out* file is more relevant for physical than electronic documents. One reason for this is that many people find it satisfying to be able to see what they have done. It can help with practising awareness too. If you have a colleague, assistant or secretary to whom you are passing on work, another reason is that collecting a pile of items reduces interruptions. If you create a stack of things that need to be passed on or filed, then this reduces scattiness.

It is for the same reason that I recommend you have a *File* slot. The aim is that you store up physical items for filing and do it periodically rather than every few minutes. The principle is always to know the real task with which you are involved and to cut down on interruptions and digressions.

Taking the stress out of meetings

Is not every meeting actually a critical moment in the world's evolution?
Athys Floride

Meetings seem to be widely disliked and yet they are potentially one of the most enriching and fruitful parts of working life. When meetings work well, as they could and should, they become profound opportunities for people to share, even if it is only to take care of routine business. Meetings should be an opportunity to get away from machines and lonesome working in order to find common partnership for planning and learning.

Successful meetings depend on three things: their preparation, the process of the meeting, and the follow-up. Practices that make for happy meetings include:

- Prepare beforehand: make sure everyone comes prepared. Plan a process to achieve the goals of the meeting;
- Label topics 'for information' or 'for decision';
- Take care of the people and the process and the answers will come;
- Make sure decisions are confirmed;
- Organize and execute follow up.

Preparation

I believe that it is often not recognized how important the practical and mental *preparation* for a meeting is for its success. In a sense, the meeting actually begins with the preparation process.

Whoever is responsible for the meeting needs to ensure that all the right people are properly invited and can come, that they know the purpose of the meeting and have all the information they need in order to prepare for it. They should also ensure that the meeting spaces are properly prepared. This is an important aspect of Venus care:[17] a clean room, refreshments, paper, technology facilities, perhaps even flowers: whatever is needed, aim to make sure it is there. First impressions count and the meeting will probably flow better with fewer interruptions.

Many people who are 'good at meetings', whether chairing or partici-pating, but especially chair people, have commented that creating a clear mental picture of what you hope and want the meeting to be like is extre-mely effective: great athletes imagine the forthcoming event. We can do it too.

Individuals who are going to attend the meeting might need to do their own preparation, whether as research or simply thinking about the goals of the meeting and their own personal goals. It is important that those who come to the meeting also organize their own schedules so that they can be there on time, as far as possible, unstressed and free of the business of whatever came before. Of course this is not always possible, which brings us to how to manage the meeting itself.

The process of the meeting

During the *process* of the meeting, there is what is going on 'above the table' and what is going on 'below the table'. The first of these is the visible or obvious part of the meeting. It includes what people say, how long is spent on various points, obviously meaningful behaviour, and so on. The second component is the invisible part of the meeting. It is all the internal thoughts and emo-tions that people experience but which they do not bring into the open, hence they remain 'below the table'. It includes needs and assumptions and feelings that con-dition the visible, and it is usually here that problems lie. I shall go into this in

> *What people say or make obvious through their actions*
>
> ABOVE THE TABLE
> _____
> BELOW THE TABLE
>
> *What people think and feel and want without overtly expressing, or even without knowing it.*

more detail in the next chapter. A kind of grey area between these two components is the body language of those in the meeting. Body language is visible gesture that indicates inner activity, but because much of it is subtle, those who are not alert may not notice it. On the other hand it may be the key to reading what is really happening under the surface and therefore instrumental in achieving a successful meeting.

Managing the meeting effectively means not only managing the visible part of the meeting, but also the invisible and subtle parts. It is for this reason that it can be helpful to separate the person who is responsible for the *process* of the meeting from the person who will bring most of the *content or expertise*. That is why many large companies have a separate managing director and chair. Suppose you are the most expert person, and also the most senior person in a meeting, and now you also have to chair it. The probability is that you will do most of the talking and spend most of your mental energy focusing on your own thoughts and ideas rather than those of others and what is happening in the emotional realm. The job of the chair is to manage the social process as a purposeful project.

A 'business meeting'—whether it is of a group of mothers planning a bring and buy cake stall or a board meeting of a company—is neither a therapy session nor just a group of people socializing and enjoying each other's ideas and emotions. However, despite its business goals, it does need to take account of the emotional life of those involved, because the ultimate purpose of the meeting is to ensure that everyone feels committed and enthusiastic towards whatever is agreed. A meeting with good humour and laughter generally produces better results than a tense or dull one.

It is requisite for the relaxation of the mind that we make use, from time to time, of playful deeds and jokes.

Thomas Aquinas

That leads to the second most important part of managing a successful meeting. Every meeting and every item within the meeting should have a purpose and each objective should normally be clear to everyone concerned before the meeting so that they may prepare. This means that meetings should be organized not around a list of topics, but around realistic goals or purposes with the aim to build agreement and good will.

For example, the first item on the agenda might be labelled 'Introduction', but what is its purpose? It is normally helpful that the first item in each meeting should have the purpose of bringing everyone together to ground and warm the meeting. An appropriate process is needed that enables this to happen, such as helping everyone to get to know each other, say something about their expectations and become conscious of any baggage that they are bringing from earlier in the day. Proper preparation beforehand also helps this.

Some items on the agenda might only be for communicating information to ensure that everyone is properly informed. Others might be to get a decision. For example, one item might be: 'We need agreement to go ahead with the proposed new supplier,' or: 'We need to decide which supplier we are going to appoint.'

Each item then needs an appropriate process, with co-operation and good management to ensure everyone understands and is supportive of the way ahead. Without these, decisions will probably not be effective. When there is a meeting of hearts and minds it can generate the most wonderful feeling of shared commitment.

Follow up

The third stage of the meeting is the *follow up*. Meetings are designed to bring about change and this needs action. One of the most frustrating aspects of many meetings is the fact that it is quite clear that the decisions will never really be realized. So, part of the meeting discipline is the taking of notes, usually best accomplished by recording decisions, and this should be distributed very fast, preferably even at the meeting itself. When planning a meeting, put into your diary not only the meeting time, but also realistic preparation and follow-up time. This will reduce stress and helps to make you more effective.

The spiritual significance of meetings

These are practical suggestions. But, there is another perspective. Bearing in mind Athys Floride's question, 'Is not every meeting actually a critical moment in the world's evolution?' what really happens in a meeting? Surely, a meeting brings different streams of human experience together for the purpose of shaping (at least slightly) the future of the participants and of the world. It is a karmic encounter. Invisibly present in the room are both the past and the future, both of which are influencing the present. There is the call for what needs to be brought about, for the future always exists in vision before it becomes material. And there are also helpful and hindering emotional presences from the past: the resonance of experiences that live on as emotional mines waiting to be stepped on.

In the meeting the *communi*cation is a *communi*ty building process in which the sharing of ideas, feeling and intentions builds a kind of spiritual substance, a force of will and ideas that transforms the world. It brings to birth the decision which must then be nurtured by its parents until it can live its own life.

> The preparation, deeds of the meeting and subsequent taking up and implementation of the mission(s) and tasks agreed within the meeting follow a model seen in great stories of civilization. Two significant meetings that changed the world are the Last Supper and the gathering at Pentecost when the apostles experienced their spiritual mission. The latter meeting was first carefully prepared—for at least the forty days during which Christ met with them individually and in groups. Then in the meeting itself the apostles were inspired by a common impulse. Finally, they immediately went out and began to put this into practice—continuing to great effect for the rest of their lives.

Meetings are places where individuals learn to sacrifice personal preferences while contributing ideas and goodwill. Individual positions need to be offered but then, in a free deed, allowed to die to allow the birth or resurrection of common will. In this way, meetings become the means for something greater than the individual to come to pass, while also enabling the individual to become greater.

Organizing change to minimize stress

Change is not made without inconvenience, even from worse to better.
Richard Hooker, English theologian c.1554–1600 ACE

Organizational change can be very stressful. Indeed, as we shall see, those involved in it may go through the classic grieving cycle normally associated with death (see page 212). Radical change, such as re-organization, large-scale redundancies, acquisition and mergers, shock people out of their patterns and assumptions. Managers introducing significant change can therefore benefit from following these principles through the three stages of shock, avoidance or resistance, and acceptance.

AT THE SHOCK STAGE

- Give as much information as possible about the reasons for the change and what its effects are likely to be for both the staff and the organization;
- Be clear about the timing and processes that will take place;
- Cover both the beneficial and the less welcome aspects;
- Allow some discussion of both, accepting the expression of concerns people may have initially, but also encouraging exploration of the possible benefits;
- Allow time for things to sink in;
- Be available for support.

AT THE AVOIDANCE/RESISTANCE STAGE

- Assure people that the change will happen;
- Listen to and acknowledge people's feelings;
- Respond to the concerns that people raise;
- Invite further suggestions and allow people affected to influence how the change will be implemented;
- Accept that tension or discomfort is an essential part of the process.

AT THE ACCEPTANCE STAGE

- Be prepared to utilize fully the extra energy released here;
- Set goals and priorities and monitor movement towards them;
- Help people to manage necessary adjustments to working practices as far as possible themselves;
- Look out for other processes that might need to change as a result;
- Continue to support.

Using work rhythms to reduce stress

Themis is a daughter of the Earth Mother Gaia [to the Greeks]. Her name expresses the regularity of nature, the peaceful law shared by all its creatures ... [Her daughters, the Horai,] bore the names of Thallo, Auxo, Karpo, from sprouting, growing, ripening ... *Horai* means periods of time, rhythmic periods of the world's unfolding. Developing into symbols of an ideal—lawful, just, peaceful—world order, they bear witness to the deep-noted belief that a just order has its natural foundation in Themis, the earthly maternal principle, which protects and brings forth growth and fruit.

Karl Kerényi, *Prometheus, Archetypal Image of Human Existence*

The universe is formed from rhythm, whether you see in it 'God's cycle' of the week or the cosmic cycles of planets and stars and galaxies and their seasons. Traditional lifestyles were strongly linked to seasons and festivals and daily rhythms. Their rhythms helped to bring order, security, health and good humour. Absence of rhythm introduces more stress; increasing rhythm reduces stress.

Rhythm here means things like regular times of waking and sleeping and eating, starting and finishing work, rhythms of more physical and more mental work, individual and group work, patterns of work and regularity of jobs within the day and from day to day.

When life and work-styles become more chaotic, we disturb our personal bio-sphere and so add mental stress. The cause might be lack of self-leadership to fashion order in life and work. Alternatively, outside pressures might mean we need to work harder at doing so. Either way failure of rhythm increases distress.

Workplaces and organizations that lack rhythm put more pressure on employees. For example, they increase the 'Mercury stress' to flexibility, since the arhythmical or chaotic demands more flexibility. Personal lifestyles that seriously lack rhythm are a form of self-abuse and signal lack of self-awareness ('Moon stress') as well as a lack of basic self-regard and care ('Venus quality'). For example, I have found that if a call-centre builds a rhythm into the day and avoids shunting shifts and time about, productivity and health increase.

It is therefore helpful to think: 'I may be able to cope, but if I increase the level of ordered rhythm both within my day and from day to day, I will reduce stress and perform better.' Planning some regularity into your days (from day to day) and some pattern into each day and week, eating together at regular times, taking a break at a particular time, taking up a regular exercise or activity, can all help.

One valuable way to build rhythm into your life is through the regular practice of meditation or concentration exercises such as those already described at various points through the book. Meditation creates a strong 'punctuation' in the day. The meditator pauses, changes pace and consciously and deliberately makes a mental journey into the subject of the meditation. As Chapter 11 will describe, meditation normally involves the repetition of the same thing at about the same time of day for weeks, months or years. As such, it not only relaxes the mind, it tends toward an improvement in physical health and a more vibrant personal biosphere and immune system.

CHAPTER 9

WHEN PEOPLE SEND US CRAZY

*The aftermath of non-violence is the creation of the beloved community,
while the aftermath of violence is tragic bitterness.*

Martin Luther King

Sometimes other people send us crazy. Conflict may lead to wrenching of the guts, fear, freezing up, doubt in one's own abilities, violent antipathy, and anger. The distress can be extraordinary. This chapter therefore focuses on the second of the three primary causes of stress outlined in Chapter 1: being out of tune with other people.

Assyrians going to war, from a frieze in the British Museum

There is no greater stress than conflict. Conflict between peoples—Serbs and Croats, Jews and Palestinians, Irish Catholics and Protestants, Indians and Pakistanis—on the grounds of cultural or religious rivalry is an anti-social plague that ravages communities. Most organizations significantly under-perform, largely because people don't work well enough together. Conflict in boardrooms and management teams costs uncounted billions of dollars, as well as the more significant emotional costs of destroyed careers, motivation and well-being. Conflict in families wrecks marriages and damages children.

Conflict amongst friends and family leads to social ulcers and weeping sores that leave trails of sadness and tragedy through the years. Conflict erects walls that block happiness, creativity and decision-making. Eggshell politeness and open hostility are frequent but ineffective solutions.

> A former friend of mine has refused to communicate in any way with his mother for over twenty years after a most terrible conflict erupted. A conflict between two leaders of a charity with which I was working led to both of them being requested to resign to allow a slow recovery of normalcy. A chief executive was ready to sack one of his reporting directors, despite the individual being the most successful member of his team, because of conflict.

Where there is a will, conflict can be avoided or healed. The ability to do this is a social art, one that may yet become civilization's most prized achievement.

What can be done? How can we reduce or deal with such conflict and stress? I will explore this from four points of view:

- The need to overcome personal alienation through empathy, over-coming one-sided projections;
- The importance of taking personal responsibility and developing emotional maturity rather than blaming others;
- Non-violent communication skills;
- How to heal painful relationships.

The pain of individuality and separation

Out beyond ideas of wrongdoing and right-doing, there is a field. I'll meet you there.

Rumi

Chapter 4 outlined the way humanity's evolution of individuality led to a sense of alienation one from another. Most conflict is caused by mis-understandings and misconceptions born of this, our divided humanity, whether divided by age or gender or skin, experience or attitudes or beliefs, ambitions or dreams.

Such divisions begin in our almost universal experience of separation, as we contemplate the world through the isolation of our own skin and skull.

Perhaps you know aloneness:
the full skull and watcher's world
inside seeing outsides,
as though a surgeon had severed connection?

(the author)

The separation expressed in these lines may be painful, indeed it frequently is. After all, how much do we value a friend or a lover and how lonely is it without one? Recently a man in our village commented that it had been three weeks since he had had a real conversation with another bloke.

It might seem a cruel joke that we are so often so separate, each within our own physical and psychic skin. Such pain is surely the major cause of stress, and yet also of self-development through love. Erich Fromm in *The Art of Loving* describes it like this:

Being separate means being cut off, without any capacity to use my human powers. Hence to be separate means to be helpless, unable to grasp the world—things and people—actively; it means that the world can invade me without my ability to react. Thus separateness is the source of intense anxiety. Beyond that, it arouses shame and a feeling of guilt. This

Conflict: from an Athenian frieze in the British Museum

experience of guilt and shame in separateness is expressed in the Biblical story of Adam and Eve ... The deepest need of man, then, is the need to overcome his separateness, to leave the prison of his aloneness ... It is hardly necessary to stress the fact that the ability to love as an active giving depends on the character development of the person.

Without this, where would this individual isolation end? It might be in a Great War of All Against All, in which no one would understand or comprehend anyone else. Each person would interpret events only from his or her own personal perspective so that the other's perspective would be unfathomable and alien. There would be no truth but one's own point of view, the castle walls from which to hurl incomprehension and antipathy like burning oil upon the outsiders.

That is the dark journey!

Yet each little experience of discomfort with others may also be a spur to take another journey. Experiencing an enemy or a difficult-to-get-on-with person may encourage us to develop the social powers of understanding and compassion and love needed to avoid such a fate. Thus the person who drives us crazy may become our great inspirer and teacher. What others do that we do not like becomes a key for our own behaviour. Feeling isolated and misunderstood can stimulate us to reach out to others. Our own anxiety and vulnerability can help us to recognize pain in others. Gradually, he or she who drove us crazy may teach us the art to realize their yearning for love.

Vulnerability breeds aggression

Love your neighbour as your self.

Jesus Christ

In looking back at my own childhood, I noticed how I had developed various defensive techniques for when I felt threatened. Many children feel that schools and playgrounds, and sometimes even families, are risky places. There are the threats of bullying, social ostracism and failure. I certainly found this to be true. As a child nervous of physical violence, I developed aggressive intellectual and verbal techniques to defend myself, the individual equivalent and beginning of the behaviour that led to global rivalry in the insanity of mutually assured destruction (MAD).

The Cold War, the superpower battle that was the tense backdrop to my childhood and teenage years, and its language of confrontation and threat, merely extrapolates the tension and stress of two children threatening each other in the playground.

The irony is that it is nervousness and anxiety that commonly trigger such aggression. This may take many forms. It is not uncommon for adults to be anxious that they are being misunderstood or are not being properly recognized and appreciated. Bullies are commonly cowards, and fear stimulates fight/flight reactions.

The great irony is that the more we adopt aggressive, accusatory, blaming postures
and language the more we engender our own further stress
by triggering distress in others.

When language is aggressive and inflammatory, when it generalizes wildly and accuses others, when it projects personal feelings in the form of blame statements, then it tends to increase social tension, just as pulling a rubber band increases physical tension. When people say 'You' instead of 'I', for example, 'You hurt me' rather than, 'I feel hurt', and order each other about with statements like, 'Don't be so horrible', there is likely to be a succession of responses and counter-responses, accusations and counter-accusations. (This will be reviewed in more detail later in the chapter.) Marshall Rosenberg said: 'We have enemy images that make us think the other person is an object, not an alive human being. When we learn to communicate not in terms of needs but in terms of enemy images the bombs are never very far away.'

The challenge to transform social relations, whether in the playground or among the superpowers, takes us to the heart of spiritual development and true empowerment. Fromm calls *giving* the 'highest expression of potency'.

In Whitman's early and delightful poem, 'The Base of all Metaphysics', the base of all metaphysics is said to be:

> The dear love of man for his comrade, the attraction of friend to friend,
> Of well-married husband and wife, of children and parents,
> Of city for city and land for land.

And in the final sublime poem in Whitman's *Leaves of Grass*, 'So Long', written shortly before he died, he writes his vision of what will come after him:

I announce adhesiveness, I say it shall be limitless, unloosen'd,
I say you shall yet find the friend you were looking for.

The mechanisms that make us vulnerable

> In contemporary western society the union with a group is the prevalent
> way of overcoming separateness. It is a union in which the individual self
> disappears to a large extent, and where the aim is to belong to the herd . . .
>   Most people are not even aware of their need to conform.
>
>   *Erich Fromm*

Why are people so vulnerable to each other? What mechanisms explain
our mutual vulnerability and division and how can we heal these breaches?
How far can we legitimately allocate to others responsibility for our own
feelings?

Blaming others for how we feel

It is common to believe that the behaviour of others naturally has the
immediate power to cause strong, negative reactions: that there is something
inherent in what others do that must cause offence. People put this belief into
practice every time they make blame statements like these: 'He did this, and
so I felt. . . .' 'I hate him because he didn't deserve the promotion he got.' 'I
won't talk to her because she criticized my cooking.'

From my experience, I would say that there is a strong tendency for certain
sorts of behaviour (or communication) to breed reciprocal aggression. For
example, in leadership workshops run with colleagues we have observed
how when a person does something 'aggressive', for example to achieve
superiority over another, *or where it is so interpreted*, then even if there is no
immediate response, later the aggrieved party will where possible 'get their
own back'. For example, they might choose not to agree to a proposal being
made by the former aggressor. Sometimes, they even appear to be unconscious of this stimulus-response mechanism.

Here the aggressive action is like a punch that provokes, sometimes storing
up for later, a counter-punch. This of course easily becomes an ongoing
vendetta cycle, or even saga! This suggests that those who want to reduce
stress need to:

- Avoid generating counter-punches from angry rivals;
- Notice and deal with their own instinctive, possibly festering rancour that will otherwise dish up a mess of immediate stress through internal psychological and chemical reactions and at some point trigger the next step in the war.

Later in the chapter, I will describe how to communicate in ways that prevent such bloody ping-pong.

Some reactions do tend to be more instinctual, habitual or pre-conditioned. Psychologists, such as Maslow, who have studied human needs have found that people commonly share powerful drives or wishes for things like survival and safety, well being, belonging and self-esteem. Situations, behaviour and comments that appear to threaten any of these are likely to trigger various reactive responses including anger, anxiety, or fight-flight adrenaline rushes that grab the gut.

However, we know that some people have consciously chosen, because of other preferences, to forgo some or all of these so-called needs that Maslow described. For example, hunger strikers (or martyrs) such as Emmeline Pankhurst, Gandhi, Palestinian freedom fighters, and some IRA prisoners have threatened or taken their own health and life to make a point. If someone else can consciously choose to die of hunger, however much you or I might find that odd, then it becomes debatable what you or I are actually *forced* to do.

So, before rushing to agree that when others do something 'wrong' you must willy-nilly take offence (at the least), it is worth remembering the advice of stoic philosopher and former Roman slave Epictetus (55–125 ACE): 'It is not the things themselves that disturb people but the judgements they make about these things.'

Others' behaviour is mediated and interpreted by our values and opinions and thus stimulates the angry or approving response. What we see and hear and experience is open to choice. A sign of maturity is the ability to choose not to take offence, breaking the vicious spiral towards social hell that reactions such as the following tend to provoke:

A. 'What did that look mean? Is he sneering at me? I won't talk to him.'
B. 'She cuts me dead for no reason. How rude! I don't know why I liked her. Does she think I'm beneath her? I'll show her.'
A. 'So now he rubbishes the book I'm reading—just to show how superior he is! Well, he's got the intellect of an ant!'

When Alexander the Great first fought against the Persian Empire he did them the honour of burying their dead—as the Greeks did. Unfortunately this caused great grief and insult because the Persians thought of the dark soil as a contamination and had quite other treatment for their dead. Such misunderstandings are at the root of most tension on both small and large scales.

Childhood demons

Another factor that shapes conflict is that responses such as feeling threatened, put down or rejected may be reactions triggered by childhood or early experience. For example, something someone does might provoke a recurrence of childhood fear and insecurity. This helps to explain some of the irrational mental processes that so provoke distress. For example, if our experience of our boss reanimates, perhaps unconsciously, a childhood feeling of helplessness, then it is likely to affect how we interpret what is now happening. Thus old memories distort reality and increase stress.

Parents, for example, are often blamed for this. Philip Larkin expresses the resentment that is all too common in his poem 'This Be the Verse':

> They fuck you up, your mum and dad
> They may not mean to but they do.

The cited cause may be a single traumatic event or a pattern of parental behaviour. For example, the poet John Berryman was haunted by his childhood experience of his father committing suicide: 'Shadowed by your father/in his terrible pose,' in the words of his poet lover, Tracey Herd. Eventually he committed suicide himself but not before his pain traumatized his relationships.

But we can also review and make new sense of the past through empathy and acceptance, and thus heal both the image of our parents and our present ability to relate to the world. In one of the most moving poems I know, Robert Hayden describes how he comes to see with a renewed eye the life and influence of his father. Each winter Sunday, his father, whose chronic angers the house feared, got up in the freezing morning and with hands that Hayden described as cracked and aching from weekday labour banked warming fires and thanklessly polished the family's shoes. Hayden asks:[18]

> What did I know, what did I know
> of love's austere and lonely offices?

Again, I shall suggest ways to free yourself from such a problem if it applies to you. It is important to do so not just for your own benefit, but because otherwise you will be more likely to blame others when in fact the real cause stems from your own lurking chimeras, as with Annabel:

> Annabel remembered her first maths teacher as someone who thought she was stupid and incompetent. From this she became riddled with doubt about her ability, while also feeling angry with him. Whenever as an adult she engaged in mathematical tasks, especially with an authority figure, she tended to become flustered and irritable, blaming others for explaining badly.

I have indeed noticed how easy it is, when I remember my own childhood, to become sunk in maudlin self-pity or perhaps self-satisfaction. As James Hillman comments, 'Our lives may be determined less by our childhood than by the way we have learned to imagine our childhoods.' The great danger is to be an adult unconsciously haunted by, stalked by, a series of children—our childhood selves of five and nine and thirteen. In moments of stress, these 'children' may suddenly come into the forefront with their unresolved emotional wounds and immature prejudices to fashion our feelings and behaviour. Such moments may add to a spiral of stress, as what we then do provokes reactions that make the situation worse.

There is a meditative exercise by Rudolf Steiner that can help to free you from this tempestuous inner sea, helping you get to know yourself and so develop inner freedom from your childhood shadows. 'Remember yourself as a child but as if this child was another person, another child, so that you have a completely objective picture of the child as a stranger.'[19] By getting to know these children objectively we not only increase self-knowledge but we gain greater objectivity and self-awareness in dealing with the present. We enfranchise the slave. We gain freedom from the power of 'remembered perspectives', those distorting lenses that serve us up pseudo-facts instead of experience-in-the-present.

If, instead of wallowing in our own past, we observe it objectively, then we gradually gain the imaginative power to see things as they truly are, to see the wonder of the present. In the process we also give true weight and honour to the childhood experiences and personality that are part of who we are *today*.

Past lives re-emerging?

> The Body of B. Franklin,
> Printer,
> Like the Cover of an Old Book,
> Its contents Torn Out
> And
> Stripped of Its Lettering and Gilding,
> Lies Here
> Food for Worms,
> But the Work shall not be Lost,
> For it Will as He Believed
> Appear Once More
> In a New and more Elegant Edition
> Revised and Corrected
> By the Author.
>
> *Benjamin Franklin, aged 22, reconfirmed aged 79*

Another way in which many diagnose or interpret otherwise irrational responses to others is to see the conflict as connected to experiences in a past life. While reincarnation is not a traditional western concept, 25 per cent or more of the British and American populations are reported as believing in reincarnation, not to mention the billions in Asia. I find it interesting that reincarnation was a significant belief in Celtic, Roman, Jewish and Early Christian religious systems—i.e. the most important in European heritage— and was only later removed from Christianity.

Reincarnation seems to explain phenomena that are otherwise puzzles, and for that reason has been respected by many significant western thinkers, including Benjamin Franklin (as his proposed text for his gravestone demonstrates), Goethe, Lessing, Blake, Schiller, Wordsworth, Coleridge, Sir Walter Scott, Herman Melville, Shelley, Flaubert, Dostoevsky, Ibsen, Rosetti and Tolstoy.

Reincarnation was also a feature of several influential European and American movements over the centuries, including alchemy. The well-known image of a snake or dragon biting its own tail (shown in the image below) symbolizes rebirth. The snake is a frequent symbol because of the way it also casts its skin and is thereby 'reborn'.

For these reasons it is worth listening to the strategies for dealing with conflict that reincarnation theory suggests.

'Ourobos', the snake/dragon biting its tail, is an ancient symbol of reincarnation

At the core of reincarnation philosophy there is a humane point of view that everyone can usefully adopt. This is simply to assume that there is a special value to be gained from each relationship, and most especially from those involving conflict or love. The aim is to garner this value while healing the conflict or developing the love. This seems good advice.

How many people are there from whom you have parted with 'unfinished business'? Perhaps it is unfinished because of love untimely ended or just very intense. The great poet and sage, Rabindranath Tagore, describes his experience of undying relationship in his poem 'Unending Love' translated by William Radice:

> I seem to have loved you in numberless forms, numberless times,
> In life after life, in age after age forever...
> Whenever I hear old chronicles of love, its age-old pain,
> Its ancient tale of being apart or together,
> As I stare on and on into the past, in the end you emerge...

Alternatively, an unresolved conflict is also unfinished business. In the Epilogue to Beaumont and Fletcher's, *Honest Man's Fortune*, we read:

> Our acts our angels are, or good or ill,
> Our fatal shadows that walk by us still.

Unresolved conflict leaves those involved peculiarly *connected* in a mutual distress. Research shows that when people are reminded of someone they feel strongly about, perhaps by a photograph or having their name mentioned, it can alter breathing, heart rate, sweating and electrical energy patterns on the surface of the skin, glandular activity as well as mental processes and imagery. We may have parted physically, but in our soul we remain highly connected! Of course, it is not only conflict that does this. All strong emotional relationships live on.

According to the law of karma (or 'cause and effect') we may remain connected in just such a way to people from past lives with whom we have unfinished conflicts, and this may pass on from life to life until it is resolved through healing, compassion and understanding. Perhaps we have caused harm to the other person or they to us? Whatever the cause, there is always some important learning that each partner in conflict can give to the other, and this needs investigating.[20]

Whatever your outlook, up to a point it does not matter whether the problem has come about through behaviour in the here and now, or prompts from earlier in this life or from another life. Whatever the case, if you find yourself in a conflict-pattern, two or three attitudes seem to be most helpful, specifically to think:

- There is something important here for me to learn, something that will help me not only now but in the future, and unless I learn this I will keep stumbling into the same problem again and again;
- Unless I forgive I harm not only the other person but, no less importantly, myself;
- I can choose how I want this conflict to continue.

A painful experience, precisely because it is painful, has great learning potential. The irony is that until I have learnt what I need to learn, I find that I keep stumbling into the very situation I am trying to avoid—whether from day-to-day or year-to-year or life-to-life. Usually, these are lessons to do with maturity, compassion, respect, love and freedom, but they also include practical skills of communication and listening. In each case, the crisis is a challenge to acquire new capacities and social skills for the future, qualities that will make you a finer, wiser and more loving person. Thinking this way becomes a path to maturity through taking responsibility for your own inner condition.

The way out: taking true responsibility

You say you're lookin' for someone/never weak but always strong/to protect you and defend you/whether you are right or wrong/someone to open ev'ry door:/but it ain't me, Babe;/no, no, no, it ain't me Babe...

Bob Dylan

The more one forgets himself—by giving himself a cause to serve or another person to love—the more human he is and the more he actualizes himself.

Viktor Frankl

As we have seen, a sign of wisdom is to recognize your own responsibility for conflict and develop the skills and qualities that you need in all life-situations. When I feel hurt I can go through life thinking, 'He has hurt me, badly treated me, is to blame!' And when it is he who feels hurt, I can also think, 'It wasn't me, it's his fault, and he should get a grip!' If I do that, I never progress and I stumble from crisis to crisis and stress to stress. Alternatively, when it is *he* who feels hurt, I can think, 'What did I do that might have contributed to that?' And when I feel hurt, I can think, 'In what way have *I* contributed to this feeling of hurt?'

Perhaps you will think that this is some kind of nightmare: as if you are to blame whatever the situation? Perhaps you think that that is not fair? To my mind this is not so. Rather it is a sign of maturity to begin to free yourself from pain and suffering. As a compassionate person, you do whatever you can to prevent unnecessary pain in others. And as a strong person you develop resilience and emotional intelligence to avoid unnecessary vulnerability, which leads others to wound you when they would not wish to (or even if they would). Through such growth, you can also assist your otherwise partner in conflict to become free from the bitter emotions that cause and perpetuate suffering.

In this way, you follow Confucius's balanced principle, articulated by his disciple Tsêng Tzǔ as: 'Conscientiousness within and consideration for others.'

Nor is it a question of blaming either yourself or the other. As Epictetus said: 'It is the action of an uneducated person to lay the blame for his own bad condition upon others; of one who has made a start on his education to lay the blame on himself; and of the one who is fully educated, to blame neither others nor himself.'

Blame is clearly not a helpful concept here. More helpful is the idea of taking responsibility for your own self-development and reactions as well as the consequences for others of what you think, feel and do. In this way you move towards freedom.

When you think that others are to blame, that others hurt and harm you, you are in danger of missing your own responsibility for your life. Such a thought divides you from others and is the cause of great suffering. Furthermore, blame has a tendency to weaken your powers of self-leadership. It is a kind of myopia, for if you do not take responsibility you will not learn and hence crass actions will breed more conflict. Thus you will bind yourself to a primitive cycle of revenge or duty. This is one reason why religions have been such sources of conflict.

Abdicating responsibility for one's own actions means to be a kind of voluntary slave. Marshall Rosenberg, who teaches non-violent communication, says that in reading psychological interviews with Nazi war criminals what struck him was not their abnormality, but that they used a language that denied choice. For example, Adolf Eichmann was asked, 'Was it difficult for you to send those tens of thousands of people to their death?' Eichmann replied, 'To tell you the truth, it was easy. Our language made it easy.' Asked to explain, Eichmann said, 'My fellow officers and I coined our own name for our language. We called it an "amtssprache"—"office talk." In our "office talk" you deny responsibility for your actions. So if anybody says, "Why did you do it?" you say, "I had to." "Why did you have to?" "Superiors' orders. Company policy. It's the law".'

Rather than blaming and avoiding responsibility, I should think, 'What have I done, what is in me that so affects him or her?' In acknowledging my own responsibility, I create freedom. Indeed, learning to take responsibility for our own actions is the essence of what Rudolf Steiner called ethical individualism,[21] and therefore the hallmark of the free individual.

If I blame others for what I do, or I do things because I feel I am expected to do them by outside forces, whether the military, the police or the Church or my teachers or my boss, I am not free. According to Steiner, 'Man is free insofar as he is able to obey himself in every moment of his life. A moral deed is *my* deed only if it can be called a free one in this sense.' Ethical individualism is the process of acting out of one's own inner love or judgement of the action, as opposed to a sense of external compulsion or conditioned habit. When we accord to others the right to determine how we will behave we are unfree.

Notice that I am saying here that there is a relationship between blaming others for the way you feel or are behaving, and following an external moral code, however good that code may be. In both cases, you are handing over authority for yourself and your own actions to another. Even if that external moral code is said to be the word of God, nevertheless there is a difference between what you do out of your own inner love of the action prompted by

The Good Samaritan, from St Ely Cathedral

the inner voice of the divine that we call conscience and an externally presented set of instructions. Notwithstanding the doctrinal Church and the vagaries of translation, it is reasonable to believe that Jesus Christ replaced the old Way that was called the Law[22] with a new Way that means acting out of love and the impulse of the higher Christ-like I or Self, as in the story of the good Samaritan, who should be you or me, who succours the alien stranger, who might be you or me.

Life brings many challenging circumstances that test your ability to make a moral choice and do what is right. This is the responsibility of what Marshall Rosenberg calls the *inner chooser*, and what I have called the higher I. Rudolf Steiner described it like this: 'We ourselves must give birth to a new, higher being within us. This higher self then becomes the inner ruler, directing the affairs of the outer person with a sure hand.'

This is most needed whenever we meet the Sun challenge of moral courage that I described in Chapter 5. At any time, you might find a crisis that tests your moral courage. Having the capacity to choose effectively depends on regular prior practice in thinking and speaking that takes responsibility for your own experiences. This is the path to living in social and environmental harmony.

Thus the process of experiencing and dealing with stress effectively is also a process of developing moral stature. Without self-awareness, it is easy to be storm-tossed and at the mercy of a stressful sea of prejudice and blame and fear. As I practise recognition for my own responsibility I learn to calm these waters and take charge of my boat.

Communication that connects

'He beat me, he robbed me. Look at how he abused and injured me.' Live
with those thoughts and you will never stop hating. 'He beat me, he
robbed me. Look at how he abused and injured me.' Abandon such
thoughts and your hatred and your suffering will cease. Hating can never
overcome hatred. Only love can bring the end of hating.
This is the eternal law.

Buddha, Dhammapada, *3, 4 & 5*

Given the potential stress in social relationships, it is helpful to learn methods
of communication that do not generate conflict, such as Marshall Rosenberg's wonderful guidelines to improve dialogue and communication
between people. These have been put into practice in thousands of teaching
centres in many of the world's most difficult places. You will find a reference
to his book, *Non-Violent Communication*, in the Appendix.

I shall describe a four step process for communication that facilitates honest
conversation and dialogue, without hurting feelings, broadly based on his
ideas and teaching. These steps are:

1. Close and accurate observation of the 'facts';
2. Recognition of your own feelings;
3. The assumptions and needs in you that led to these feelings;
4. Stating what you would positively like to request.

This is a respectful process for meaningful communication—not a way of
developing power. According to Rosenberg: 'Non-violent communication
is not designed to get people to do what you want. If that is your aim, go to a
dog training school and learn how to use punishments and rewards.'

Communication is always two-way, so how we listen to verbal and non-
verbal messages is as important as how we speak. Let me illustrate with a
classic situation. One of my colleagues arrived late for a meeting. I was angry.
'She's always late', I thought. 'She's treating us like we don't matter and what
we're doing isn't important. It's so unprofessional!'

I might have left it there, filled with prejudice and unspoken rancour that
would have been bound to bubble up later in the meeting to create an even
bigger problem. Fortunately, 'Hang on' I thought. 'Let's review that. She
arrived late for just the last four meetings. Two situations were abnormal—a
broken train and a meeting scheduled at a time she had said would be difficult
for her. I don't know why she's late this time though. I am feeling angry and

disappointed and worried because *I need* to feel valued by her in what *I am doing. I want* her commitment. And *I'm thinking* she might not be committed. These are all my issues. So let me communicate and discover reality, or forgive.'

So I relayed this to her. 'I know you were late the last couple of times for reasons you couldn't really help, but now I see you're twenty-five minutes late, and I don't know why. I'm feeling concerned and upset because I want you to be fully on board with what we're doing, and I think you have an important part to play. I value your support. So would you mind telling me if there's a problem?'

This led to a far more productive exchange than accusation and blame would have stimulated, and moved the project on. I've found that the process has often blown away assumptions that 'They don't care.' At other times it has at least led to co-operative dialogue about real issues.

There are four steps in non-violent communication that I will discuss:

1. Perceived 'Trigger' Facts;
2. How you feel;
3. Because I . . . ;
4. Positive, Actionable Request.

Perceived 'Trigger' Facts or Events

Have you ever experienced a breakdown in relationships in which those involved seem to be in different worlds, speaking about the same events as if they were completely different? As Boethius put it:

> This discord in the pact of things,
> This endless war 'twixt truth and truth,
> That singly held, yet gives the lie . . .

One cause of this is that those concerned observe lazily and with different biases, mixing up their opinions with the so-called 'facts'. In such cases each describes their own interpretation of what is going on, sure that it is the truth. It seems clear that sometimes they actually look through the spectacles of their prejudice. I begin to overcome my egocentricity when I experience that what I take to be data—facts—are only points of view. The more I strive for certainty in a *single* point of view, the more I commit a partial lie. And the more I perceive facts that make the other to blame, the more I deceive myself.

One measure of maturity is the ability to distinguish between the fact of what happened, my observation of this, and my subsequent opinion about it. This is neither easy nor trivial. The ability to see things as they truly are might first seem to be a simple, even a naïve and childish task compared with the job of intelligent analysis. Yet, it is useful to remember Christ's remark that, 'Unless you are like children, you cannot enter the kingdom of heaven.' Indeed, Krishnamurti once said that true observation was the highest form of human intelligence. Blake, seeing heaven in a grain of sand, might well have agreed.

Rosenberg's non-violent communication method begins with asking yourself: 'Exactly what did this person do or say—or what is it in this situation—that I don't like?' Your aim is to identify at a factual level the events or phenomena that trigger the conflict.

The secret is to eliminate anything that is not pure observation. 'He criticizes me,' is not observation, it is opinion. Suppose someone was to say, 'You hardly seemed to think before you gave the answer.' This might seem to be a criticism of you. In fact though, he or she might be expressing amazement and wonder at your apparent brilliance, your ability to produce answers in a moment and without needing the long period of thought that he/she needs.

A direct quote, such as, 'Yesterday afternoon I believe you said, "You are stupid",' attempts to be observation because it tries to present a fact, not an opinion. It may be mistaken, but at least it is less biased. Compare this with, for example, 'So you think I'm stupid!' Try therefore to be exact with your observation.

Listening

How we hear things depends on what kind of ears we choose to wear. With empathic ears you can hear no criticism. Criticism simply ceases to exist, because criticism is simply a tragic expression of another person's unmet need. With empathic ears you can't hear praise or blame. Instead you hear the need that keeps the person saying yes—because you hear just what's alive in this person at this moment. With empathic ears the other person is always giving me a precious gift of what's alive in him or her.

Marshall Rosenberg

Good observation includes good listening. Listening tends to be filtered by attitudes and prejudices. If expecting aggression, we listen for aggression;

expecting love we listen for love. Key words take on more emphasis; others are overlooked, discounted or forgotten. Listening also tends to be reduced to a narrow wavelength. We hear the words of aggression and overlook the signs of vulnerability and fear and need.

The key is to open yourself to the full and honest reality of what the other person is saying across both verbal and non-verbal dimensions.

Unconsciously you will probably be taking in visual cues such as body language as well as aural cues such as tone and emotional resonance. Even those relatively inexpert in such matters still take in much in this way. Some experts believe up to 85 per cent of communication is non-verbal.

It therefore matters to be more conscious and aware—to notice the signals that are influencing you and to look more generously for other signals. When you listen with the heart, you will hear the surging needs of the human being and the enemy will evaporate like clouds on a sunny day.

How You Feel

After collecting mental observations and phenomena and perhaps communicating them, the next step is to recognize how you feel: *your emotions*. Just as an opinion is not an observation, nor is a thought an emotion. For example, 'I think he hates me' is not an emotion, it is a thought. Emotions are things like anger, sadness, frustration, joy, happiness, disappointment, bitterness, wistfulness, misery and excitement.

'I feel he is ignoring me', or 'I feel she doesn't care' masquerade as emotions but are opinions full of blame. Recognizing the emotion you have—and it can be hard if you have not practised it[23]—immediately tends to remove such blame because you are now talking about yourself, not the other person. You therefore reveal the truth of your response both to yourself and the other. Stating (not shouting) that you feel angry, sad or disappointed is more honest than accusatory.

When you feel happy, warm, joyful or grateful and reveal these positive emotions, others will probably feel warmed and grateful, glad that you have revealed yourself. Thus you improve the relationship. After all, showing emotion is the basis of all 'love-making'.

Because I . . .

Anything we say that implies blame is a tragic, violent way of expressing needs.

Marshall Rosenberg

Once you have identified the emotions, the third step is to recognize your *own responsibility* for these attitudes and emotions as well as your real *needs* by using 'I-language' not 'you-language'. All too often 'you-language' simply projects our own unacknowledged feelings and needs. Emotional response doesn't leap from 'facts', i.e. words or events that happened, straight to emotion. Experience first passes through a filter of thoughts and needs.

Let us finally realize that it is not the 'facts' that breed fear, aversion, desire or hate. Fear, desire, aversion and hate, are caused because fear, desire, aversion and hatred are within me. When I know things through the filter of my pre-suppositions and partiality and separation I never truly know them. Thus my bias will have a tendency to lead me into social disharmony and even conflict. Unacknowledged or unexpressed needs can prime a violent or negative attitude. Yet it does not have to be so. As Walt Whitman put it: 'Were mankind murderous or jealous upon you, my brother, my sister? I am sorry for you, they are not murderous or jealous upon me. All has been gentle with me, I keep no account with lamentation, (What have I to do with lamentation?)'.

Whitman beautifully expresses the truth that the world we meet depends on how we meet it. Certainly unpleasant things can happen even to the most innocent and lovely of people. However, the old proverb that those who live by the sword die by the sword reflects the karmic principle that we bring upon ourselves according to what we bring to others. The accusers will be accused and the blamers will be blamed, while the lovers will be loved.

An appropriate next step is therefore to say, 'I feel like this *because I . . .*' At this point you would explain, at least to yourself, your own thinking and the needs that drive your feelings.

> Andrew met a young woman and really liked her. He asked her to go out with him and she said she would ring him back. A few days later she had still not called. Andrew felt miserable and angry. He accused her of being unkind.

It is important, as in the example above, to distinguish between your real needs—for example for friendship or love or financial security—and your interpretation. Thinking about it, Andrew realized that it was because he wanted love and blamed her for not giving him what he wanted. He interpreted the lack of a call as meaning that she didn't care, was not interested and was perhaps not a very nice person. Here is the core stress of feeling alone and out of tune with others twisting the mind and thereby further promoting the very problem Andrew wanted to solve.

There may or may not be truth in Andrew's interpretation, but the key point is that another person with different needs and a different rational interpretation of the absence of a call might have had a very different response. It is therefore your response, your interpretation or assumption, which drives your reaction, not the other person. Furthermore, Andrew's negative interpretation, driven by his own unrecognized needs, leads him to think badly of the girl, a conflict-generating as well as stress-inducing response.

Those who ascribe to the other what belongs to them are unconsciously doing violence. Check the two columns below to see if you recognize your own patterns of thought and communication. Language in the first column tends to blame others, fuelling violence and counter-violence. The second column expresses the situation more honestly, owning responsibility and disarming conflict.

'You' statements imposing on the other person	'I' statements expressing the truth
You are right	I agree with you
You were wrong	I disagree with you
You did well	I like what you did
You did badly	I don't like what you did

Mature individuals therefore own the responsibility for their reactions, recognizing them as arising from their own, inner, psychic world. It is not a question of deciding it's wrong to have a particular reaction but of recognizing the cause. In dialogue this is called surfacing the assumptions. These assumptions are driven by our past education and experience and by our unmet needs. Marshall Rosenberg therefore recommends paying attention to your *inner educator*, the inner faculty that brings your needs to your attention.

There are two reasons why this is a good way to behave. The first is personal and amounts to a more effective way of dealing with stress. Suppose you are feeling angry because you need security and think your security might be threatened. If this is so, it's important for you to know that. Acknowledging inner drives helps you to recognize what is really going on and develop a strategy to deal with the stress. You might decide that you need to reconsider your assumptions and to open your mind to other ways to think about what has happened. You might also review how important or how much at risk your need really is.

This is empowering. I have noticed that I become less at the mercy of my emotions as I become more aware of them. Paradoxically, self-awareness does not make you a cold fish, far from it. Increased awareness of emotion tends to enrich the emotional life, just as increased awareness of the world of nature stimulates the senses. Instead of being driven, perhaps unconsciously, by emotion, I can become more aware, more responsive and more alive as well as more in charge of myself.

Since distress comes not from the external stimulus but from the internal response, the more aware you are of how you react, the more possible it is to develop mastery. When inner awareness is perfect we gain the freedom to choose the response we want. Distress then disappears. In Buddhism, this is called the Buddha nature.

You might think that such an attitude could not be sustained in a 'truly vicious environment', such as a Nazi concentration camp. Yet even in—perhaps precisely in—conditions that would rationally lead everyone to condemnation, Viktor Frankl and Bruno Bettelheim described how different people had vastly different reactions, reactions that were also vastly different in their effectiveness.

The second reason for recognizing your internal cause with the 'Because I' statement is that it can help you in your communication. Even if you cannot perfectly master and transform your attitude, you can avoid escalating the conflict. Taking responsibility for your feelings tends to avoid such escalation because you are no longer blaming the other person. That is less threatening and inflammatory. You have said what the problem is without directly accusing them. Furthermore, by giving a personal explanation for why you have those feelings you make yourself more open, revealing how you work and what you really think and need. By divulging this and surfacing your assumptions you make it easier for others to warm to you and clarify any misunderstanding you may have.

Positive, Actionable Request

> Never express pain without expressing the request. Without expressing
> what you want, it will probably be interpreted as blame.
>
> *Marshall Rosenberg*

So now you have communicated to yourself and the other person or people where you stand:

1. What you have observed;
2. And how you are feeling;
3. As a result of your assumptions and needs.

The final stage that Rosenberg recommends is to make a positive and actionable request. You might for example say, according to circumstances, any of the following:

- I would be grateful if you could tell me your point of view;
- I would appreciate it if you would arrive at the meetings in time for the scheduled start in future;
- Would you wash up whenever I cook?

A *positive* request is simply one that asks the other person to do something rather than not to do something. 'Stop leaving it to me to cook and clear the dishes,' is more conflict generating and less helpful than, 'Please wash the dishes when I cook'. The advantage is that you communicate what you actually want rather than, potentially, delivering a veiled blame statement.

A *request* is not an order. However much we may want the other person to do something, except in special circumstances, ordering it is not appropriate or helpful. An order is more likely to be perceived as confrontational and aggressive, as well as being unnecessary. Therefore, instead of creating conditions for a willing, positive response, we may trigger more confrontational behaviour in response. 'If it feels like a demand, there is no joy in doing it', said Marshall Rosenberg.

An *actionable* request means that the request is specific and capable of being performed. 'Listen' is not an actionable request. General statements like, 'I would like you to improve your performance,' if not made within a very clear context, do not specifically say what you want done. A small change, like, 'I would like you to think about ways in which you can improve your performance,' demonstrates the difference. Here there is a specific action. Instead of saying, 'Treat our meetings with more respect,' ask, 'Please arrive on time.'

Summary

So, in summary, these four steps help to ensure that communication avoids blame and encourages understanding and social harmony:

1. State the 'Trigger' Facts: observing and communicating the actual events or triggers for concern without adding opinion and blame;
2. Express your Emotions: saying how you feel, your actual emotions, leaving out all opinions of the other person;
3. Because I: take responsibility and own your needs and the beliefs that drive these emotions by using 'I' language;

4. State your Positive, Actionable Request: what you request the person to do that would help.

Healing relationships

Blessed are the merciful, for they shall obtain mercy ... Blessed are the peacemakers, for they shall be called the children of God.

Jesus Christ, Matthew 5, 3

Perhaps paradoxically, a good way to deal with conflict-based stress is the opposite of what one might think: it is to learn to appreciate what is good in the conflict-partner.

Those who learn to see their negative feelings as primarily rooted and nourished within their own soul, rather than caused by someone outside, learn to take responsibility for those feelings and so grow and create a mutual space for freedom and love. Instead of thinking ill or of trying not to think at all of people with whom you are in conflict, perhaps avoiding physical and mental contact, try to take an interest in finding out as much as possible about your conflict-partner's life history and how they see things. Try to find as many good qualities as you can. In a word, try to appreciate the person you might otherwise hate.

Positive interest in the other is a warm, sun quality that unties the emotional knots and may, in time, stimulate love.

I well remember one individual with whom I had difficulty over several years. We met in professional situations where we should have engaged with each other as colleagues. Instead, I rarely felt positive about his ideas and he clearly seemed to feel the same about mine. Taking the situation in hand, I found an opportunity to ask him about his life and for two hours I listened and asked questions as he let me know intimate details of important periods in his life. His willingness to share and mine to listen projected a kind of warming radiance into the relationship that without any other words or deeds healed the difference and built mutual respect. Not too much later, he died. I feel as if we have parted on quite different terms than might have been the case.

Undoing knots

> O Great Spirit, help me never to judge another until I have walked two
> weeks in his moccasins.
>
> *Cherokee Prayer*

Sometimes people feel totally and helplessly knotted in conflict. I well
remember the severe conflict that I had with another professional colleague.
At first, we worked well together but then the time came when each meeting
seemed to lead to conflict. I would flare up with anger while he retreated into
a position of cold obstruction. Even when we were not meeting, simply
thinking about him produced violent reactions. In response to the mental
picture that I formed of him, my stomach would knot up, my heart would
begin to race and adrenaline would run in my veins. My shoulders would
tense, my lips become narrow and hard and my thoughts turn ugly as I
blamed him for whatever I thought was going on. In this situation I was far
from seeing the truth and I expect the same applied to him.

This was many years ago and while we worked together I was not able
to find any healing path. It was only later, after I moved away, indeed,
after the situation helped to drive me away, that I was able to do anything
about it. However, for several years after we parted I continued to blame
him. Each time I thought about him the same kind of reactions rushed
into my stomach and head. Not only had my thoughts become bitter and
twisted, but to the extent that I saw the events of this period of my life
and my own personality through my canker, part of my character was also
becoming bitter and twisted. Fortunately, I found a way to free myself
from this anguish.

Forgiveness is the key that unlocks the door of resentment and the handcuffs of hate.
It is the power that breaks the chains of bitterness and the shackles of selfishness.
Corrie Ten Boom

I had always avoided thinking about him because I did not enjoy the anger
that erupted each time I did. However, by learning to observe my mental
picture of him and my own reactions, I gradually found my way towards
equanimity, and something strange came about in the process. *My own
responsibility for the situation* gradually appeared. I saw how my own deeds, and
the unnoticed needs and thoughts that lay behind them, contributed to the

poison in the situation. I saw how I had continued to stir this poisonous brew, like the witches in Macbeth.

This helped me to understand and forgive him and to recognize the forgiveness I also needed. I recognized what I needed to do to change myself.[24] Thus, although we have not overtly made things up since we parted, inside I feel very differently towards him. Our relationship is now on a new ground for the future.

It is my impression that when one conflict partner, unilaterally, takes steps to transform the conflict pattern that lives within his or her own soul, this also helps the other conflict partner. Christ expressed something of this view when he said, 'Judge not, that ye be not judged.' (Matthew 7, 1).

Healing feelings and attitudes

The time for the healing of the wounds has come. The moment to bridge the chasms that divide us has come. The time to build is upon us.

Nelson Mandela

As the two personal cases I have just described show, it is important to be in touch with one's own emotions. Lack of emotional awareness causes many social problems and conflicts. It can signal a kind of lack of intelligence in dealing with the world. A book by Daniel Goleman[25] has popularized the idea of *emotional intelligence*, an ability that contributes to social intelligence, perhaps the kind of intelligence most needed in the world today. Awareness of one's own emotional life can help to regulate, balance and positively direct it in ways that we choose. Without this awareness, we are like a ship without a rudder upon a stormy sea, blown hither and thither by the emotions that move us.

Emotions power reactions.

The word *emotion* derives from Latin roots, the letter *e* meaning *out*, and *motion* meaning not too different from what it means today. Emotion powers the internal motion that moves us.

As I have described, one of the greatest dangers is projecting our emotions on to others. For example, instead of thinking, 'I am feeling angry,' I might think, 'He hates me.' This leads to increased conflict. Accurate awareness of your emotional life helps to develop awareness of others, leading to empathy. The mere act of becoming aware of your feelings and emotions already starts to bring control.

There is a very important image that has appeared countless times throughout the Christian era which I think represents this. It is the image of Michael and the dragon, often represented as St George and the dragon: the archangel Michael, perhaps on his horse, is thrusting his lance down to hold the dragon at bay. This may be seen as a picture of intelligence (Michael is regarded as the angelic guardian of intelligence) projected through the lance of awareness into the turbulent, uncontrolled and violent world of emotional bestiality that erupts in the stomach. According to Jung, 'The dragon, or serpent, represents the initial state of unconsciousness, for this animal loves, as the alchemists say, to dwell "in caverns and dark places". Unconsciousness has to be sacrificed; only then can one find the entrance into the head and a way to conscious knowledge and understanding.'[26]

I therefore believe the image expresses in mythic language the human aspiration to master the lower nature, the unrefined passions and emotions that lead to abuse and conflict.

The dragon in this myth is generally regarded as Lucifer, the light-bearing

Michael and the Dragon based on an image at Lincoln Cathedral

archangel who led the revolt in heaven. As the snake (or dragon), Biblical legends describe how he brought about the banishment of humanity from the Garden of Eden into a world of shame and pain. Legends of such a fall are also found in almost all the other world traditions. It is as a result of the loss of emotional purity that we live at odds with ourselves and in revolt between one person and another. Transformation of negative emotions into positive ones is therefore a process of redemption whereby the earth-bound serpent, the fearsome dragon, is freed and transformed once again into the bright light-bearer.

Identifying the negative emotion is like taking Michael's spear and using it to hold down the writhing, squirming beast that threatens you.

In the majority of these pictures, Michael or St George thrusts his lance into the dragon but does not kill it. This is important because I think that, in general, it is not possible to kill emotions, unless perhaps by starvation. It is only possible to suppress or transform them, and the first step in this is generally to penetrate them with awareness. The dragon as emotion is not *suppressed* but mastered. Michael does not avoid the dragon, he engages with it.

An emotion-transforming exercise

An exercise that helps is to take a deep interest in your own feelings and attitudes about the conflict partner. Look objectively and with keen attention at the fluttering in your stomach: the feeling of sickness or rage, how the blood rushes to the head or the hands go cold, or the shoulders tense up. If you can look at this feeling or experience with the greatest of interest and intensity, thus penetrating the dragon with your lance, you progressively free yourself from negative feelings and in due course from the bad behaviour or cold or angry feelings of the other. It becomes possible to forgive your conflict partner and treat the experience as a learning situation. Spinoza comments in his *Ethics*: 'Emotion, which is suffering, ceases to be suffering as soon as we form a clear and precise picture of it.'

It is very helpful, once you can observe your emotions, to then ask: What beliefs or needs in me cause these emotions? In this way you discover how the emotions are *triggered* by outside stimuli but *caused* by you. This is not in order to blame yourself; rather it is to develop self-knowledge and to grow towards maturity. Those who practise this gain certainty about their responsibility but also their potential for freedom.

Through such an exercise, a number of options might emerge; you might even become friends with the individual; you might find mutual freedom to separate and go your own ways, but without any residual hostility or bitterness; you might be able to achieve a breakthrough and work more effectively together.

We grow through others

> I will not grieve that people do not know me; I will grieve that I do not know people.
>
> *Confucius,* Analects *I-xvi*

The greatest block to discovering reality in relationships, or in the observation of nature or events, is to be too certain that you already know 'the Facts'. Such facts, however, are not what is directly present to observation—the leaf on the mushroom in a haiku by Bashô—but rather what is remembered, what you think and bring to mind. With time, maturity and perspective the meaning and significance of relationships changes, as in the poem by Robert Hayden about his angry father, quoted earlier. Georg Kühlewind wrote:

> . . . experience is never completed . . . Therefore the face of the fact can change, and does change in most cases during life. Today's misfortune can prove to be a blessing; the joy of today can prove to be a tragic error. The one for whom the facts do not change or develop can well suspect that he is not on the right path. Facts gradually turn out to be what they really are. They have no final face for us, they live with us: as long as we live, they only begin. The facts have not occurred: they occur constantly.

In the course of my life I have several times re-evaluated basic 'facts' of my upbringing according to my mood or whether I was disposed to see things as positive or negative or when new consequences or factors in my personality emerged.

For example, in my first week at secondary school a woodwork teacher caned me with a wooden dowel—the first time I had been caned—largely to make an example to the class. For a long time I saw this as grossly unfair, and still there lurks a part of me that can turn to the hurt child and complain; and this same child is ever ready to spring forth in response to some event I experience. Yet I also see that my *fear* of the pain exceeded the reality. Once it happened my nervousness decreased and I became braver and wiser, a lesson that holds good for much of life. From the experience, I also learnt the importance of scrupulous fairness. Out of my own, totally selfish experience, I gained a little compassion and justice in my dealings with others. That man and his deed has in many ways actually been good to me.

Sometimes, the ongoing memory or experience of the 'enemy' can be still too raw to allow respect. In such cases, time can help with healing and recognition. Taking the trouble to practise the emotion transforming exercise just given in the last section will help to gentle the rawness and speed healing and recognition.

There is another meditative exercise that cultivates appreciation of the significance of others in forming who we are—drawing on the Jewish saying 'The one in front of you is your teacher'—while increasing self-knowledge:

- Dwell on what you have gained from all the people you have met either directly (such as teachers) or indirectly (for example in books). Try to build up in inner pictures within the soul what each has done for you. Picture without liking or disliking but merely seeing what you owe to this person or that, how you are in their debt for who you are. Never mind how much the learning may seem to have depended on your interpretive wisdom. Note only the significance of the people and the experiences.
- Develop thereby an objective experience of a vast crowd of people who have formed the substance of who you are.[27]

Walt Whitman's wonderful poem, 'There was a child went forth', evokes this:

> There was a child went forth every day,
> And the first object he look'd upon, that object he became,
> And the object became part of him for the day or a certain part of the day,
> Or for many years or stretching cycles of years...
> The early lilacs became part of this child,
> And grass and white and red clover, and the song of the phoebe bird...
> And the old drunkard staggering home from the outhouse of the tavern
>   whence he had lately risen,
> And the schoolmistress that pass'd on her way to the school,
> And the friendly boys that pass'd, and the quarrelsome boys,

And the tidy and fresh-cheek'd girls, and the barefoot negro boy and girl,
And all the changes of city and country wherever he went . . .
His own parents, he that had father'd him and she that had conceiv'd him
   in her womb and birth'd him,
They gave this child more of themselves than that,
They gave him afterward every day, they became part of him . . .

Recognising the contributions of others develops a capacity that serves us in each present moment. What happens is that separateness from others is reduced, and now as you meet someone in the moment you more truly meet them, you more truly picture who they are, not just how you feel about them. One of my most valuable lessons from this exercise has been to realize how important to me have been those who have challenged me, whether in full-throated conflict or in something milder. Learning to value not only those we love but also those we have hated is an amazing and maturing experience.

Each time I learn to value my enemy, I gain immeasurable power to love and appreciate each person I meet. Each time I learn to love my enemy I overcome a portion of the great divide that separates me from the universe and its maker. This is the path demonstrated for us by Christ, Buddha and others. It is thus to become Christ-like or Buddha-like, to become as a son of God. At its end, each individual, and not merely humanity at large, becomes an image of the divine and we learn to value what each individual in our life means for us.

This is the true potential of the higher self, the true I.[28]

Wonder, reverence and love

What food is to the body, feelings are to the soul. If we feed the body
stones instead of bread, it will cease to function. It is the same with the
soul. We nourish it with reverence, respect and devotion.

Rudolf Steiner

Wonder is the root of compassion and love. Wonder and reverence form the rainbow bridge to the love that heals the divided universe and the stresses of social life. As each of us reveals more and more of our unique presence, and as our wonder and interest in each other illumine the ever-present beauty and value in each individual, love is born and conflict healed.

The stresses of egotism, aloneness, hatred, bitterness and scorn are killing, as I described in Chapter 1 and discussed through the myth of Cain and Abel. Through such emotions the value of life declines in bitter pain. In the increasing reality of individualism/individuality there is therefore both the potential for nightmare—as separation, division and hatred—and supreme goodness in the form of love. Race, religion and gender have separated us in the past with demonic apparitions in the last century. This is cured only as we warm to know and appreciate others.

It is a sad fact that probably the most influential psychologist of the twentieth century possessed a pathological attitude towards others. Freud commented, ' I have found little good about human beings. In my experience, most of them, on the whole, are trash.' How we see others seems to be a measure of our own nature. Rudolf Steiner commented that in our lower natures we can find commonality 'twelve to the dozen,' but in our higher nature we find real individuality that never has conflict with others.

Individuality thus becomes a true gift only when consummated by passing from mere egotism to discovering the true value and interconnectedness of each human being. The more I think I am separate and alone and the sole arbiter of things, the more I become divided from the real. The more I realize that I am indissoluble from the gifts of and interactions with others, the more I recover my community self. This is to be more not less an individual, it is individuality enriched, as Whitman suggests in this moving phrase from 'The Song of Thyself': 'Walt Whitman, a Kosmos, of Manhattan the son.'

Whitman's whole great opus, *Leaves of Grass*, is a paean to the world and the individual (hence its repeated quotation in this chapter). Perhaps lines from one verse (also in 'The Song of Myself') best express something of the emerging reverence of the individual and the love that flows from this:

> And I say to mankind, Be not curious about God,
> For I who am curious about each am not curious about God,
> (No array of terms can say how much I am at peace about God and about
>   death)
> I hear and behold God in every object, yet understand God not in the
>   least,
> Nor can I understand who there can be more wonderful than myself
> Why should I wish to see God better than this day?
> I see something of God each hour of the twenty-four, and each moment
>   then,
> In the face of men and women I see God . . .

Cultivating wonder in others and nature heals the breach that is called the Fall. It is the capacity that allows Whitman to see God in his neighbours and a mouse as 'miracle enough to stagger sextillions of infidels'.

A poem by E.E. Cummings, 'i thank You God' in his book *XAIPE* (1950) beautifully captures the opening of the eye to wonder and its healing power:

> i thank You God for most this amazing
> day: for the leaping greenly spirits of trees
> and a blue true dream of sky;

Cummings goes on to describe how he feels alive again on this 'day of life and of love and wings' and that this lifts him beyond all doubt of the 'unimaginable You', since:

> (now the ears of my ears awake and
> now the eyes of my eyes are opened)

From such perception grows healing reverence. In nature it means learning to love the created world. In the social realm, this happens when wonder leads to this appreciation of others and of our inter-dependence. Wonder is the organ or power that discovers the virtues of each person while cultivating the community. There is a social or moral law formulated by Rudolf Steiner that can serve as a meditation on this principle:

> The healthy social life is found
> When in the mirror of each human soul
> The whole community finds its reflection,
> And when in the community
> The virtue of each one is living.

We can also cultivate wonder by practising exercises like those described above, whereby we transform our own hatred, get to know others and acknowledge their value, potential and how they have formed our nature. Such acts are also a gift to others, as Viktor Frankl wrote:

> Love is the only way to grasp another human being in the innermost core of his personality. No one can become fully aware of the very essence of another human being unless he loves him. By his love he is enabled to see the essential traits and features in the beloved person; and even more, he sees that which is potential in him, which is not yet actualised but yet ought to be actualised. Furthermore, by his love, the loving person enables the beloved person to actualise these potentialities. By making him aware of what he can be and of what he should become, he makes these potentialities come true.

CHAPTER 10

TRIALS THAT GUIDE US TO OUR HIGHER SELF

We dedicate this day to all the heroes and heroines in this country and the rest of the world who sacrificed in many ways and surrendered their lives so that we could be free. Their dreams have become reality. Freedom is their reward.

Nelson Mandela in his inauguration speech

President Harry S. Truman's harsh comment, 'If you can't stand the heat, get out of the kitchen,' does make some sense. Clearly, one of the strategies for coping with stress is to reduce it. Human life is full of stories of struggle and pain, difficult decisions and situations of uncertainty that became the source of growth and insight for those who were 'suffering' them. For example, despite its inherently vile nature, Oprah Winfrey said of her experience of physical and sexual abuse that it made her a 'stronger and more vital woman'. After his journey through the Nazi concentration camps, Viktor Frankl entitled one of his books *Saying yes to life in spite of everything* and commented that what mattered was finding meaning even in suffering.

As well as such evils, life brings other kinds of challenges and trials associated with the human pursuit of excellence, from Sir Edmund Hillary's conquest of Everest because 'it was there' to the struggle to achieve creative mastery, as for example in the case of Martha Graham and her troupe.

Martha Graham, one of the most important artistic figures of the twentieth century, was instrumental in the development of new dance forms. For seventy years she danced and choreographed with intense energy. She believed that 'Everyone is born with genius but most people only keep it a few minutes.' Involvement with the Graham company was more like a crusade than a profession. She had little understanding of those who lacked dedication and audacity. She said, 'Everyone has the right to fail. You fail and from your failure you go up one step—if you've got the courage to get yourself up.' In other words, for Martha Graham life was to be lived intensively for the cultivation of imagination, insight and artistic practice. As a choreographer, she aimed to code every gesture with significance. What she put into her art she first found as a principle of life.[29]

Any exploration of stress therefore needs to recognize and celebrate life's trials for what they are or can be. As Seneca commented, 'There are times when even to live is an act of bravery.' Nietzsche said, 'What you have experienced, no power on earth can take from you.'

To develop this idea, I will describe trials known traditionally as the fire, water and air trials. Each brings special gifts. My aim is to show how such developmental trials occur naturally in life, with the hope that you may come to see some stressful experiences in a new light.

Life as a 'trial by fire'

> ... as far back as consciousness can go ... one of the greatest properties of fire was its power to transform, to remove the impermanent and perishable from the permanent and the imperishable, the false from the true, and let these move on and grow into the future.
>
> *Laurens van der Post*

According to Goethe, 'Genius is formed in quiet; character in the stream of human life.' This, it seems to me, points to an important pair of truths that illuminate the theme of stress. The trial by fire that is the trouble and strife of daily life, the obstacles that trip us up as we blithely make our way, the 'heat in the kitchen' that Truman referred to, are nevertheless the means to develop 'character', that depth and strength of personality that can stand life's buffets and give help to others. Trials like the death of a loved one, redundancy, divorce, illness and even conflict add substance to our souls through the mere fact that we have borne and accepted them. Quiet reflection afterwards on the meaning of this experience then gives wisdom, the only true genius.

For what matters is not simply the experience, but learning from it. There is an old question: Have you really had twenty years experience, or have you had one year's experience repeated twenty times? What happens to experience depends on a person's attitude. Those who are convinced they know the answers, or that fate is unkind, or that there are no mysteries to plumb, gain little from experience. Instead they continue to repeat their lives based on assumptions; or they rail against life and other people, accusing rather than gaining; or they pass through their experiences blindly, never noticing the manifest secrets of existence. However, those who investigate their experiences in search of unselfish insight develop ripe knowledge, breadth of mind, the acuity to see what others miss and wisdom to understand what leaves others confused. I shall try to explain how I believe this happens.

The meaning of the fire trial

The fire trial is a term used in many forms of initiation and spiritual development, from the European Rosicrucians and Masons to Asian or African rituals. Mozart and his librettist and producer Schikaneder made use of it in his opera, *The Magic Flute*, when the hero Tamino is required to cross a red-hot bed of coals in order to win acceptance and his love. This required courage and fortitude, qualities that are the prelude to the revelation of secrets and development of love.

While some fire trials were and are physically real (for example some practitioners of NLP, or Neurolinguistic programming, a set of psychological tools and methods, use it in personal development courses for managers and staff), others are symbolic, referring to everyday challenges that 'cook' our character, as in the image below of a king being roasted. Similarly, Jung quotes the *Aurora consurgens*, which says that through baptism by fire, 'man, who before was dead, is made a living soul', an idea based on the words of St Paul. Treading the path of life well requires resolution; through faith in the future comes breakthrough. For example coping with major life trials leads to inner development and new life wisdom.

This image by alchemist Michael Maier, left, from his book Atalanta Fugiens *published in 1618, makes a symbolic point that before becoming king, i.e. a wise and fit leader, purification through the fire of life-experience is required. A contemporary clip art image, right, makes a similar powerful point! Learning to deal with life's trials leads to wisdom and patience.*

Have any of these 'top 10' stress-inducing life events affected you recently? If so, what have you done to help yourself through this period of stress? What have you learnt?

FIRE TRIALS IN EVERYDAY LIFE

- Death of a partner;
- Divorce;
- Separation from marital partner;
- Detention in prison or other institution;
- Death of a close family member;
- Major personal injury or illness;
- Marriage;
- Being fired from work;
- Marital reconciliation;
- Retirement.

The fire trial leads to a different perception of the world. In this simple sentence I hope to convey a rather profound meaning. Let me develop the idea in stages. Two people walk down the road. The first one notices the trees growing through holes in the pavement every few yards. She sees the state of the leaves and hears the birds that are nesting above. The second one notices all the people: what they look like, what they are wearing and what they are doing. The same real world, but two different experiences! The difference lies not in the world but in the outlook of the person.

The fact that on numerous occasions people who have tried to walk across a bed of coals have severely burnt their feet serves to show how significant it is that others are able to walk calmly across twenty feet of burning, red-hot coals. Fire walking demonstrates the principle that the world I experience truly depends on my outlook.[30] The effect of a lifetime of deep and richly challenging experience is a shift in outlook through the development of life-wisdom. As a result, the world becomes a different place. Take the story of Betty, below, which is a classic example of Moon stress (see Chapter 5).

Betty was an administrator of a community school. She began with an idealistic commitment, but did not feel she was recognized as being as important as the teachers. Over the years she began to feel put upon and disgruntled. So she began complaining in the hope of getting appreciated. After a while, parents, colleagues and others began avoiding her because she spent so much time complaining to them about how busy she was. Betty's response created a vicious cycle that only she could break free from. The more time she spent telling herself how busy she was, the less energy and enthusiasm she had for the tasks. In her mind her work grew into a massive and un-appreciated burden. She therefore alienated those she hoped would sympathize, so creating yet more reasons to complain.

Betty's solution was to recognize how much energy she wasted and that her complaints were really a cry for help from her own nervous system that only she could really answer. Complaining, she realized, achieved nothing: it only contributed to negative rather than positive mental attitude. By improving her lifestyle, taking time to plan more effectively and working in a more disciplined way she gradually took charge of her own life. As a result, every detail of her life became different.

Before, what had surrounded her had been charged with gloom: although she would not have described it so, she invested the people and tasks of her working life with rank meaning and dark soul, as though they were out to spoil her life, as though they deliberately mistreated and threatened her. I think it is natural to invest the world with meaning, and those who do not find positive meanings tend to invent negative ones. When Betty rethought her life, to use a saying of Blake's, the doors of perception were cleansed.

And into this world a new and splendid character emerged, one who had been obliterated under a pile of mental rubbish. This was Betty herself. At this point the real being of Betty began to emerge, even for Betty, from its obscurity. The character of her work also changed. Now, Betty saw that her working tasks and circumstances could not have been designed better to help her discover her own real power and potential; the challenge had helped her achieve a personal breakthrough to new potential and possibilities.

As a result of maturing experience, Betty's reflections on the world changed: instead of seeing herself as a victim of difficult circumstances with the world around her to blame, she begins to see her role and potential. At this point, Betty's world is a New World, an entirely new continent of experience with new meaning. Thus the human being has the capacity to mature through difficult times and feelings.

Human potential is limitless and therefore so also must be the path to its unfolding. Each step is accompanied by new challenge. Each challenge successfully met develops character and prepares for the possibility of new challenge, by changing not only inner capacity but also how the challenge itself is viewed. As you become changed, so the world changes. As you become inwardly richer and wiser, the world becomes richer and more filled with wisdom.

A tree is not just a tree, a task not just a task. They are invested with beauty or pain, value or irrelevance, scientific or poetic explanation. Experience of life gradually refines this, reduces the random, partial or shallow interpretations in favour of richer, wiser deeper perspectives, the fount of wisdom and character.

Through life experience in the trials by fire, an invisible world increasingly becomes visible. Or, to put it a different way, the soul of things gradually develops through enriched understanding. Take awareness of thought, the ability to observe our own thoughts or to understand what others are trying to communicate. Deep experiences that furrow their way into our character seem to give us the means of getting to know the world of thought in a new way. Life's experiences have gradually unfolded meaning for us. The very pain that we have experienced not only gives us emotional depth, it seems to open a window in our soul. For example, many people report that the pain that they have experienced becomes the source of understanding and compassion for others. In effect, my pain can help me to see into the mood and situation of another, can help me to understand and empathize. In the very middle of life, the opportunity extends to cultivate the imagination that 'gets us through'. As Sally Jenkinson put it in *The Genius of Play*:

> Rationality works with the now, the finite. Imagination, on the other hand, is timeless and engages with the possibility of what might be. Imagination penetrates the veil of the future, and trawls the past to supply the human psyche with the multiplicity of meanings it needs; it lends wisdom to the soul. The mind's eye is the blind eye that also sees. It is the imagination of spring that helps us through the dark days of winter; the vision of spring's return, which allows winter's privations to be borne. Inner vision draws us on, giving us staying power and furnishing us with the necessary courage to win through against adversity. In troubled times our imagination, unbounded by time or place, reminds us that things will not always be as they are. (Page 57.)

Furthermore, as a result of life's trials, we may increasingly begin to observe that the world and all around us, all the events, all forms of life, and all situations are filled with meaning. Everything becomes coded with personal meaning, yet loaded with significance not merely personal but also increasingly insightful. All great art seems to me to seek to express this. It is as though the world becomes a language or a secret script so that everything tells a story that can enrich our understanding. The world becomes ensouled.[31]

Perhaps you have had the experience of 'feeling blue', or you might have seen a person that you thought was 'looking grey', but more in the mood than the skin tone. These are first examples of seeing the colour or aura of things. In Chapter 6, I described listening to the difference in quality between the sound of an animal and an object. This is to experience the soul of the sound. It is a first step in allowing the soul-spiritual nature of things to speak or sound to us. What is the difference between walking in a straight line and in curves, or between being in a round or a square room? Let the form of things become meaningful.

At one end of the spectrum this leads to the ah-ha! moment when we suddenly realize the world anew. At the other, there are the highest of peak or mystical experiences that reveal secrets of nature and existence, such as Wordsworth's of a divine nature, or this one by Happold, who went on to collect many testimonies:

> Another experience happened to me on the evening of 18th of April 1936, the evening of the day before my son was born. My first child had been still-born and I was very anxious about my wife and much disturbed in mind. And then a great peace came over me. I was conscious of a lovely, unexplainable pattern in the whole texture of things, a pattern of which everyone and everything was a part; and weaving the pattern was a Power; and that Power was what we faintly call Love.
>
> F.C. Happold, *Adventure in Search of a Creed*

Yet, life can be very lonely, or difficult, leaving many questioning its meaning and point. The philosopher Hobbes described it as, 'Nasty, brutish and short.' Frankl said that when concentration camp prisoners thought this they soon died. However, as we learn to read the world's script aright, it increasingly regains meaning and value. Even death takes on new meaning.

Never forget that we may find meaning in life even when confronted with a hopeless situation, when facing a fate that cannot be changed. For what then matters is to bear witness to the uniquely human potential at its best, which is to transform a personal tragedy into a triumph, to turn one's pre-dicament into a human achievement. Echoing Seneca, Frankl commented on the experience in the death camps:

> ... the hopelessness of our struggle did not detract from its dignity and its meaning... Not only our experiences, but all we have done, whatever

great thoughts we may have had, and all we have suffered, all this is not lost, though it is past; we have brought it into being. Having been is also a kind of being, and perhaps the surest kind.

When we are no longer able to change a situation—just think of an incurable disease such as inoperable cancer—we are challenged to change ourselves.

At a certain point, this ability to see the real nature of things takes a decisive step. Not only do we feel that life has increased significance and value for us personally, which is already enough to give comfort, but something else emerges.

Let me go back to my example of Ms Stress, our guide in life. Possibly, when I introduced this idea, if you did not reject it out of hand, you may have thought of the idea as a quaint metaphor. But as a result of the *deepest* experiences of the trial by fire, the world becomes filled with active wisdom and we come to notice wise agencies in life and all around us. (In Betty's case these active agencies included the tasks that at first she thought were wrecking her life, and that she later realized were helping her.) Through life experience, we begin to notice how every event or thing we meet has its own wisdom and that the meeting is not just coincidence.

I can observe the shape of a tree and recognize that there is nothing on its left; once another tree must have grown there, for the tree has twisted away to get sunlight. The invisible, now vanished tree affected the tree that remains. The scene now tells a dramatic story. In the same way, through life experience, I begin to notice how every event or thing I meet has its own wisdom and that the meeting is not just coincidence. (What happens naturally through life experience will happen more quickly amongst those who reflect deeply on their experiences, and still more quickly amongst those who practise an effective path of spiritual development.)

My own destiny and life process now ceases to be a series of haphazard and chance experiences and instead becomes a meaningful and planned process of self-development. When this happens, what is normally apparent only from hindsight at best, begins to be noticed in real time. I begin to see that the people I meet and the events that happen to me have purpose and value. I can begin to see the 'why' in what happens. Let me explore these ideas in two important aspects of the fire trial; karma and then death and loss.

Karma

> All things that are accidental we must transform into purposeful living.
>
> *Novalis*

In Chapter 4 I considered the role of destiny in human life and the Acorn theory put forward by James Hillman describing how it might influence our attitude to and handling of stress. I cited some examples including these:

- My wife responded to a charity advert and we ended up getting married. If she hadn't responded, would we have married?
- R. G. Collingwood (1889–1943), a brilliant English philosopher, took a book by Kant off the shelf, could understand nothing but felt a calling: 'I must think.'
- My son aged seventeen took up a book by Plato, was filled with excitement and the feeling of finding what he had searched for 'all his life' and switched (without ever really reading Plato again) from being a good to an excellent student. Suppose Plato hadn't been there, or he hadn't looked into it?

Other examples also reveal the way destiny can work into life:

- A colleague remembered visiting a particular school for disadvantaged children that gave us a connection in her initial job interview and led to her being offered the job and us becoming friends. Without this connection, would she have had the job offer? How many other such 'chance coincidences' serve to bring people together every day?
- Ella Fitzgerald, an awkward sixteen-year old, had already been announced to dance at Amateur Night at Harlem Opera House when she suddenly changed her mind, decided to sing, won three encores and first prize, and changed her life. Suppose she had danced?
- Martha Graham was convinced that she was born as a dancer. 'I didn't

choose to become a dancer. I was chosen to be a dancer,' she said. She discouraged anyone who didn't feel the sense of calling from making dancing their career. What brings about a feeling that you really want to be something?

- Another woman I worked with described how she was descending in a hotel lift in Las Vegas with a group of girlfriends when a party of Englishmen joined them. The other women loved the accents and followed the men, drawing my colleague along with them. They were sitting in a large bar when there was a sudden commotion; the men began laughing. Looking round she saw a huge man carrying another tall man in his arms. The giant walked over and deposited the other man on the floor at her feet. Even though the men were only there for that one last night before returning home this was enough: today she is happily married to the man who was deposited at her feet. She commented that, 'I was led to him and he was brought to me in a way that is absolutely uncharacteristic of my normal life.'

- The composer Julian Anderson came across a collection of old records of field recordings of folk songs from Latvia and this transformed his musical language and approach. The sounds he heard chimed perfectly with his ability and personality to provide a new direction. Is it chance when a person meets their destiny in this way, or is it something else?

Such examples, which can be multiplied many times, may be cynically downplayed, but the aware mind finds significance. In Chapter 4 I also proposed that life has meaning, in the sense that we meet things that we need, and that we prepare these experiences for ourselves. There are many clever voices arguing that life is random or based on blind mechanisms, voices that argue with certainty and authority and yet actually represent no more than a factional point of view. As I discussed in the previous chapter in connection with relationships, the idea of a meaningful destiny is intellectually robust and has a powerful heritage in the idea of karma. Karma is actually, in various forms and names (fate, destiny, purpose etc.), one of the most widely held and, in mature form, most sophisticated and powerful philosophies in both eastern and western cultures. The word is borrowed from Indian philosophy and means something like 'the law of action'. In its most developed form, it holds that throughout our life we meet events that have been planned for and by us in the interests of becoming and doing what fulfils our destiny and calling.

Actions have effects: I cut the branch off the tree and now for all time the tree lacks the branch. This deed and effect in the world is now part of me, part of who I am.

To an all-seeing being observing me, the fact that I cut the branch would reveal part of who I am. So would all my other deeds. I too in my higher nature can see that I should take responsibility for this deed and its effects and in so doing I remake who I am.

A branch might seem a trivial matter but suppose it is not just a branch but a forest, or perhaps it is someone's car that I smash up. Across Europe, paper manufacturers are not permitted to cut down a single tree without having measures to more than replace it. Across the world, if I smashed someone's car I would be expected to have insurance to take care of it. Thus we accept the karmic principle as a normal part of life and earthly existence.

Furthermore we see the effects of our actions determining the future of our lives in many obvious ways. For example, I have frequently and ruefully lived with the consequence of promising to be on the other side of the country early in the morning, of losing my temper with someone, or of promising to do a lot of work in a small amount of time. On the other hand I have enjoyed the benefit of apologizing or being gracious.

The notion of karma takes this principle to its conclusion in the idea that nothing is ever overlooked. I can't 'get away with it' just because no one saw that it was me who cut the trees or smashed the car. Nor is the unobserved kindly deed lost; rather it shapes my future. The fact is that the deed and its consequences are now part of me, something I now live with—in my character, who I am, my future destiny. Most of the world's great drama and literature dramatizes just this: think of Macbeth and Lady Macbeth. I can't dodge consequences, because I carry them; and the world, nature, God, circumstances, destiny or what you wish to call it will reflect this. However, karma is not about retribution: it is about learning and improving.

The essence of any mature view of karma and especially the western tradition is that what comes to meet us is not a blunt eye for an eye but an artistic response designed to let us learn, rather as a hangover is a good way to learn about how to drink. Everybody goes through life with a leitmotiv, or distinctive pattern, or more likely several. Angry people keep getting into conflict; caring people keep getting asked to help, or finding opportunities to do so. Relationships or jobs break down for similar reasons until the lessons have been learned and some adjustment made. Backache returns until posture or exercise is corrected. Karma in its fully developed form suggests that many of our characteristics are never resolved or healed in a single life. Thus we carry our need to learn something through life and sometimes from life to life.

The fire trial thus includes necessary learning experiences. These include the opportunity to put right anything we have previously done wrong. Karma and reincarnation extends this principle over lifetimes. Suppose in a previous time or life I hurt or caused stress to someone, now I have the opportunity to put that right. Suppose in a previous life I have an unfinished relationship with someone; now in this life I meet this person again and have the opportunity to complete the relationship that I had hoped for. Perhaps in a previous life I had a childhood friend, then our ways parted and I did not see her again, yet when I died I had a longing to know her in later life. As a result, I meet her in this life as a mature individual (although perhaps this time 'she' has become a man). From the aspect of the fire trial, the key point is that through such experiences and awakened awareness I learn to look at what happens as a code containing a deeper meaning of great import for me to discover. The fire trial is the means to learn how to see into the secrets of nature, including the dark and light secrets of our own personality.

All that is happening is designed to give the opportunity to develop freedom.

Suddenly, the people I meet and how they treat me ceases to become mere chance and coincidence. It becomes the result of purpose, whether initiated in this life or earlier.

Thus the concept of karma accords perfectly with the philosophy of this book: that stresses are learning opportunities and each of us meets according to our unique personality a unique mix of stresses when we need them (even if we don't want them). This idea can be very healing. An example is given by psychotherapist Roger Woolger of one of his clients, 'Peter':

Peter was a client who during a therapy session suddenly described an intense experience as an indentured labourer and then migrant worker who is treated harshly as a social misfit all his life. The memory is powerful and vivid, and also cathartic. Afterwards Peter recognizes how he has been unconsciously challenging authority figures in his present life as an after-image of this former life, a discovery that releases him from the obsession. 'I feel very different,' he says. Such a story, if taken seriously, indicates how a stress leitmotiv may develop.

Roger Woolger, *Other Loves, Other Selves*

Karma also provides a profound route to explore questions that trouble not just philosophers but every thinking person:

- Can an evil person get away with it?
- Why do unpleasant things happen to good people?
- Does the pattern of life have meaning?

In my experience your answers will be partly a matter of faith, based on your outlook in life, and partly a matter of growing perception or insight. The more deeply you observe phenomena, the more you pay attention to the sub-text in events, the possible layers of meaning, the more you are likely to see that nothing is random and that life is a meaningful destiny that we continuously form. If you ask why something is happening to you from the perspective of what it especially enables, answers begin to glow in the mind.

This is a hard thing to prove, especially in a short space, but it is an easy thing to experiment with. Live with or try out this possibility—that the trials of life, the events that come to meet us arise from what we already bring and that this in turn stems from what we have already done (or not done, another kind of doing). Then if you seriously, in the mood of open-minded research, live with this thought and pay attention to your experience I believe it will come to make sense.

At the very least you will have become a more open-minded person and will probably notice the simple things you do—and do not need to do—the promise to meet across the country, the cutting of a neighbour's hedge or the offer to make tea. Such increased consciousness will then help you reduce your stress levels. The retrospective exercise that I mentioned also helps with this observation process.

Increased consciousness creates increased choice. What happens has purpose and meaning, but does not take away our freedom. Quite the contrary, destiny is the means to develop freedom and to develop ourselves to our fullest potential. But everything depends on how we react. Those with courage, compassion, forgiveness and tolerance develop inner freedom.

Dealing with Death

> Call upon Me in the day of trouble, and I will deliver you.
>
> *Psalm 50*

The maturing wisdom and insight that emerges through the fire trials begins to reveal the real nature of things. The deepest of the secrets that is unveiled is the nature of death. We live with death from birth: the first breath is the beginning of death. Yet through life wisdom the sting of fear and loneliness that death wields is lessened.

Usually, when someone close to us has died, the feeling of bereavement is a difficult and even bitter experience. In fact it ranks high amongst the most stressful experiences of life. Elisabeth Kubler-Ross observed the grieving process amongst friends and relatives of those who have passed on. Her grieving model (see below) is widely accepted as an accurate description of what commonly happens. It shows fluctuating changes in emotional and personal energy, beginning with *immobilization*, rising to *anger* and falling into *depression*, before final *acceptance*.

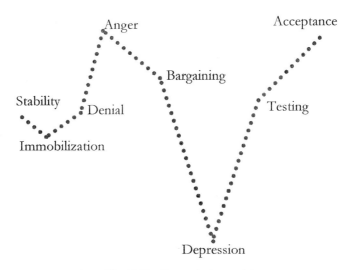

The Kubler-Ross grieving model

It should immediately be acknowledged that the pain of bereavement can be enormous, it may feel like an ocean of suffering. As the Kubler-Ross model indicates, the pain of grieving affects us in our thinking, feeling and will. First, people find it difficult to believe that this could have happened to them. Bereavement can be like having a part of your world rubbed out or amputated. Then comes anger: for who has done the rubbing out, who is the cause of this pain that hurts so much? Finally, we sink into depression, when the will turns inward to make sense of the loss and difference in our life.

And yet this depression is not simply a 'down', it is a sinking down, an immersion into the experience of death and also the experience of the life of the person we have lost. I believe that it is important to have the time and emotional space to do this properly, to have the opportunity to reflect deeply on the life and death of the person we have loved. I remember that it was quite some time after the death of my mother before I was really able to recognize my loss and the love that I felt for her. Partly, this was because at first I did not give myself the space to absorb what was happening; partly I just needed time. When this moment finally came I was wracked with sobs, but it was also a cathartic experience by which I came to know the being of my mother in a deeper way and to appreciate the fullness of my relationship with her. As a result I re-entered normal life, but with a new relationship to her. Through giving the space to enter deeply into grief, we not only honour the life, we also have the best opportunity to learn from it and to come to terms with our own future, the process Kubler-Ross calls Acceptance.

For every death is also a birth. The death of the older generation is also the space into which the next generation can grow. Equanimity is a virtue (encouraged in Chapter 6) that is entirely consistent with a healthy grief process, I believe, for equanimity does not mean absence of feeling. Instead it means that we have the inner courage and balance to be able fully to absorb tragedy or difficulty without falling apart. Equanimity means transforming the impulses towards denial and anger and the darkness of depression so that the fullness of feeling may be owned and accepted and the new situation embraced.

So what is acceptance? Is it just the acceptance of loss or is it, as I believe, the acceptance of a new relationship with the loved one who has departed? Acceptance certainly includes the process of transformation by which we are able to go on with a life without the presence of our loved one. But what is death really? I think the experience of life helps with the answer to this question. The deeper and more powerful our trials and crises, the more I believe we experience the cycle of death and resurrection that is at the heart of all existence. In our own depression, we go through a kind of mini-death; and in our acceptance of the new situation, a resurrection of the soul takes place. As Walt Whitman said: 'No array of terms can say how much I am at peace about God and about death.'

When the time comes that we are truly able to see the world filled with soul, the observation of death is itself transformed. I believe that death is only the departure of that which gives life to the body. The word 'spirit' means breath, and it is the spirit that quickens the body. Once it has departed, the body returns to the elements from which it has been formed: as the saying in the Christian funeral service goes, 'earth to Earth . . .'

What appears to be death in the visible world, the world of the senses, is something very different in the invisible world, the spiritual world. From this higher perspective, there is a birth as the eternal human being passes over into the world of pure being. Death in this world is birth in the soul world. This brings us close to the realm of miracle, for as the transformed pain of life gradually matures into new vision of the world, one of the things that becomes obvious is that those who have died have not left us. Far from it, for the so-called dead are very close to us. In the world we begin to know that is full of active wisdom, we begin to discover how those who have died remain in active connection with us.

Suppose for example you now find yourself in a crisis, let us say there is a conflict in your family, consider how it would help to take this idea seriously. My experience is that you can actively ask those who are close to you but have passed over to help you in such situations. It is not necessary that you are able to see them or that you go to a spiritualist. It is enough to make a personal connection in your mind through the memories that you have of the person before he or she died. Then simply ask for help, though it can be helpful to try and make this request as pictorial as possible, for example imagining the one who has died calming the difficult situation or giving advice. Speak simply, from the heart. All you then need to do is to observe the situation and your own thoughts. Perhaps thinking of those you love and their past help to you puts you in a mood to find your own solution. Alternatively, I suggest that your loved one then gifts ideas to you, although these will at first seem to be your own ideas. Even if you are sceptical, try it. Just talking to those you love in your imagination can really help.

Other forms of loss and the pains of attachment

> Monks, the All is aflame ... Aflame I tell you, with birth, ageing and
> death, with sorrows, lamentations, pains, distress and despairs.
>
> *Buddha,* Fire Sermon

Although grief at the death of a loved one is perhaps the most severe form of grieving, there are also other circumstances when it occurs. Kubler-Ross's model was developed in studies of bereavement and grief, but it has been shown to relate much more broadly. When any major change takes place, such as being made redundant, mergers (when 'your' company 'vanishes'), divorce, children leaving home and so on, most people feel as though they are losing 'part of themselves'. The change is like having a limb lopped off.

Change is in fact a kind of death. Research shows that employees who go through significant change processes commonly react in the same way as people suffering bereavement. The grieving model applies in both cases.

This is generally because people believe themselves to be tied up with what they do and their social circle. Losing some of this is like losing part of themselves. Just as the lines on our faces are worn in by movement and become part of the self-image, so our everyday actions and responsibilities are worn into our self. The stronger the habit, the stiffer you become and the more it feels like an amputation when the habitual experience is no longer possible. The more ingrained the habit, the more likely that grief or pain is felt. Old age and growing old are experienced by many as a slow loss—of vitality, youth, passion. As Nobel prize-winning poet Octavio Paz put it:[32]

> and I find myself at the end of time
> with bad eyes and a cough, rummaging through
> the old photos

Paz's answer, from the same poem was:

> better to be stoned in the plaza than to turn the mill that
> squeezes out the juice of life

The exercises for flexibility given in Chapter 6 help to prevent such a fate. However, if a 'death' experience does meet you, it helps to follow the same process described earlier: of inwardly honouring what has passed on, while letting the death in whatever form it takes become a space for new life.

> Deborah's marriage turned dull, and she felt imprisoned without really realizing it. Then she found that her husband was having an affair. For a while she felt terrible. First she found it difficult to believe: this did not fit her mental picture of marriage. Then she was angry: she blamed herself and felt unworthy, arguing that if she had been a 'better person' this would not have happened; and she was angry with her husband. She became depressed and felt she was staring into a void. But after the divorce she began to find and assert her own life and interests, including renewing her love of painting, which she had put aside throughout her marriage. She found a new meaningful career. After a while she realized that the crisis had been one of the best things to happen in her life.

Deborah's experience is a common pattern. Denial, anger, self-blame and depression are common stages in dealing with what seems to be failure. But, at a deeper level, Deborah's process allowed her to come to terms with what was really important and necessary in her life. The pain of the experience was transmuted into a more vibrant soul.

Similarly, we feel loss and disappointment when things that we expect to have or experience or enjoy are not available. Here is a meeting point between religious thinking and practical life. Buddha described how the cause of all suffering, i.e. stress, is human desire and attachment. For example, I like ice cream. There are times in my life when my liking for ice cream leads me by the nose, or perhaps I should say by the tongue, in search of a vanilla special. When I can't have one it feels like a loss or absence or gap. It is a pain. Following our desires in this way prevents clear thinking. It blinds us. In Buddha's celebrated Fire Sermon (quoted above) he described each of the senses as aflame with the fires of passion, aversion and delusion.

Octavio Paz echoes this in lines from the poem quoted above:

> eyes are flames,
> what they see is flames, the ear a flame
> and sounds a flame, lips are coals,
> the tongue is a poker, touch and the touched,
> thought and the thought-of, he who thinks
> is flame, all is burning, the universe
> is flame . . .

Those who achieve wisdom are released from these fires. The fire trials and life-stresses teach us not to behave like an untrained dog sniffing after our every whim. In this way, through self-development and balanced self-discipline, our thinking evolves and thus our ability to make free decisions. Preferences, wishes and opinions belong more to our unfreedom than our freedom. As we become released from such unconscious mental attachments and see more clearly, we prepare for the water trial.

Life as a 'trial by water'

> Life ultimately means taking responsibility to find the right answer to its problems and to fulfil the tasks which it constantly sets for each individual.
>
> *Viktor Frankl*

The trial by fire is preparation for the more advanced 'trial by water'. It is easy to imagine that a trial by water must be different from the trial by fire. Whereas 'fire' indicates the difficulties and even tragedies that meet us in life and thereby harrow and yet purify our souls, the trial by water approaches from a different pole. Success in dealing with these trials depends on what we have gained through fire.

The name 'trial by water' traditionally indicated an experience in which you lack normal support because the normal ground for decision-making is gone. You are 'all at sea'. Saturn stress as described in Chapter 5 is an example of this. I described situations in which it was very hard to know what would be the right thing to do because there was no immediate feedback available. For example it is hard to know what it will be like to live in a new neighbourhood until you have really moved there. The trial by water has this quality of unknowing. Successful resolution leads to the decision-making freedom of the true leader.

Most people are unaware how much of their behaviour is conditioned by outer circumstances. For example, we commonly behave the way we do because that is what is expected of a male or female, a parent or manager, a 'good person' or a 'good Christian', a son or husband. Ultimately, all such conditioning or socialization tends to make people unfree. It is not that there is anything necessarily wrong with any set of expectations. No, unfreedom depends on you feeling instructively constrained and therefore unable to act differently. In effect, each of us is to some extent locked into our self-image. In fact the deepest level of unfreedom arises when I do not even know that I am constrained to behave the way I do, but simply act from habits ingrained into my nature.

One of the profoundly instinctive responses of the human being is to assert the essential freedom of human nature. Just a few pages ago I was describing how the fire trial helps us to develop freedom, yet here I am describing how unfree the ordinary person is. It is just out of this paradox that behaviourist philosophers have laughed at human aspirations for freedom. I believe that life teaches that freedom lies deep in our nature as *potential* but needs to be acquired in *practice*. Each time we find ourselves with no *given* answer and a need to find a decision, we face the water trial and the potential for freedom. Each time we make a real choice 'real' freedom comes a little closer.

This brings us to another paradox, for the action that we take in such a situation should not depend on our own preferences, our personal wishes and opinions, for when we act in this way this is not true freedom. Instead it should derive from wisdom. This is why successful achievement of the water trial depends on the heightened perception and insight that arises through the fire trial. Let me illustrate this.

When thinking about moving house, as is the case as I write this text, I naturally think about where and in what kind of a house I want to live. But, suppose instead of looking at what I want, I see it as my responsibility to discover where the *right* home is? How would that be different?

Perhaps this personal example illustrates this. About 15 years ago my wife and I bought the house in which (at the time of writing) we currently live. We looked at a number of houses and rejected even more without bothering to view them. Most of the time, there is no doubt that we considered the houses mainly on the basis of what we liked or did not like combined with practical matters such as what we could afford. But something else also played into the process and was most apparent in our choice of the house into which we eventually moved. A simple way to describe this would be to call it the 'feel-right' test: the house we ended up buying felt right, there was an almost immediate intuition that this was the right place to live, and it certainly proved to be the case. Our children had good conditions for growing up and met other children who have been very important to them. There is also little doubt that we have positively changed the lives of several of our neighbours just as they have changed ours. I would say that we were called to meet each other by destiny.

Simply buying the house based on liking it would not have been freedom; it would have been no more than following an urge. What made the difference was consciously choosing to go with what presented itself as right.

Of course some readers may reasonably point to all sorts of factors that may have been the real instruments of our choice. They might say, 'Most houses seem to be chosen in the first few seconds and all kinds of minor and often unnoticed factors seem to be decisive in this choice. Perhaps there was a particular smell that you liked, for example coffee brewing?' This is certainly how many decisions are made. Nevertheless, I think it is interesting that so many houses, new employees or suppliers do seem to be chosen in the first few seconds. What brings this about? Is it the smell of coffee or the voice of destiny? In our case, I think there was a genuine intuition and if pushed to describe how it 'felt-right', I would say that my wife and I could see the *rightness* of the place. This was not in anything material but in its subtle, soul nature and our relationship to it. The 'right house' has special meaning in our life; it has a different quality than just its colour, size or shape, perhaps to do with people we will meet. If life has meaning, it would be right to be able to see this. I think this is connected with what in Chapter 1 I also called the ecology of life. It is a kind of feng shui. It is also an example of the kind of matured and wiser seeing that came about through the fire trial—seeing into the nature of things.

Fortunately, for the purpose of this book it is not essential for you to decide whether I am right or wrong, for this is only a personal instance of a general principle. But, the trial by water is a situation in which we are called to act, to meet some responsibility, not just a desire, but the only way we can know the right or wrong thing to do is when the ensouled world gives us this feedback. We cannot rely on any normal standards. It is only during the trial by fire that we gradually develop the ability to recognize the language of nature and how every event or circumstance that we meet is loaded with meaning. This was called being able to 'read the language of nature' or its secret script. Now in the trial by water we put this to good practice by letting Nature or the spiritual world or our intuition advise us directly. When our insight is sufficiently developed, perceptions appear of things invisible to the ordinary senses.

Every situation has its own 'form' and we can change or sculpt this spiritual form as much as we can change things in the material world. Perhaps you have had a sudden intuition to do something, or not to do something. This is a first and possibly unconscious step in higher decision-making.

There is an NLP (Neuro-linguistic Programming) technique that illustrates this principle. You start with a problem situation that you want to examine from a higher perspective. At the first stage, you try to re-enact the problem situation as closely and as accurately as you can, paying attention to the details. If possible you try to dramatize it, for example laying out tables and chairs, and acting out the events that happen physically. Then in the second stage you step back, physically, and observe the situation as if other characters were involved. Finally, you step back again and if at all possible climb up to a higher level, such as on to a table. I have experienced that at this third stage something miraculous often takes place. Suddenly, everything becomes clear: why things have been happening and exactly what to do.

Life gives opportunities to train the higher senses further through responsible decisions that are crammed with uncertainty. Making such decisions is stressful, but gaining the capacity to make them through practice means personal growth and freedom. When such a situation comes, you need self-control, calm and thoughtful contemplation. Those at the mercy of their wishes and opinions cannot 'listen' to what the situation is asking for. If I am in panic, how will I come to a good decision? But, suppose that I can consider the alternatives thoughtfully and carefully and weigh up in my mind what each of them is telling me. Then I can start to open my perception to the rightness or wrongness of each alternative, first by common sense and then by seeing its colour or hearing its sound. If I become capable of doing this, then I have the potential to be of great value to others, as well as being able to go through my own life in a more effective way.

I become free: less at the mercy of my own stresses or desires and more help to others. In this way I steadily transform my lower self to be more like my higher self. Thus we see a relationship between moral character and decision-making ability. Decision-making in the water trial—finding the right answer to the mystery of the situation—does not simply depend on cleverness. Indeed cleverness usually leads to problems, as for example in our ecological disasters. To decide right needs right-thinking, and right-thinking needs right-being. Before moving on to the air trial, it is therefore necessary to explore 'rightness'.

Finding balance and moral clarity

Spirit is a purified act.

Novalis

Wherever we look in the cosmos we see pattern, and processes or states of balance and imbalance. Energies interact with energies in a continually developing, transforming and dynamically interwoven pattern or patterns. For example, ecological theories such as the Gaia principle describe an evolving balance of nature energies that maintain life, populations and the environment and shows how destructiveness comes about when balance is lost.

Spirituality has always found a specific aspect of this principle, assuming the human being to be an image of the macrocosmic divine and believing that life and society should harmoniously reflect the divine mind. However, instead of being in tune, the individual frequently becomes aligned with energies that cause alienation and stress, including jealousy, anger and greed.

Distress therefore means an imbalance with the universal pattern.

The fire and water trials equip human beings to perceive the underlying pattern and nature of things, to read their meaning and significance, but also their moral dimension. Culture has always recognized a moral drama

Yin-Yang symbol expresses balance

between right and wrong, good and evil. Sometimes this has itself led to evils, for example when religions attack non-conformists and vice-versa, but all such aberrations only point to the need for more genuinely enlightened, wise and compassionate reading of people, situations and actions.

I want to propose that there are two primary archetypal sets of energies or beings and that alienation and distress arises because we don't live in the right balance with them. Balance represents a third state or energy or being. The yin-yang symbol in Taoism beautifully expresses this.

Life experience gives feedback when we slip out of balance, just as a high-wire artist feels each time he or she is in danger of overbalancing. And just as the experience of being out of balance may be scary to anyone not supremely comfortable with high-wire walking, so can life experience be uncomfortable, culminating in the equivalent of the artiste's ignominious fall into the net. Gradually from this experience comes mastery of life-balance and improved decision-making.

Distress means an imbalance with the universal pattern.

The first of these archetypal beings or states is naturally and psychically hot, excited, animated, enthusiastic, brilliant. It expands and is expansive. It is feverishly creative, stimulated and stimulating, synthetic, bright, arrogant. Some literature calls this Lucifer, the light-bearer, the fire-bringer.[33]

The second of these archetypal beings or states is naturally and psychically cold, congealing, crystallizing, compulsive. It is reductive, grey, bitter, sharp, coldly analytic, repetitive and brilliantly formulaic, without humility. Some literature calls this Satan, others Mephistopheles or Ahriman, the dark lord.[34]

The first is electric, rhapsodic, artistic, beautiful, flowing and soft. It is playful wind, gorgeous sunset, animating oxygen, the advertiser's idea, lust for life, fantasy and abstraction, perpetual variation, seduction and desire.

The second is compelling and repelling like magnetism, reclusive, hard, algorithmic, scientific and matter of fact. It is hail, sand, matter-building nitrogen, the accountant's decision, the template for an estate of standard houses, lust for power, logic and fact, tyranny and procedure, the legal trap.

The luciferic nature is one pole, the ahrimanic another. When a business is too luciferic it is chaotic or constantly inventing new unrealized dreams. When a business is too ahrimanic it is bureaucratic and stuck.

When an idea is too luciferic it is too big and bright and abstract to see the details that are really involved, including people. Then Mao announces a great leap forward; a new dam sweeps away communities; the chief executive's theoretically brilliant reorganization disrupts all that has been learnt and loved.

When an idea is too ahrimanic it is too cold and uncaring to appreciate life and feelings, too clever to think it might be wrong, too logical and frigid and reductive to create beauty. Then a scientist thinks human beings are no more than conditioning and chemical processes; the smart man has no need to listen to concerns; Mao says that political power issues from the point of a gun; the politician approves ugly buildings as places for the human spirit to try to thrive because they are cheap; children get ugly toys; teachers are measured exclusively by the academic grades their pupils get.

Both of these poles induce stress. One is more likely to be fun, at least for a while. The other may be very attractive to the winner who gains by its power. But both set in motion strains and consequences that become exhausting. The water trial means finding insightful balance.

Balance means seeing the beautiful idea and the consequent details; observing the physicality of the body and the power of conditioning while relishing the quality of the human spirit; it means creating irrigation dams that nurture environment and community; stimulating change through participation; seeing beauty in all things; inventing things that work with and for people like the wonderful microcredit banking system that is revolutionizing poor communities; designing organic beauty and functional utility into products and places.

Christ's temptation to plunge, without harm, from the pinnacle of the temple in order to prove his power was the luciferic temptation of grandiosity. The temptation to turn stones into bread was an ahrimanic incitement to tame and control nature by brutal spiritual power rather than through the natural means by which grain grows in the earth ('stones'). The temptation to take power over all lands was a dual temptation: ahrimanic domination and luciferic lust.

Learning to live rightly means always finding balance and harmony in action and thought. There is an ancient Indian term for this: *dharma*; and it is the principle that guides you in the drama of finding life-balance in right-action and right-thinking, a drama that is of the essence in the water trial. Tuning your nature to right-thinking and right-action then prepares you for the third trial, when all options are open and none certain.

Life as a 'trial by air'

We are closer to things invisible than to things visible.

Novalis

As we mature, a third type of trial presents itself. This time there are no guidelines for action. Everything is now up to us. In this situation nothing shows us how to act. Instead, you and I must each find our own way, by ourselves and out of ourselves. Nothing and no-one can help us to take action. Nothing outside us can provide the insight, strength or resources required. Here what matters is simply the ability to be 'together'—to collect oneself promptly and act decisively. Doing this means we must discover the 'higher self'. When this capacity is fully developed a person can listen to the inspiration of the moment and show complete presence of mind.

Through the water trials we develop free decision-making, the test of human leadership. With the air trials, we develop truly creative decision-making: making something out of nothing.

With the water trial, we know that we have a task to perform and we can let the secret script guide us. We use our developed wisdom to read the mystery of the situation. Now we have no such help, hence this trial is named after air, which is even less supportive than water. Instead we must act out of our own higher nature. If we have advanced far in dealing with the seven stresses that I described in Chapter 5, then we will have developed many of the necessary qualities that we need, in particular, presence of mind. For what does presence of mind rely on? In my experience it depends on just the kind of qualities that were mentioned:

- Courage (Mars);
- The ability to size up a complex situation in a moment and see its pattern (Jupiter);
- Awareness of the state of what is happening, especially across a large field of activity (Moon);
- Quickness and flexibility (Mercury);
- Interest and care about others or about a situation (Venus);
- Moral balance and judgement (Sun);
- The ability to act decisively to determine the future (Saturn).

It is for this reason that I am sure that everyday life, including especially the challenges of work, can be so helpful in developing our fullest potential. Such crises constantly demand of us that we learn to act rapidly and decisively, without any undue hesitation or reflection, employing empathy, initiative and presence of mind. At such moments we need the ability to be able to see what needs to be done out of a higher perspective.

The trials by air develop the capacity to act with this level of creative insight and presence of mind, in the right and immediate moment, which the Greeks called Kairos time.

During a conference I attended in 2000 there was an intensely awkward moment. We were sitting 'in the round' in dialogue mode when, immediately after one speaker another woman got up and launched into an attack on what the speaker had been saying, claiming that the remarks were hurtful. Up to that point the mood had been vibrant but convivial and harmonious and there was a spirit of listening and reflection. For a moment the whole room held its breath as though watching a chandelier falling and anticipating the awful crash.

Suddenly, from the outer circle, a man leapt up with passion and yet clarity, and metaphorically caught the chandelier. In a moment of immediate magic he succeeded in fully acknowledging the pain and concern of the second speaker while at the same time linking it creatively to what the previous speaker had said and the theme of the dialogue so that all hostility vanished, there was a collective sigh of relief and the conversation moved on. He spoke for only a minute or two, I cannot remember his words, but the effect was miraculous. What he said had been totally unpremeditated and with no ulterior goal. It required tremendous vision, social grace and unegoistic authority. Hesitation would have been decisive. Reacting would have been primitive. The situation needed fully awake and alive creative responsiveness and there it was.

Crossing Thresholds

Suddenly the Thing happened, and, as everybody knows, it cannot be described in words. The Bible phrase, 'I saw the heavens open', seems as good as any if not taken literally. I remember saying to myself in awe and rapture, 'So it's like this; now I know what Heaven is like, now I know what they mean in church.' The words of the twenty-third Psalm came into my head and I began repeating them: He makes me to lie down in green pastures; He leads me beside the still waters. Soon it faded and I was alone in the meadow with the baby and the brook and the sweet-smelling lime trees. But though it passed and only the earthly beauty remained, I was filled with great gladness.

Margaret Isherwood, The Root of the Matter

Between our present self and our potential lies a threshold, one that each person must cross, again and again. This threshold is a transition, a window, a door, a portal, a barrier, a fence, a shore between our self and our Self. Crossing the threshold is a step out of a fenced to a fenceless existence, a step towards freedom; a step from selfishness and alienation towards loving community of being. Trials are means to encourage such inner breakthrough. Fear of the threshold and discomfort in the crossing induce stress. The three types of alienation introduced in Chapter 1 (with nature, people and spirit) all need thresholds to be crossed if the alienation is to be healed, as Octavio Paz indicates in 'Letter of Testimony':

To love:
To open the forbidden door,
the passageway
That takes us to the other side of time.

All around, in the garden, in the wild, nature teaches us the language of threshold. An estuary, a river, a mountain range, delving roots, a seed, a chrysalis, a hearth, a fence, the roof of a tower block, the point between past and future, a stone's flight in parabolic curve, all are emblems of crossing thresholds. To overcome alienation means the interpenetration of worlds:

A garden fence wards off nature:
And on it a robin sings.

Suburban homes and gardens may also symbolize our inner world. The garden fence is the human threshold, or barrier, to wildness and otherness. In the garden of our soul we cultivate a private life, but birds fly in (like thoughts) and weeds find ways to prosper.

A butterfly is a living, visible symbol of metamorphosis, and an inspiration to the metamorphosis of soul.

In Roget's Thesaurus the word *threshold* is associated with *door* and its synonyms, with *beginning* and with *nearness* and *enquiry*. When I enquire and learn something new, I cross a threshold. Each real new act of knowledge is a transformation of self and outlook. When I get to know another person, I cross his or her threshold, if only slightly, and he or she crosses mine. Begin to look for thresholds and you can be dizzied with the wonder of the nearness and ubiquity of thresholds in our lives. Each day is a new beginning, when we cross back to this world; each night takes us again across the edge of consciousness.

'Threshold' therefore weaves through all experience and is a suitable metaphor for resolving and summarizing the trials. Day by day, it is an 'open secret' that life brings us the three trials of *Fire* (the test of courage and fortitude), of *Water* (to act only out of inner knowledge of right) and of *Air* (to find purpose and presence of mind in isolation and emptiness). The trials of daily life are threshold moments on the path:

- Reluctance is but a trial by fire, calling for resolution to cross the inner threshold barrier. 'What can I do?' invites action. 'I am afraid,' asks for the courage to go on. 'I can't,' calls for perseverance. 'I do not like this person,' is an invitation to love.
- 'What should I do?' asks for true willingness to become open to insight: success in the trial by water means truly perceiving what is needed.
- 'I feel empty and inadequate,' can be a moment before fullness, when we cross the inner threshold of the air trial and step into, or on to, airy inner space with only conviction as support and find that we can indeed cope.

We should not belittle the experience of crossing the threshold. It can become a sublime moment. Neither, however, should we belittle the tender flowerings of threshold consciousness on our journey up the mountain peak.

Death is a great threshold mystery. Yet each day I die. I am not quite who I was. Any real learning is a real dying. To join a new group my solitariness and self must die, at least a little, I must ingest a being, an 'other'. All projects and changes are transitions: something must die for the new to be born. When the moral technique of change is crass, the process is felt to be destructive, the grieving becomes abrupt, unexpected, unwanted. A bit of our self lives in each of our surroundings and places in the world.[35] When this is lopped off, like the branch of a tree, we have a (perhaps minor) threshold experience.

Illness, too, is often a threshold experience. We are brought into consciousness of our fallen nature and invited to take a step into a new personal dimension.

Old forms, conventions and habits must be passed through. Each doubt, fear, reluctance, antipathy, and feeling of hatred arises as a strong force to challenge moral flabbiness, to build our moral and spiritual strength, love and freedom. Each time we notice the inner substance that acts as barrier, we also perceive an aspect of our lower self, the 'other man', our inner double, doppelganger or shadow that opposes progress, who holds us in selfish complacency or fear. The more we tread towards the threshold, the more there is resistance, until the full spectacle of the unredeemed self who bars our path can be confronted, known and transformed.

What powers of soul carry us over the threshold?

Wonder, interest, surprise and enthusiasm expand our willing senses to penetrate the outer mystery. Reverence, compassion, love, attention and listening help us find the mature Self of our own humanity in others. Courage, consciousness, self-knowledge and forgiveness enlighten a pathway through the dark forests of the interior continent.

The threshold becomes deeper and more profound as we are more willing to let the trials grow greater. We do not need to look for our threshold. We are on it, we are it, and it is all around. Those who travel the threshold reach their highest potential. One way to travel faster and more reliably is through cultivating healthy inner practices or meditation. This is the subject of the next chapter.

Your personal reflections

> The Master [Confucius] said: 'Learning without thinking is useless.
> Thinking without learning is dangerous.'
>
> Analects *II-xv*

The idea that underlies this chapter is that life is schooling us in the development of our spiritual potential and resourcefulness. I hope you find this as inspiring a thought as I do. At this stage, I would like to invite you to reflect on your life through three questions:

1. What experience do you have of these trials?
2. Do you see any new value in old struggles or difficulties that you have had?
3. What should you do to develop the inner capacities that you need?

CHAPTER 11

MEDITATION

Watchful among the thoughtless, awake among the sleepers, the
meditating one advances like a racer, without hindrance.

Buddha, Dhammapada*, 29*

Meditation is not just for odd people. Many people know how healthy
and good it is to meditate, how it can help with the stresses and strains of
life. Many meditations are also like deep prayers, bringing some healing or
help to the world. The word means 'to come into the middle', to become
centred. Sound meditation generally makes people calmer, stronger and
wiser.

Meditation's fruits include overcoming nervousness, developing a strong
active creative intelligence, equanimity, purposefulness and the ability to
manage time more effectively. Sound meditation helps to develop people
who have an abundance of positive energy to give to others. Instead of being
stressed, irritable, tired, unhappy, self-absorbed or selfish, they have healthy
energy and ideas. Meditation may also become a path to the deepest wisdom,
as Blake put it in 'Jerusalem':

To open the eternal worlds, to open the immortal eyes
Of Man Inwards, into the worlds of thought, into Eternity.

The reality of such an inner world is extensively documented as well as the
means to discover it. As Plato wrote in the *Symposium*: 'The mind's eye
begins to see clearly when the outer eyes grow dim.'

A good first step is to reflect on the following 'thoughts for the day'
formulated by Rudolf Steiner. They also connect to the seven self-leadership
challenges outlined in Chapter 5 and have a common source in Buddha's
Eight-fold Path. These are widely recognized as wonderful maxims for a
balanced daily life.

Thoughts for the days of the week

SATURDAY Paying attention to one's ideas	To think only significant thoughts. To learn little by little to separate in one's thoughts the essential from the non-essential, truth from mere opinion, the eternal from the transitory. In listening to the talk of others, seek to become quite still inwardly, avoiding all agreement and still more all unfavourable judgements such as criticism and rejection, even in thoughts and feelings. This may be called 'Right Opinion'
SUNDAY Right judgements	To come to a decision on even the most insignificant matter only after fully reasoned deliberation. All thoughtless action, all meaningless behaviour should be kept far away from the soul. Always have well-weighed reasons for everything. And definitely abstain from doing anything for which there is no significant reason. If convinced of the rightness of a decision, hold fast to it with inner resoluteness. This may be called 'Right Judgement' formed independently of agreement and disagreement
MONDAY Talking	Only what has sense and meaning should come from the lips of one striving for higher development. All talking for the sake of talking—to kill time—is in this sense harmful. The usual type of conversation, full of disjointed and confused remarks, should be avoided. Yet this does not mean cutting oneself off from conversation with others, it is just in conversation that talk should gradually be led to significance. Adopt a thoughtful attitude to every speech and answer, taking all aspects into consideration. Never to talk without cause—be happy to keep silence. One tries not to talk too much or too little. In the first place acquire the power of accurate listening. This may be called the 'Right Word'
TUESDAY External actions	These should not be disturbing for others. Where circumstances call for action out of inner conscience, carefully weigh up how best to meet the occasion—for the good of the whole, the lasting happiness of humanity, the eternal. Where acting out of one's own impulse or initiative: consider most thoroughly beforehand the effects of the actions. This may be called the 'Right Deed'

Contd.

Contd.

WEDNESDAY The adjustment of life	To live in balance with Nature and Spirit. Not to be swamped by external trivialities of life. To avoid all that brings unrest and haste into life. To hurry over nothing, but also not to be indolent and inert. To look on life as a means for working towards higher development and behave accordingly. <center>This is connected with 'Right Standpoint'</center>
THURSDAY Human endeavour	To take care to do nothing that lies beyond one's powers – but also to leave nothing undone which lies within them. To look beyond the everyday, momentary, and set oneself aims and ideals connected with the highest duties of a human being. For instance, in the sense of these exercises, to try to develop so that afterwards one may be able all the more to help and advise others—although perhaps not in the immediate future. <center>This may also be stated as 'To let these exercises become a habit'</center>
FRIDAY The endeavour to learn as much as possible from life	Nothing goes by us without giving us a chance to gain experiences that are useful to life. If one has done something incorrectly or imperfectly, this then becomes a motive for doing it rightly or more perfectly, later on. If one sees others doing something, one observes them in the same way (yet not coldly or heartlessly). And one does nothing without looking back to past experience that can help decisions and achievements. One can learn from everyone— even from children, if one is attentive. <center>This may be called the 'Right Memory' (Remembering one's experiences)</center>
DAILY SUMMARY	To turn one's gaze inwards from time to time, even if only for five minutes daily at the same time. In so doing one should sink down into oneself, carefully take counsel with oneself, test and picture one's principles of life, run through in thought one's knowledge— or lack of it—weigh up one's duties, think over the contents and true purpose of life, feel genuinely pained by one's own errors and imperfections. In a word: strive to discover the essential, the enduring, and earnestly work towards the goal, for instance, virtues to be acquired. (Not to fall into the mistake of thinking that one had done something well, but to strive ever further towards the highest standards.) <center>This may be called 'Right Examination'</center>

Seven practices to develop seven self-leadership qualities

The world of the happy man is a different one from that of the unhappy man.

Wittgenstein

There is a relationship between these seven exercises or practices and the seven self-leadership qualities outlined in Chapter 5.

Saturday's meditation, *Right Opinion*, is linked to what I called the Saturn quality. (Saturday is Saturn's day.) The exercise is to separate what is merely current opinion from what is enduring, and, by inner openness, to avoid putting what others say through the prejudice of agreement and disagreement. Its practice enables a person to develop a long view and one that is centred on what is really important. This helps develop at least two great leadership qualities. It promotes the social healing described in Chapter 9. It also develops the capacity to maintain focus on what is really important, thereby avoiding diversion of energy into non-essential areas or goals.

Sunday's meditation, *Right Judgement*, is strongly connected with what I called the Sun leadership quality and with ideas that eastern thinkers would associate with Dharma and Tao ('Way') or the Confucian concept of conscientiousness, and westerners with conscience. It leads to action that is more wise and appropriate. Fear and stress that might arise from challenges to doing what is right are reduced or eliminated. What does it matter if I gain the world and lose my soul? And how can a person be truly effective, whether as prime minister, business leader or simply human being, when at the mercy of the opinion poll or the first idea that comes into his or her head. How may a person be a balanced, true leader who only follows his or her instincts of what is liked or not liked? To discover what is right and stick to it is the basis of greatness.

Monday's meditation, *Right Word*, relates to what I called 'Moon' stress, and its associated leadership quality. (Monday means Moon-day.) A person who is scatty in speech will probably be scatty in life. Meaningful dialogue with other people requires a self-reflexive capacity—the ability to listen and be conscious both of what the other person is saying and of your own inner responses. This leads to considered communication and, more broadly, the ability to engage with the required range of tasks in a more conscious way. Instead of dashing aimlessly, it leads to becoming more aware and more conscious. It's practice means reflecting on the world and then responsibly doing what is required to further progress.

Tuesday's meditation, *Right Deed*, which is concerned with external actions, is connected with what I called the Mars self-leadership capacity. (In French, Tuesday is called Mardi, Mars' day.) Here the meditation emphasizes not simply the forcefulness and courage that we need, but the increased sensitivity required as a person becomes more capable of taking forceful action.

Wednesday's meditation, *Right Standpoint*, is connected with adjustment of life to reality and with what I called the Mercury self-leadership capacity. (In French, Wednesday is called Mercredi, or Mercury's day.) When I discussed this capacity I emphasized the ability to adjust continuously and flexibly to changing circumstances. Here the meditation emphasizes how the mature individual adjusts in such a way as to keep in balance the higher, bigger picture ('Spirit') and worldly realities ('Nature'). The true hero doesn't simply twist and turn; he or she adapts to circumstances in such a way that the real goal is maintained.

Thursday's meditation, concerned with a balanced and comprehensive *Human Endeavour*, proposes making all the other exercises a habit. This exercise is connected with what I called the Jupiter leadership capacity, the ability to transcend complexity and see the overall pattern. This exercise is concerned with full expression of abilities and powers, fulfilment of destiny, but without vain delusion; the ability to take the right action taking everything into account, including both spiritual and mundane needs, your own needs and the needs of others including Mother Nature. The American psychologist, Abraham Maslow, whom I have already mentioned, described the highest needs of the human being as self-actualization and self-transcendence. The first means making real—actual—one's full potential and the second means going beyond the boundaries of the lower self to live one's higher potential. Living with all the meditation exercises helps to further this.

Friday's exercise or meditation, *Right Memory,* or the endeavour to learn as much as possible from life, is connected with what I called the Venus capacity. (Friday derives from the Norse or Germanic goddess, Freja, but this is simply another persona for what the Greeks called Aphrodite and the Romans, Venus. The link to Venus is preserved in the French name for this day of the week, Vendredi.) Right Memory asks us to see the value in all experience and so learn from it. The Venus capacity supports our tireless ability to care and respect things and people. Here, it means not only valuing experience, but valuing our own development. There is a kind of joke in self-development circles: Oh no, not another learning 'opportunity'. There is, however, an extraordinary power in taking responsibility for our own learning and becoming used to perceiving our actions and their effects truthfully. According to Colin Wilson, William Blake showed imagination to be the instrument of self-knowledge. This is our goal here. Accurate imagination is the instrument for perceiving likely or concealed effects, as with empathy, a form of imagination. One consequence is that we are far less likely to be 'hurt' by what others say.

The eighth exercise, *Right Examination*, belongs to every day and is the meditation I have already referred to several times. Practice of it preserves us from the rat race and helps us focus on what is enduringly important in our lives. This daily meditation need only take a few moments each day. For example, colleagues in my company met for many years for a morning tea or coffee, read the relevant 'thought for the day', had a moment's quiet and then discussed issues of the day. Other people simply read or remember the meditation each day. A few minutes contemplation helps to make them into active life principles.

For something emerges from these meditations. They are not concerned with withdrawal from the world but with more effective engagement with it. Our own activity can become a subject for meditation when observed truthfully. So indeed can the problems of the world. In many cases prayer and meditation cross over as deeds aimed to help people or world conditions.

Another reason for me to recommend these—or similar practices that you might choose—is that they connect what we do in meditation with what we do in life. Healthy meditation is not only useful for life; it also sets up a resonance that makes it uncomfortable to have a basic inconsistency between thought, word and deed.

I am sure most readers will have registered how often so-called leaders proclaim principles that they do not live up to. Either they follow other tenets in secret or they never put into practice their promises. Confucius characterised good leadership when he said: 'His words correspond to his actions and his actions correspond to his words. Isn't the superior person earnest and genuine?'

Meditation is a way *of* life not a way *out* of life. The spiritual life and the practical life are not apart. The healthy life is that which makes the spiritual life and the practical life one. A person with this ability knows self-leadership and so has the ability to lead others in ways that are fruitful for all and avoids conflict and unnecessary stress. Confucius also said:

Love of learning is akin to wisdom. To practise with vigour is akin to humanity. To know to be shameful is akin to courage. He who knows these three things knows how to cultivate his personal life. Knowing how to cultivate his personal life, he knows how to govern other people. And knowing how to govern other people, he knows how to govern the empire, its state and the families.

A western way to meditate

Cultivate the seed points; foster forces of development; recognize that which is of the future.

Rudolf Steiner

There are many forms of meditation practised by different groups. Some people chant, some use music, some physical exercises; some would call their meditation 'prayer' and others 'contemplation' or 'introspection'. I would like to describe a modern, western path of meditation that aids self-development. This method is outlined in great detail in various works by Rudolf Steiner and others. I shall, however, aim to give the essential points.

This meditation is not based on elimination of the ego, like some eastern techniques, nor does it need to be religious. Instead it is based on calm development and transformation of the lower self by the imaginative power of the higher. Another way of putting this is to say that it aims to free the individual from conditioning, prejudice and inertia so that thinking becomes free, feeling becomes loving and will becomes purposeful and ethical.

We are all used to having or creating thought pictures, although some find it easier than others. For example, if you think of the room you sleep in, you should be able to recall (some kind of) memory picture of it. Meditation is based on *choosing* certain *specific kinds* of thought-pictures and then repeatedly dwelling purposefully and deeply on them.

The meditation process already stimulates calm and strength, while the thought-pictures gradually gain in power and generate insight. In effect, the person who meditates makes an inner journey from a place of restless activity to a point of stillness that is richly creative.

Meditation requires the right inner attitudes
The normal mind is very busy, and restless. Try for yourself to sit quietly and mentally still for five or ten minutes, or try to pay attention to just one object, like a stone or candle flame for that time. Most people find that they cannot

do this. The flitting mind lacks concentration and focus. Meditation gradually changes this, but we must also seek an attitude of calm.

Meditation needs to begin with right inner attitude. True meditation depends on many of the ideas already developed in this book. For example, it depends on the inner attitude of responsibility for our personal thoughts, feelings and actions. It depends on a will to live in harmony with others and therefore to overcome anger, intolerance and hatred. It depends on seeking calm not only in the moment but through living a healthy life. It depends on patience in the meditation itself.

At its simplest level, meditation helps to increase calm and purposeful energy. With more advanced practice, the secrets of the universe that form perennial wisdom become revealed.

Please do not try to force your way into such secrets. That would be like trying to open a door by forcing it closed. On the other hand, please do not fear that you will suddenly be whisked into an awesome world. If you practise these ideas in a straightforward, purposeful and patient way you will gradually gain a benefit, but great breakthroughs only occur when inner change has prepared them. When inner stillness is truly achieved it becomes possible to make the transition from the world of ordinary thoughts to the creative source of the soul or mind.

So how should you begin?

Steps in meditation

First, find the time and place when you can regularly be uninterrupted and quiet. Early morning and/or evening are favourites. In the morning you will (hopefully) be fresh and undisturbed. In the evening, you may reflect on the day and then sleep with the effects working through the night.

- Begin by mentally quietening yourself. Get comfortable, sitting in an ergonomic posture to reduce strain. No special posture is required, although an upright sitting position is helpful. Practice will show you what works for you;
- Consciously relax your body, breathing deeply and then quietly, noticing any stress and letting it go. You may find it helpful to relax from feet to head, beginning with each leg separately, moving consciously from foot to ankle, calf, knee and thigh; then stomach and chest, releasing the lungs by breathing out fully; relax each arm in the same way as with the legs;

then the shoulders, neck, mouth, and upper head. Maintain your relaxed state during the meditation;

- Then calm and focus yourself by concentrating on a single restful idea—for example the word 'calm', or the opening line of the verse at the beginning of the book: 'Quiet I bear within me' (see also below);
- If it is in the evening, do the retrospective exercise: reviewing the day backwards, seeing it objectively and without in the least bit blaming yourself. Simply observe. (This was described in more detail on page 122);
- That can be enough. However, it is helpful to take one verse with a theme that resonates for you and to work with it consistently each day, for a period of at least several weeks. Repetition is at the heart of the effectiveness of meditation and its healing and soothing power. Remember: do not worry if no result seems at first to be happening.

When choosing a meditation you might ask someone you respect to suggest one for you, or you may choose your own. Alternatively, I have selected many here related to different themes I have discussed. You may decide on one or other based on your felt need to develop calm, order, courage, care, resourcefulness or other qualities. Remember though, that you should aim to develop these through meditation in a balanced way over time.

An example of how to meditate
Take the meditation by Rudolf Steiner that is also at the beginning of the book, which is a particularly effective meditation for calm, rest and inner reinforcement.

> Quiet I bear within me.
> I bear within myself
> Forces to make me strong.
> Now will I be imbued
> With their glowing warmth.
> Now will I fill myself
> With my own will's resolve.
> And I will feel the quiet
> Pouring through all my being,
> When by my steadfast striving
> I become strong
> To find within myself
> The source of strength,
> The strength of inner quiet.

This verse includes thought pictures that are of nothing that you will see in the ordinary world. It proposes that you imagine *Quiet* as something you have within you.

It weaves two images together in a kind of circle: the images of quiet and of forces of strength and glowing warmth. The picture is not described, nor is it simply something you have seen and can remember. That is important because it is only the energy that you put into meditation that counts. This daily inner resolve exercises the inner spiritual athlete and creates the inner fitness that brings about self-leadership and self-development. This resolve is the very source of the *Quiet* the verse speaks of.

So, you are free to make your own images. As time goes by you will develop how you think they should be; they may change somewhat over time. During meditation don't speculate about the meaning. (The rest of the day is time enough for that.) Instead just fill yourself with the meditation and the rhythm of the images/ideas (see below).

Quiet does not come about by stopping the world. It comes from one's own inner world. A quiet inner world is open to everything, it is warm and receptive. All may flow through it, yet nothing can disturb it: it is immensely strong. This quiet might therefore be imagined as an inner sun. Its warmth and light flow through every part of you, its source is your own I's will.

Fill the words of the verse with your own depth of feeling and meaning. A further step follows that is described below. First, however, it is important to consider rhythm within meditation.

Meditation and rhythm

Feel the series of ideas also as a rhythm. In this meditation, they are like successive waves in a calm ocean, or like successive spirals that a bird might fly. If you feel this rhythm it will calm you and your own rhythms, for example your breathing.

This is a principal difference between this meditation method and older eastern methods. Many forms of yoga for example use special breathing to still the mind. This certainly works. There is a very subtle correspondence between breathing rhythms and mental state. For example, anxiety is associated with disturbed breath, such as panting, while calm is associated with slow even breaths. The physical association is achieved through various means, including the mediation of the cerebro-spinal-fluid, which transfers breath rhythms into impulses in the fluids that surround the brain. If you change your breathing, it affects your mind and vice versa. Hence the importance to remind someone (yourself) to 'Breathe!' when he or she is angry or in panic. It may therefore be helpful to begin meditation by breathing out deeply and then having two or three even breaths. As you surrender into the meditation you will probably find your breathing becomes slower and calmer.

I follow this way of meditating because it has been found to help modern individuals in contemporary culture. In particular it heals the fractured, vulnerable, modern egoism that is so normal a condition. Instead of trying to master the ego through the body, this meditation develops the self through surrendering to one's own higher purpose. The selection of a verse therefore represents a direction of development you wish to make. For example, the golfer Tiger Woods meditated daily from early childhood on a verse that expressed the essence of empowerment. By focusing fully on a key idea, you move in its direction. If you select wisely, you do not give up your purpose. You find it.

Stay awake. Watch and reflect. Work with careful attention.
In this way you will find the light within yourself.
Buddha, *Dhammapada*, 27

After contemplating the meditation content

After you have filled yourself with the thought pictures of the meditation, empty your mind fully. At this point an image may appear. Such an image represents an in-streaming symbolic reply from your own creative higher nature.

Just as the sleeping mind creates symbolic images we call dreams, when the ordinary day consciousness is quieted, deeply meaningful pictures may appear. They are no more than symbols of reality, yet they may contain truths of profound wisdom and therefore become in themselves subjects for meditation, for they are gifts of the higher Imagination that many people, including artists, poets and philosophers, have celebrated.

Further steps in meditation do exist. Those interested are recommended to study further (see Readings). Briefly, however, after contemplating the imagination that has spontaneously appeared, you can further eliminate this and a new and deeper/higher level of content may spontaneously emerge, this time more in the form of an inspired idea. This too can be put aside for a third and even more profound experience during which you will have an experience of oneness with a higher power and being of the cosmos, knowing 'it' from the inside. This is comparatively rare.

Once you have finished doing your meditation: finish! Do not drift between states idly. Consciously end and go about your responsibilities (or sleep). Should you go to sleep during meditation (especially at first) do not worry, but try to cultivate wakeful awareness.

Summary of how to meditate

Find a verse that suits you, preferably from a wise source such as the Bible or Tao Te Ching, or an acknowledged guide such as Steiner or James Allen, and practise it regularly for at least a few minutes each day. You should be patient and not expect immediate results. Patience is vital on any path towards maturity, and in dealing with stress. A brief summary of how to meditate is given below.

- First prepare your mood; try to be calm, perhaps take a deep breath and give a sigh to relax;
- Meditating after the retrospective exercise (see page 122) is a very good time;
- Let go of anything that is occupying your mind, and then focus on the words as deeply as you can, either silently in your mind or aloud, making a thought-picture as far as you can to accompany them. As you inwardly say the words, fill yourself with their meaning, but not in an intellectual or speculative way;
- Strive with your heart to penetrate the inner wisdom;
- Then empty your mind completely for a moment, or as long as you can. You may find an image or something like an experience of light or lightness, or it may just be a moment of peace or calm;
- Then consciously end your meditation and go about your life (or sleep). Try to stay wakeful, but it is OK if you fall asleep while meditating.

Other ways to meditate

> When I closed my eyes and bent my head representing to myself a flower
> right at the centre of the organ of sight, new flowers sprang out of this
> heart, with coloured petals and green leaves ... There was no way of
> stopping this effusion, that went on as long as my contemplation lasted,
> neither slowing nor accelerating.
>
> *Goethe, from his notebooks*

In his experimental studies into the psychology of meditation,[36] Arthur
Deikman identified the investment of special attention in the sensory
experience as important to changing consciousness. He described how
meditation involved withdrawing attention from intellectual thinking and
reinvesting it in percepts—i.e. what you are perceiving or paying attention
to—amounting to a reverse of the normal learning sequence. Through this
process a habit of automated thinking is 'de-automized', so that what has
otherwise been at best a dead abstraction, and perhaps even invisible, now
becomes vivid and present to a new imaginative consciousness.

The quotation from Goethe above suggests another way to meditate—on
natural phenomena. Goethe gave an example of this in his scientific work on
plants and colour. He used a method which he called 'exact sensorial imagination' by which he first *paid attention* to something he considered to be an
important phenomenon in nature and then re-represented it to himself
exactly in his imagination. Thus we can say that he contemplated nature in
the laboratory of his imagination, not coldly as in the analytic mode, but with
reverence, a reverence that became more real as the imagination became
more exact. This is no less than meditation, but it is also science.

He then carried out various studies in this mode, allowing as it were the
object in his imagination to come to life. For example he observed the
relationship between a series of leaves on a single plant from the first and
lowest to the last and highest and through his exact sensory imagination
observed not only the metamorphosis between the leaves but the active
principle that shaped this metamorphosis. He described this as equivalent to
observing footprints in the snow and then seeing the person or animal that
makes the footprints.

Notice that such a process serves to heal the rift between the human being
and nature and also between science and art (Goethe was a supreme example
of both). I will return to this in the next and final chapter.

For the moment, however, let me try to relate what I have just been saying to the previous section, using verses or verbal meditations. I have not been advocating that you pay attention to words but rather that you pay attention to an idea in your meditation that shines through the words. The aim is to use the vehicle of the words along with their rhythm to bring the idea into a vivid presence as an object of attention. Thus you want to avoid the intellectual abstractions yet you want to observe the idea. In the case of a series of ideas in, say, a verse you want to observe these as a unity in the way Goethe observed a series of leaves on a plant as a unity connected by an active principle. In either case, what would otherwise have been invisible or reduced to an abstract thought becomes, in time and with due practice, present in its fullness.

Meditating on key ideas or verses is therefore a way of entering into their reality and seeing what they have to offer as a portal into the deep nature of things. Similarly everything has meaning—situations, all objects and things, life histories, processes and natural phenomena. Each may reveal its soul or spirit nature through exact sensorial imagination when attention is rightly given to it.

Specific meditations

> Think of the lilies: they neither spin nor weave; yet I tell you, even
> Solomon in all his splendour was not attired like one of them.
>
> *Jesus Christ*

Many of these meditations were composed or described by Rudolf Steiner. Rather than repeat this each time, I have tried to indicate where someone else is the source of the meditation. However, many meditations have a long tradition of use and were formulated for different languages and cultures, and it is not always clear, at least to me, who is the ultimate source.

Fundamental meditations for increasing sensitivity
Chapter 6 included several very effective exercises. Many of these may be considered as either meditations or valuable preparations for meditation.

How do you see your ideal self?
All meditation needs to be accompanied by a conscious quest for the realization of one's own 'higher self'. Of course people put this to themselves in different ways according to their spiritual and religious beliefs and

experience. (I have generally avoided including meditations that are specifically related to one religion or another, although there are two below that would suit someone looking for a meditation that specifically connects to 'God'.)

One very helpful meditation is therefore simply this: Formulate your own

picture of your own higher self. If you fully realized your potential for love, wisdom, tolerance, physical energy, peacefulness, understanding of others and humility, how would you be? You may also imagine it in the form: what is my idea of a fully-developed person?

There is no need to worry about a 'wrong' answer. If you put feeling and energy into this meditation your imagination will itself mature. Some people might imagine Buddha or Christ or an angel. That is fine too. Imagine your ideal for yourself as you choose. Practice makes perfect!

Observing your own life (as a source of meditation)

You may use the experiences of your life as a source of meditation. I have many times stressed the importance of learning to observe your mind and behaviour. The ultimate way to do this is to treat it as a subject for meditation. The retrospective exercise is an excellent way to do this. It avoids the danger that you become self-obsessive and egotistical.

I also recommend a regular examination of how you see yourself versus your ideal. First, *imagine your ideal* as discussed. (This is a complementary meditation.) Then see one way that you fall short of your own ideal. See this not as a failing—no blame should follow—but as an ideal to achieve and make real. Imagine this being changed. When I say 'see' here I mean exactly this, using the principle of 'exact sensorial imagination' from Goethe mentioned above. Try to see yourself as a vivid percept and then 'see' what you strive to become, as for example a first leaf on a plant will lead to the flower. Obviously the leaf cannot blame itself for not being a flower—it is part of the process. Blame will only get in the way.

Usually it is best to persist with this one area of development for some time through repeated meditation before turning to your next goal.

Meditating from emotions and feelings in everyday life

One example of how to meditate on life and so deepen and enrich your emotional life is to develop your own content in the following way: Perhaps some incident has triggered a feeling such as joy or love or sadness. For example, on one occasion my daughter decided to go to South Africa and work in a township kindergarten, so awakening in me feelings of respect and love. Today my wife has done something very kind.

The feeling—love, joy and so on—was caused by one or more qualities I perceived in the person or incident (for example kindness or good-heartedness or courage). If I now take that quality that gives rise to the emotion and contemplate it not as something related to one incident but as a general property of the world, I will be meditating on it as an *idea*.

I can now immerse myself in radiant kindness and see all the happiness and comfort it brings. If I now let this general happiness live on in my heart I will be immersed in a profound meditation.

When your mind is so assaulted you can't quieten it

The unmanaged mind lacks purpose and owns pride and blame. An old tale illustrates this.

> There were four monks who entered into a silent retreat during the holy period. As darkness came on the first evening, one said, 'Shall we light a candle?' The second promptly exclaimed, 'You are not supposed to speak.' The third muttered, 'You have both failed.' Then the fourth monk proclaimed, 'I am the only one who has not spoken.'

The following meditation is based on the ancient symbol of healing, the Mercury or Caduceus Staff (see page 102). The Caduceus consists of a staff and two snakes and was carried by the healing God Mercury (or Hermes) and is still featured on every doctor's certificate. This is a very ancient symbol and has a special and cross-cultural resonance. If you energetically place this image in your mind you will find that it calms you.

- Picture to yourself the radiant upright staff around which there twines a black snake. (The black snake symbolizes all the troubling thoughts.)
- Then in the opposite direction, imagine a shining white snake also twisting around the staff. (The shining snake symbolizes the higher resolution of all the troubles and strife.)

To enrich thinking, feeling and will

The following meditation develops an enriched and balanced soul, strengthening your capacity to deal with life's challenges and opportunities.⋆

> Dwelling in silence
> on the beauties of life
> gives the soul strength
> of Feeling.
>
> Thinking clearly
> on the truths of existence
> brings to the Spirit
> the light of Will.

Meditations on images

There are many meditations based on images that symbolically point to fundamental truths or puzzles of existence. Here I suggest a few you might find helpful. Practising them also encourages the creativity and flexibility of the mind.

Here is one I am personally connected to, partly through my birth sign (Cancer) to which it is related: it is the ancient symbol of *Change* shown alongside. Because my company works as consultants in change, it also forms a part of our logo. You may contemplate it as drawn here or better still imagine it in your own mind. By living with it, you will gradually come to see how this dynamic appears throughout life, as well as coming to appreciate the significance of the 'empty moment' of transition—for example how things have to die to allow new life. It also symbolizes the relationship between our inner and outer nature. You may contemplate the associated question: 'What is "disappearing into oneself" and, out of this, "disappearing" to arise anew?'

In the second example: imagine how a point becomes a circle and a circle becomes a point.

This meditation is important in understanding many secrets. One is how

---

⋆ The seven meditations on pages 245–8 are all by Rudolf Steiner from his *Verses and Meditations*.

you may experience yourself as both an individual in a point-centred radiating consciousness (how most people normally experience themselves, perceiving the world from their centre) and also the reverse (a much less common experience): to experience yourself from the world. I have been created out of the natural cosmos and all my life experiences. Hence, the ancient Indian Rig Veda indicates: I am That (Tvat Tram Asi). To experience your self from, and as the gift of, 'the periphery' as well as from your own centre is a way to overcome one-sidedness and alienation. The poem I cited in Chapter 9 by Walt Whitman ('I was a child') is an example of such peripheral consciousness as is this ancient meditation from the classical era: 'God is a circle whose centre is everywhere.'

'Spiritual' meditations

The following four meditations connect to the higher I, or spiritual sphere.

The first helps those who use it to experience themselves as a part of the great cosmos and its meaning. You may imagine Spirit in whatever way you choose, for example as the realm of God or Ideas or Pure Energy or the Higher Nature of the Cosmos.

> The sphere of the Spirit is the soul's true home,
> And Man will surely reach it
> By walking in the path of honest Thought;
> By choosing as his guide the fount of Love
> Implanted in his heart;
> By opening the eye of his soul
> To Nature's script
> Spread out before him through all the Universe,
> Telling the story of the Spirit
> In all that lives and thrives,
> And in the silent spaciousness of lifeless things,
> And in the stream of Time—the process of becoming.

The next meditation focuses on the experience of the eternal higher self that during life seems so much beyond us and yet remains an ideal to attain eventually. The Light is a real and frequently described experience (see Chapter 4) that may occur to those who are patient and achieve inner stillness and quiet after contemplation of the words.

> I look into the Darkness:
> In it there arises Light,

Living Light.
Who is this Light in the Darkness?
It is I, my Self, in my Reality.
This reality of the 'I'
Enters not into my earthly life;
I am only its image.
But I shall find it again
When with good will for the spirit
I shall have passed through the Gate of Death.

The next meditation should be appreciated by those looking for courage and renewed health, for example after or during depression or illness. It also has the character of a prayer.

Spirit of God,
Fill Thou me,
Fill me in my soul.
To my soul give strength,
Strength also to my heart,
My heart that seeks for Thee,
Seeks Thee with earnest longing,
Longing to be whole and well,
Whole and well and full of courage,
Courage the gift from the hand of God,
Gift from Thee, O Spirit of God.
Spirit of God,
Fill Thou me.

The fourth meditation affirms the higher self as one's true nature.

More radiant than the sun,
Purer than the snow,
Finer than the ethereal
Is the Self,
The Spirit in my heart of hearts.
I am this Self.
This Self am I.

Ancient Indian meditations

The following seven meditations are at least four to five thousand years old. They were translated by Paul Reps from the Malini Vijaya Tantra. They may be used both as meditations, i.e. as thoughts to contemplate, and as exercises to perform whenever life circumstances allow. For example, with the second one, 'Intone a sound', you can make a tone and gradually bring it into silence, and then continue to make your inner self quiet and harmonious. With the fourth, 'Some desire', the contemplation of the idea may serve as preparation for actually performing the deed. And so on.

1. Unminding mind, keep in the middle—until!
2. Intone a sound audibly, then less and less audibly as feeling deepens into this silent harmony.
3. Gracious one, play! The universe is an empty shell wherein your mind frolics infinitely.
4. When some desire comes, consider it. Then suddenly, quit it!
5. At the start of sneezing, during fright, in anxiety, above a chasm, flying in battle, in extreme curiosity, at the beginning of hunger, at the end of hunger, be uninterruptedly aware!
6. Wherever your attention alights, at this very point, experience!
7. Each thing is perceived through knowing. The self shines in space through knowing. Perceive one being as knower and known.

For self-leadership

The short meditation on page 46, 'Take care of your thoughts', which is also a maxim for life, briefly expresses many of the ideas of the book in a way suitable for regular contemplation:

> Take care of your thoughts, because they will become your words.
> Take care of your words, because they will become your deeds.
> Take care of your deeds, because they will become your habits.
> Take care of your habits, because they form your character.
> Take care of your character, because it defines your destiny.

Do you wish to develop purpose and energy for your work and destiny? If so, this should help.

> In the free being of Man
> The Universe is gathered up.
> Then in the free resolve of your heart
> Take your own life in hand,
> And you will find the World.
> The Spirit of the World will find itself in you.

The next very simple but effective meditation should be focused on for at least five minutes a day to the exclusion of all else for at least a month. It contains a profound truth of life which is at the heart of the message of this book.

> Steadfastness is of higher value than any success.

At the end of Chapter 4, I gave another meditation beginning, 'Wishes of the soul bud forth' (page 79). This excellent meditation also helps the individual to seek out and discover the destiny that is within his or her potential and to achieve it with courage.

Facing the future with courage

> In late 1916, during the Battle of the Somme, I crouched in the darkness in a front-line trench … stinking with unburied corpses… At dawn my battalion was due to attack. I watched the slow movement of my luminous wristwatch dreading the moment when I must get up and lead my men forward towards the German lines. And suddenly, with absolute certainty, I knew that I was utterly safe.
>
> *F.C. Happold,* Adventure in Search of a Creed

Uncertainty about the future can be fearful. Perhaps there is organizational change that might threaten your career, or health risks, or other stresses. Sometimes people experience sudden panics, possibly stimulated by physical conditions such as the side effects of certain drugs (e.g. Beta Blockers) or the SAD syndrome caused by light deprivation. While all physical and practical conditions should also be taken care of, you can also use mental activity to help in the form of meditation and positive thinking. This section therefore includes meditations that develop faith and courage for the future.

There is a very famous saying, cited at the beginning of Chapter 1, by the fourteenth-century English mystic, one of the most significant women of the Middle Ages, Julian of Norwich. (One reason for her popularity today is that she had an un-gendered view of God.[37]) The following short meditation is the essence of her teaching and brings strength and serenity to many people:

> But all shall be well, and all shall be well,
> and all manner of things shall be well.

Ralph Waldo Emerson echoed this in his essay, Self-Reliance:

The soul raised over passion beholds identity and eternal causation, perceives the self-existence of Truth and Right and calms itself with knowing that all things go well.

Bob Marley provided a contemporary version when he sang:

Don't worry about a thing/
'Cause every little thing is gonna be alright.

The following meditation may be considered a kind of extended meditation on this outlook. Like these, it is designed to build inner strength and hopefulness as self-leadership capacities. This meditation develops courage and optimism and is closely connected to the need for courage in vulnerability described by both Picasso (page 60) and David Whyte (page 94).

Where Steiner used the word 'must', he was not issuing a rule; he was describing what is realistically needed to deal with the challenge of the age:

We must eradicate from the soul all fear and terror
of what comes to meet us from the future.
We must look forward with absolute equanimity to whatever may come.
And we must think only that whatever comes
is given us by a world direction full of wisdom.
It is part of what we must learn in this age, namely, to act out of pure trust,
without any security in existence.
Trust in the ever-present help of the spiritual worlds.
Truly, nothing else will do if our courage is not to fail us.
Let us discipline our will and let us seek the awakening from within
ourselves, every morning and every evening.

When you feel assaulted by strange, frightening experiences, for example in the night, the 'Blue Bell Meditation' is extremely powerful:

Imagine you are covered from above to ankles by a beautiful mid-blue bell
of light—translucent and sparkling. It is there—see it.
It stays till morning.

CHAPTER 12

THE BIG IDEAS

Emancipate yourselves from mental slavery
None but ourselves can free our minds.

Bob Marley

I think there are three ideas or principles that lie at the root of this book, ideas that have been practised by great leaders and teachers from many spiritual, cultural and philosophic traditions. Indeed, I believe that the topic of 'stress' is our contemporary way, in a secular age, to discuss the fundamental spiritual questions and aspirations of former ages. These three principles are:

- You are responsible for your life, your outlook and your contribution to the world and it matters what and how you think. Your thinking determines your own experience and future character and destiny, and fashions the world around you like a stone's ripples in a pool.
- Despite the many tragedies and problems of life, the natural and spiritual world in which we live is good and loveable and is a unified, meaningful whole; in loving it we bring health and goodness to our souls and lives. In looking for meaning and beauty and value in and for the world, we not only increase our chances of finding them but also cherish the cosmos in which we have our being.
- The root of our being is relatedness, and when we live in a spirit of co-operation, cultivating love, respect, compassion and care, we heal social alienation and culture, encouraging friendship and joy.

Stuart Kaufman, one of the leaders of the 'new science' of chaos and complexity, wrote in his book *At Home in the Universe* (pp. 4–5):

> Somewhere along our path, paradise has been lost, lost to the Western mind; and in the spreading world civilization, lost to our collective mind . . . We find ourselves on a tiny planet, on the edge of a humdrum galaxy among billions like it . . . we are but accidents, we're told . . .
>
> I hold the hope that what some are calling the new sciences of complexity may help us find anew our place, that through this new science we may recover our sense of worth, our sense of sacred . . . To undergird the

pluralistic global community that is aborning, we shall need, I think, an expanded intellectual basis—a new way to think about origins, evolution, and the profound naturalness of life and its myriad patterns of unfolding.

It seems to me that Kaufman—and perhaps even more strongly in the full text from which I have quoted briefly—echoes the three principles: first, the need for rethinking and, second, for a valuing of the sacred worth of our cosmos and the forces or principles that drive its creation; and, third, the cultivation of a caring, pluralistic, global community. These for Kaufman are the challenges of our time.

Jesus Christ made a similar comment, in another context, in his teaching on what was most important for life: 'The first is, Hear O Israel; the Lord our God is One;[38] and you shall love the Lord your God with all your heart and all your spirit and all your mind and all your strength. This is the second: You shall love your neighbour as yourself. There is no other commandment greater than these.' (Mark 12, 29–31)

It matters how you think

Economics is the sum of all the strengths and weaknesses of the human heart expressed in goods and services.
Paul Hoffman, The Wisdom of Crocodiles

Judaism, Islam and Christianity share the mythologem that the world was created good and that if we now find it ill it is because a serpent has insinuated itself into our minds. Many other peoples have similar myths of loss.

If the nature of the universe is good, then our needs would naturally be met if we were not cut off from the sources of goodness. The legend of the Fall is a mythic expression of our alienation from the sources of goodness. Deprived of the source, human beings perpetually seek satisfaction for their needs and perpetually experience themselves as dissatisfied. Deprived of the sources of goodness, I compete endlessly to realize fulfilment and so get into violence and desire.

Buddha's 'four noble truths' seem to explain this:

1. That life is full of pain and stress;[39]
2. That the cause of pain lies in our desires and lack of inner comfortableness; the problem is in our minds;

3. That the ending of suffering comes about by ending these discomforting cravings;

4. And that the means to do this is through the noble eight-fold path, broadly as described in the previous chapter. (This path ultimately brings about the right relationship between a person and all 'neighbours', not merely human but all sentient existence.)

Notice, Buddha does not say that the world or cosmos itself is bad—rather that human beings bring pain upon themselves by their relationship to it. Nor is Buddhism associated only with finding personal happiness. Buddha is credited with making compassion and empathy basic goals of the good life. As we reduce dissatisfaction and alienation it becomes easier to love others.

How similar this is to St James, thought to be the brother of Jesus, when he asks: 'What causes fighting and quarrels among you? Is not their origin the appetites that war in your bodies? You want what you cannot have so you murder...'

Change yourselves within, says St James, and experience the world very differently. Don't be afraid of your light, says Mandela, for as Buddha said, 'Only love can bring the end of hating.'

It matters how we see things and how we describe them; it matters to ourselves and it matters to others to be strictly truthful, for ideas change the stress-level of the world.

Take for example this picture. What do you see? Is this an old woman or a young beauty?

In fact, it is a well-known 'ambiguous image' in Gestalt psychology, because it can be either, depending on how you look at it. (If you can't see both images, then just cover the eyelash with your finger.) Furthermore, is the young woman a beautiful lady or vain young thing; and is the old woman an 'ugly hag' or a 'wise crone' whose life experience can answer all questions? What is in the picture depends ultimately on perception, interpretation and philosophy. Similarly our experience and attitudes to life events and to each other depend on perception. Prejudice and negativity are aspects of self-ishness and great stress-inducers (in both ourselves and others).

One of the most influential figures of history, the sage Zarathustra (or Zoroaster), believed that the fate of the world depends on the individual's reaction to good and evil. In his world-view, humanity plays a decisive role in the outcome of this conflict. Whenever someone acts according to the Light, he or she will not only automatically aid the kingdom of good but will also decrease the kingdom of evil by the same amount, since the two kingdoms draw on the same power. Those, on the other hand, who follow the darkness, the evil power,[40] reduce the power of good in favour of evil and, consequently, help chaos to prevail. It seems to me that our ugly cities, our starving, our homeless, our AIDS victims, our poisoned environment, our vanishing larks and other species are aspects of such a struggle, and the fate of our children's children will depend on our ideas and how we tackle these issues. Will we add to the world's stress or reduce it?

Affirming goodness: from stress to strength to serenity

A child is love made visible.

Novalis

How should we consider happenings that seem evil and terrible?

It would I believe be wrong to suggest that there is no evil in the cosmos. Indeed I am certain that there are very active forces of evil. I have quoted from survivors of the Nazi camps and regime, and from victims of abuse, and such terrible histories are brought about by conscious purposes or dreadful compulsions. While I think people can make meaning and goodness out of suffering, that does not mean that the evil itself is dismissed. There are tyrants great and small who do evil, and thereby they walk 'in the darkness' as conscious or unconscious worshippers of darkness.

Nature also has observable and seemingly harsh competitive elements, I believe, and these, too, are inherited by human beings.

I fully value and admire those who believe that honesty means not shirking from unpleasantness. It takes a certain courage to think that life and the cosmos are nasty and yet to live on from day to day. I also value those who believe that evil is best countered by awareness and vigilance— hence their alert perceptions of the shadow-side of life. Nevertheless, I do not believe that evil or brutal competitiveness are the core reality of our world. If it is how we think that shapes what we see and experience, as in the half-full/half-empty glass question, then honesty means applying this test here too. Those who believe the world is fundamentally lacking, that it is bad or brutal, will mostly see emptiness, feel pain and struggle to explain what they see; while those who think the world is full of goodness will seek and see this goodness. Those who believe that life is a struggle for existence in scarcity and danger are more likely to promote competitiveness and to adopt it as a way of being. 'A nation that continues year on year to spend more money on military defence than on programs of social uplift is approaching spiritual death,' said Martin Luther King. Those without spirit or a rich soul experience are most likely to promote materialism or consumerism. Those who find life empty lose the wholeness and goodness of each moment. Those who are embittered miss the positive that can and usually does flow in the aftermath even of pain and tragedy.

'I tell you not to be anxious about food and drink,' says Christ. 'Can anxious thought add a single day to your life? Do not be anxious about tomorrow; tomorrow will look after itself' (Matthew 6). Incidentally, this is an excellent meditation for those who are stressed.

And Bashô, the Zen poet says:

Gazing at the flowers
of the morning glory
I eat my breakfast

Socrates is unfairly accused and goes to his death. Christ is both unfairly accused and cruelly mocked and murdered. Yet, they are the least stressed in their circles.

For one moment, so we are told, it appears that Jesus Christ is severely discomposed when he cries out, 'My God, my God, why have you forsaken me?' This is the condition of stress: to feel alone, attacked, abandoned, unsupported, unequal to the tasks of life, unwilling to take them on, separate from a supportive universe. Then to recover connection and life-faith and capacity is the essence of resurrection of the spirit.

'Delightful are those forests,' said Buddha, 'where the worldly fail to find delight. There the awakened ones are joyful, wanting nothing.' The forests, metaphor of the world and its stresses, are not the problem. The problem— or the joy—is in the way they are experienced.

A poem by David Wagoner, 'Lost',[41] expresses the joy, comfort and renewal that emerges with the right stance and relationship with Nature. Based on a traditional North American Indian story, an elder advises a worried youngster not to feel lost in the woods, because 'the trees ahead and bushes beside you/Are not lost'. 'Stand still', says the elder, for 'wherever you are is called Here', and here, he says, is a place of powerful beings that know each others' unique presence, for no two trees or branches are the same to the birds. The forest breathes and makes a place for you, says the elder, but, 'If what a tree or a bush does is lost on you/You are surely lost.'

I had the opportunity to experience this for myself recently when I worked with a Goethean scientist, Margaret Colquhoun, who has created a research centre called Pishwanton in Scotland. Meeting the woods under her 'elder guidance' meant exactly this meeting with the uniqueness of each plant and the place and presence of the wood. To experience this is to meet the inner unity, beauty and individual powers of Nature, while discovering the ravages that human beings so commonly bring through their ignorant 'lostness'.

We live in a loveable universe

> Every beloved object is the focus of a paradise.
>
> *Novalis*

This brings me to the second principle: the value of loving our creator and perceiving how we are nurtured by the cosmos: whether the creator is conceived as divine or as a natural universe. The great, concerned environmental scientist, Rachel Carson, reflects this in her essay 'The Sense of Wonder':

> I remember a summer night ... We lay and looked up at the sky and the millions of stars that blazed in the darkness. The night was so still that we could hear the buoy on the ledges out beyond the mouth of the bay. Once or twice a word spoken by someone on the far shore was carried across on

the clear air. A few lights burned in cottages. Otherwise there was no reminder of other human life; my companion and I were alone with the stars. I have never seen them more beautiful: the misty river of the Milky Way flowing across the sky, the patterns of the constellations standing out bright and clear, a blazing planet low on the horizon. Once or twice a meteor burned its way into the earth's atmospheres.

It occurred to me that if this were a sight that could be seen only once in a century or even once in a human generation, this little headland would be thronged with spectators. But it can be seen many scores of nights in any year, and so the lights burned in the cottages and the inhabitants gave not a thought to the beauty overhead: and because they could see it almost every night perhaps they will never see it.

Ancient megalithic stone circles may symbolize communities endowed with such wonder and awe, very different from the dispirited and dispiriting world described by Kaufman above (page 251). Such communities were united over centuries through creation and celebration in their love and devotion to the cosmic powers. The sacred instrument of the stone circle was a path to the cultivation of the community circle. Even today, it is no surprise that megalithic circles can touch the heart of the twenty-first century 'stressed-man'.

We cannot and should not return to megalithic simplicity, but I believe we

Megalithic circle in Moel Ty Uchaf, Wales

may and should nurture appreciation and the healthy joy it brings. Rachel Carson goes on to say that. 'Those who dwell, as scientists or laymen, among the beauties and mysteries of the earth are never alone or weary of life. Whatever the vexations or concerns of their personal lives, their thoughts can find paths that lead to inner contentment and to renewed excitement in living.' This is surely in the true spirit of the first key principle of life to which Christ points, as well as a path of renewal in our relationship with the divine.

When Christ says, 'Consider the lilies of the field,' and contrasts them with Soloman 'in all his glory,' he reminds us to celebrate the beauty of the world, a beauty that Rachel Carson perceived as giving 'reserves of strength that will endure as long as life lasts'.

'Love,' said the artist Stanley Spencer (1891–1959), 'is the essential power in the creation of art, and love is not a talent. Love reveals and more accurately describes the nature and meaning of things.' In other words, being able to see the true nature of things requires the inner openness and sympathy with them that is love, and this does not require a birth-given talent, merely a cultivated ability.

Carson's essay further outlines how the sense of loving wonder may be cultivated in children, by helping them to observe nature with feeling rather than as dry fact. She writes that all children could gain a sense of wonder so indestructible that it would 'last throughout life as an antidote against the boredom and disenchantments of later years, the sterile preoccupation with things that are artificial, the alienation from the sources of our strength'.

The wisdom in a single leaf is a marvel

Take the wisdom woven into the design of a single, living leaf which exceeds the greatest glory of our technical accomplishment and scientific understanding. It represents the most brilliant economy of design, variety of potential form, perfectly adapted to myriad environments, a miracle energy source woven from light, sustaining life, breathing with the unexplained phenomenon of Life itself. It contains wholeness. From a fragment of a leaf, a complete plant can grow. The leaf form adapts to fashion fruit, flower, seed, stalk and stamen. A leaf is sublime. It can be loved utterly.

> The first snow:
> The leaves of the daffodils
> Are bending.
>
> Bashô

Love your neighbour

> Now there abideth three things: faith, hope and love; and the greatest of
> these is love.
>
> *St Paul*

Finally, there is a fundamental relationship between having a healthy, wonder-filled loving relationship with the Cosmos and a loving relationship with one another, as in St John's deceptively simple advice in his first letter: 'My dear friends, let us love one another, because the source of love is God.'

St John perceives a world of relatedness. By contrast, many modern scientists seem to perceive a world ordered by competitive drives. However, other scientists challenge this perspective. They point out other unexplained scientific phenomena and note the tendency to 'project' opinion into data based on a particular aspect or paradigm. For example, Richard Dawkins, the archbishop of the selfish gene, implies a very different world from the one he generally champions when he describes the community, or common unity, quality of life:[42]

> Two billion years ago the remote ancestors of Mitochondria were free-living bacteria. Together with other bacteria of different kinds they took up residence inside larger cells. The resulting community of prokaryotic bacteria became the large eukaryotic cell we call our own. Each one of us is a community of a hundred million million mutually dependent eukaryotic cells. Each one of those cells is a community of thousands of

specially tamed bacteria entirely enclosed within the cell where they multiply, as bacteria will. It has been calculated that if all the mitochondria in a single human body were laid end to end they would girdle the earth not once but two thousand times. A single animal or plant is a vast community of communities packed in interacting layers like a rain forest. As for a rain forest itself it is a community seething with perhaps 10 million species of organisms every individual member of every species being itself a community of communities of domesticated bacteria.

Dawkins also argues that even 'selfish genes' must be good team players to be successful. It is the effectiveness of the combination of different cells that leads to survival (in his model) of the individual cell. One could therefore with some justification rename his theory, the 'community theory of life'!

The importance of such a perspective should not be discounted in factoring personal and world stress. Consider a forest. Do the leaves in this forest compete for light, as a conventional Darwinian opinion might state? Or do they arrange themselves so as to maximize the light captured by the forest? If you see trees competing for light you may also see yourself, people, businesses and economies as perpetually committed to competition. Such outlooks increase stress and pain.

In fact, biologists who study the morphology of plants have noticed how the mathematics of leaf arrangement around the stem of a plant optimizes light reception, as can be seen even by the amateur. In the same way, consider how trees interleave to soak up sunlight, their branches delicately approaching and interlacing with each other, so that as a consequence little light is lost to fall to the forest floor. Why not read this as co-operation rather than competition? And does it not radically shift the world in which you live? If you look at the individual leaf, or branch, or even tree critically, it may look like competition, but not from the perspective of the positive and the whole. Perhaps the fittest or best continues while the less good dies out also. (Different principles can intertwine). Even here, is this selfishness or the co-operation of the natural world towards goodness? My point is that what we see and how we choose to interpret it is neither value free nor without significance to yourself and the world. Biological theory seems to me to be in danger from the projection of our all too human anxiety. Is nature competitive and selfish, or am I?

Similarly, when we look at business do we project our own anxiety (remember this was the original meaning of the word 'business') and therefore perceive competition? Certainly there are many people competing and doing so very actively. And there are many consequences of this competition, just as there are many foul deeds done by humans to each other.

What inspires me about the whole economic enterprise are the countless myriad moments of co-operation that actually bring about success. The computer on which these words are typed required thousands of companies and fragments of the lives of millions of people in order that it may now be typed on here. A business like Dell depends on the contribution of thousands of suppliers, and they in turn depend on hundreds and thousands more. The co-operation may be loving or grudging, but it is only the *fact* of actual co-operation that brings about any desired outcome.

Atoms combine to make molecules, molecules to make substances. The world is built on 'co-operation', or what *is* it built on?

In our hearts, I think we know this. St John, an old man, much persecuted, exceedingly wise and the author of three of the recognized great spiritual texts of humanity, said that those who find love in their hearts find that pain disappears. At the heart of John's view there is a simple yet sublime message of love: 'For fear has to do with punishment, and anyone who is afraid has not attained to love in its perfection' (First Epistle of John 4).

Love becomes a path from stress to strength and on to serenity.

And from Nelson Mandela we hear:

You are a child of God:
Your playing small doesn't serve the world...
And as we let our own Light shine,
We unconsciously give other people permission to do the same.

In loving we not only cultivate the finest antidote to personal stress, but contribute to healing the world's stress. In that sense, we follow the archetypal development and healing path of Parzival outlined earlier (page 72).

We all tread the Grail path and become as Christ (or Buddha or whoever is your inspiration) when we allow goodness and love an avenue in our lives. 'The more one forgets himself—by giving himself to a cause to serve or another person to love—the more human he is and the more he actualizes himself,' said Viktor Frankl. In the beginning of our awareness of stress we are concerned with our own healing. In the end we are concerned with healing the world.

RESOURCES

Chi Wen Tzū used to think thrice before acting. The Master [Confucius]
hearing of it said: 'Twice would do.'

Analects *V-xix*

This optional section includes information about further books you might
wish to read, Notes, and a simple change planning tool. (Other resources can
also be found at www.fromstresstoserenity.com.) It begins with Goethe's
powerful inspiration about taking action:

Until one is committed there is hesitancy, the chance to draw back, always
ineffectiveness. Concerning all acts of initiative (and creation) there is one
elementary truth the ignorance of which kills countless ideas and splendid
plans: that the moment one definitely commits oneself then Providence
moves too. All sorts of things occur to help one that would never
otherwise have occurred. A whole stream of events issues from the
decision raising in one's favour all manner of unforeseen incidents and
meetings and material assistance which no man could have dreamt would
have come his way. Whatever you can do or dream you can, begin it.
Boldness has genius, power and magic in it. Begin it now.

 Perhaps these words of Goethe may be an inspiration to plan
changes in your life. The ancient symbol of the helix, which
was described as a meditation on change (see page 245), consists
of a 'before' and 'after' and a break. That break may be a great
challenge—it may be fearful, difficult, a tough habit to break,
or an unknown and new world or discipline to master. But true change
involves making that break and so making the change.

Change that represents growth is also developmental. Despite the break,
the new life has its seed in the old just as a butterfly, despite going through the
pupa stage, has its origins in the caterpillar. The helix symbol shows this too
in the way that the new element in the upper part mirrors and 'takes off' from
the old in the lower part.

So I believe that change is best planned by looking at the present and past
and using this to plan the future.

Stress reduction action plan

Your vision is the promise of what you shall one day be; your ideal is the
prophecy of what you shall at last unveil.

James Allen

Try this. Get some blank paper and draw six columns according to the following format, or download a worksheet from www.fromstresstoser-
enity.com. Then create your plan. Good luck.

Stress-related Problem

Underlying Cause In Me

Proposed Actions—Inner & Outer

'How did I Do' Review (one month)

Notes

1   C.G. Jung, *Alchemical Studies, Collected Works* Vol 13, p. 72.

2   Several books are mentioned under Readings.

3   R. Steiner, *How to Know Higher Worlds*, see Readings, Books on Self-Development.

4   Back and Bourque, 1970; Greeley, 1974, 1987; Hay and Morisy, 1978; Hood, 1974, 1975, 1977; Thomas and Cooper, 1980 all support the conclusion that 30–40 per cent of the population do have such experiences. I suspect even these studies underestimate reality.

5   R. Steiner, *Macrocosm and Microcosm*, Rudolf Steiner Press 1993.

6   C.G. Jung, *Alchemical Studies, Collected Works,* Vol. 13, p. 26.

7   From *The Complete Poems of John Keats*, edited by John Barnard, Penguin 1977, p. 549–551. In this passage, Keats actually develops a very full and wonderful theory of the soul as an immortal spark of the divinity that needs the world to develop individuality.

8   From the poem, 'Sunstone', in Octavio Paz, *The Collected Poems, 1957–1987*, Carcanet Press 1988.

9   See R. Steiner *How to Know Higher Worlds*, in Readings, Books on Self-Development.

10   *Poem for my Daughter, Collected Poems, 1955–2000*, Bloodaxe Books 2000.

11   This idea is a kind of metamorphosis of Darwinian evolution: instead of a blind reaction to a blind fate, it is a wish for a wise fate, a fate that calls forth a struggle to progress rather than merely survive.

12   C.G. Jung, *Alchemical Studies, Collected Works,* Vol. 13, pp. 36–7.

13   Excerpt of 'The Old Interior Angel' from *Fire in the Earth* by David Whyte, © 1992 by David Whyte, used by kind permission of the author and Many Rivers Press.

14   From *You Have to Say Something*, by Dainin Katagiri, Shambhala Publications, 1998.

15   These are the names John Gray gives them in *Men are from Mars, Women are from Venus, Children are from Heaven*, see Readings, Books on Self-Development.

16   I have found, however, that exaggeration of the problem sometimes works, for they also typically have a love of truth; so if your timing is right they may begin telling you how the problem is not as bad as you say.

17   See page 83.

18   'Those Winter Sundays', Robert Hayden, from *Angle of Ascent*, Liveright Pub. Corp., 1966.

19   In *Social and Anti-Social Forces in the Human Being*, Mercury Press 1982; also an e-book at www.elib.com.

20 I do not, however, recommend regression techniques that are advertised as enabling past life memories. I believe that these are often highly suspect in the same way as recovered memory syndrome. Past life memories have to be considered very carefully and it seems that it is easy to be the victim of delusion.

21 R. Steiner, *The Philosophy of Freedom*. See Readings, Books on Self-Development.

22 The Hebrew word in the Old Testament generally translated as Law more literally means 'Way', and is therefore similar to 'Tao' or 'Dharma'.

23 See also 'An emotion-transforming exercise' on page 193 for further details.

24 Later still, by following a meditational practice, I recognized the definite possibility that in a past life I had appeared to be betraying him and thus I saw how this misconception and the resulting resentment prompted both our need to be together and his distrust of me in this life.

25 See in Resources, Books on Self-Development.

26 C.G. Jung, *Alchemical Studies, Collected Works* Vol. 13, p. 89.

27 Suggestion by Rudolf Steiner.

28 An accurate translation of one of Christ's most famous sayings would be, 'The "I am" is the Way, the Truth and the Life." (John 16, 6)

29 For further information on Martha Graham, see Howard Gardner's book, *Creative Minds*, in Readings, Other Books.

30 Fire-walkers draw from the burning coals not heat but courage and will; the warmth in the world is merely energy. When it becomes a quality of soul rather than of nature it is experienced as well. Heat, anger, courage, enthusiasm, love and determination are different qualities that may be drawn from soul warmth. As the sun sends out heat, enough to start a fire in dry bush, so the sun in the soul also gives the courage for life.

31 Spiritual traditions teach that we now develop new spiritual capacities to view the cosmos. Various terms are used for this. For example Buddhism describes how our chakras open, and in particular, the 'sixteen-petalled throat chakra' that lets us see the spiritual forms of nature and events.

32 From the poem 'Sunstone', in Octavio Paz, *The Collected Poems*, 1957–1987, Calcanet Press 1988.

33 Lucifer is the bright angel who opposes God in the Bible with 'a third of the host of heaven'. Generally regarded as the same as the serpent who beguiles Adam and Eve. A similar entity is found in Greek myths as Prometheus, the Titan god who brings human beings fire and civilization in defiance of Zeus, an act that through his brother-double, Epimetheus, and his wife Pandora, leads to the opening of 'Pandora's Box' and the troubles, pains and stresses that then fall on humanity. In the Indian tradition, Mara was the God/devil who tempted Buddha with beguiling female devils.

34 In Zoroastrianism, Ahriman is the dark and evil God who opposes the light and

harms human beings. Satan, Mephistopheles and Beelzebub are names of devils in Judeo-Christian literature.

35   Represented since ancient times by the sign for the Ego or I, which is also the sun zodiac sign: a circle with a point in the middle. We live in the point and in the circle that surrounds.

36   Arthur J. Deikman, 'Bimodal Consciousness' and 'Deautomization and the Mystic Experience' in *The Nature of Human Consciousness*, ed. Robert E. Ornstein (San Francisco: W.H. Freeman, 1973).

37   'As verily as God is our Father, so verily God is our Mother; and that showed He in all, and especially in these sweet words where he sayeth: I it am. That is to say, I it am, the Might and the Goodness of the Fatherhood; I it am, the Wisdom of the Motherhood; I it am, the Light and the Grace that is all blessed Love: I it am, the Trinity; I it am, the Unity; I am the sovereign Goodness of all manner of things. I it am that maketh thee to Love: I it am, the endless fulfilling of all true desires.'

38   This is the Shema, the most important prayer in the Jewish faith, whose Hebrew meaning is hard to understand and almost impossible to translate adequately but implies something like: 'Listen, my community: we, the transcendent Divine and the living World-Being are One.' The love of God that Christ then speaks of is the love of this transcendent-immanent whole, the natural and cosmic order and its creator.

39   The word commonly used to translate the original Dukkha, which means something like 'unsatisfactoriness', is 'suffering'.

40   The evil one was called Angra Mainyu, the good power Ahura Mazda. Zoroaster asserted that in the end all will be well: the kingdom of good will vanquish the kingdom of evil.

41   © David Wagoner, from *Who Shall be the Sun?* University of Illinois Press, 1978.

42   *River Out of Eden: A Darwinian View of Life* by Richard Dawkins, Weidenfeld & Nicolson 1995.

Readings

Books I have valued are included below. If you have difficulty getting any, the Internet now also has excellent second-hand book selling services.

Books on Physical Wellbeing

The Book of Stress Survival: How to relax and live positively, Alix Kirsta, Guild Publishing 1986, with an excellent and straightforward overview of the physiology of stress and of exercises, diet and so on, expanding on Chapter 3.

Food for Free, Richard Mabey, Fontana Collins 1975: enjoy collecting wild food.

Grandmother's Secrets: Her Green Guide to Health from Plants, Jean Palaiseul, Penguin 1976, is an alternative to Geuter's book.

Herbs in Nutrition, Maria Geuter, Bio-Dynamic Agricultural Association 1982; an excellent guide to the therapeutic value of herbs in cooking.

The Owners Guide to the Body, Roger Golten, Thorsons 1999, gives a wealth of advice on posture, exercises, physical relaxation, care of the feet, etc.

Stress: Homeopathic solutions for emotional and physical stress, Miranda Castro, Pan 1995. As the title suggests, this gives both a homeopathic view of different kinds of stress and suggests very useful treatments you can take by getting medicines from companies like Nelsons and Weleda.

Books on Self-Development, Psychology and Spirituality

Alchemical Studies, C.G. Jung, Collected Works Vol. 13, Columbia University Press, 1983.

Anthroposophy in Everyday Life, Anthroposophic Press 1995, is a short but excellent book containing four of Steiner's several thousand lectures, these covering practical training in thought, overcoming nervousness, karma and the four temperaments.

The Art of Loving, Erich Fromm, Thorsons 1995.

As You Think, James Allen, New World Library 1998. Both this book and Steiner's *How to Know Higher Worlds* (see below) both first appeared in the same year, 1904, no doubt proving something.

Crisis points: working through personal problems, Julian Sleigh, Floris Books 1988. This is an excellent little book for resolving crisis problems, in particular conflict with another person.

Dhammapada, Oxford Paperbacks 2000. Collected teachings of the Buddha. Even if you don't wish to connect to the spiritual or religious side of Buddhism, this short book contains a few hundred very significant maxims for a daily life full of challenge.

The Emerald Tablet, Alchemy for Personal Transformation, Dennis William Hauck, Penguin Arkana 1999. A readable book that makes a number of bold but learned assertions about ancient spiritual traditions, and also gives some good contemporary advice.

Emotional Intelligence, Daniel Goleman, Bloomsbury, 1995.

How to Know Higher Worlds, Rudolf Steiner, Anthroposophic Press 1994, is Steiner's 'basic' work on spiritual development and describes many of the exercises that I have drawn on. Even someone not interested in 'knowing higher worlds' would probably find it insightful and helpful for experiencing *this* world better!

Man on the Threshold, Bernard Lievegoed, Hawthorn Press 1985. This book also gives considerable detail on the planets as principles influencing our lives. As a medical doctor, Lievegoed connects these archetypal principles to physical health and the organs of the body.

Man's Search for Meaning, Viktor E. Frankl, Beacon Books 1992, includes a brief but telling account of Frankl's experience in a Nazi concentration camp, followed by a summary of his logotherapy, or psychology of meaning that he used to heal many people.

Men are from Mars, Women are from Venus, Children are from Heaven, John Gray, HarperCollins 1993. One of a number of bestselling books by this author that packages good ideas well.

Non-violent Communication, Marshall Rosenberg, Puddle Dance Press 2003, is the definitive text on how to communicate without causing stress or getting stressed.

Perennial Wisdom, Aldous Huxley, HarperCollins 1990. A good background to the perennial wisdom mentioned in Chapter 12.

Phases: the Spiritual Rhythms of Adult Life, Bernard Lievegoed, Rudolf Steiner Press 1993. This book describes stages in personal development and particular crisis points such as around ages 40 to 42. Every seven years the human being goes through another stage in development and each of these has a different character. This is obvious in the first 21 years, but continues through the rest of one's life. Lievegoed describes each of the stages and the types of challenges and opportunities that they bring.

Self-Reliance, Ralph Waldo Emerson, ed. Poirier, Oxford University Press, 1990. E.E. Cummings said, 'How I hated my father for making me read Emerson's *Self-Reliance*. Now it is my Bible.'

The Philosophy of Freedom, Rudolf Steiner Press 2001: this is Steiner's seminal philosophical work demonstrating the nature of thinking as a path of freedom. It is also published as *Intuitive Thinking as a Spiritual Path*, Anthroposophic Press 1995.

The Planets Within, Thomas Moore, Lindisfarne Press 1990. Moore is one of the leading Jungian and archetypal psychologists; he reviews the astrological psychology of Marsilio Ficino and uses this to illuminate a practical psychology of health based on the planetary archetypes, as I did in Chapter 5.

The Soul's Code, In Search of Character and Calling, James Hillman, Bantam 1996. This is a wonderful analysis of destiny by one of the thought leaders in the modern 'archetypal' psychology school; Thomas Moore regards him as his mentor.

Stairway of Surprise, Michael Lipson, Anthroposophic Press 2002: describes beautifully and freshly some of the exercises I outlined in Chapter 6, and in particular the six fundamentals, which he calls thinking, doing, feeling, loving, opening, and thanking.

Understand Your Temperament, Gilbert Childs, Sophia Books 1995: a basic introduction to the temperaments.

Verses and Meditations, Rudolf Steiner, Rudolf Steiner Press, 1993.

Vital Lies, Simple Truths, Daniel Goleman, Bloomsbury 1997, on the psychology of self-deception.

Zen Flesh, Zen Bones, Zen stories and meditations compiled by Paul Reps, Penguin Books 2000.

Other books referenced or helpful

About Blady: a Pattern Out of Time, Laurens van der Post, Chatto & Windus 1991. The celebrated explorer reflecting on the trials of his life experience.

Creative Minds, Howard Gardner, Basic Books 1993. This is a study of different kinds of creativity through the biographies of a number of great men and women. It also explores the conditions that turn creativity into outstanding achievement.

The Informed Heart, Autonomy in a Mass Age, Bruno Bettelheim, Avon Books 1960.

The Mysteries, W. Otto, New York 1955.

The Outsider, Colin Wilson, Gollancz 1956: a brilliant analysis of modern alienation.

The Tao of Physics, Fritjof Capra, Flamingo 1992, 1975, 1987: describes parallels between modern physics and eastern mysticism, going into more detail on what was only briefly alluded to in Chapter 12.

The Tree of Knowledge, the Biological Roots of Human Understanding, Maturana and Varela, Shambhala Publications 1987.

The Wholeness of Nature: Goethe's Way of Science, Henri Bortoft, Floris Books 1996: a masterful description of the holistic view of science.

From Stress to Serenity website

More information can be found on the From Stress to Serenity website at www.fromstresstoserenity.com

Illustration credits

Photograph of the poet John Betjeman (p. 144) © Jane Brown, reproduced by permission of Observer Newspapers.

The photographs of the two statues by John Salter, Cain & Abel (p. 65) and Parzival and Firafiz (p. 73), are by the artist and reproduced with Mr Salter's kind permission.

The photograph of the Megalithic circle from Wales (p. 257) is reproduced by kind permission of Tenno Voerman.

The Alchemy images of the Fire Trial (pp. 4, 201), and Ourobos (p. 176) are taken from the book by Michael Maier, Atalanta Fugiens, published in 1617. An English translation exists in the British Museum, MS Sloane 3645. See also **www.levity. com/alchemy/atalanta.html** and various books, e.g. by H.M.E. De Jong.

The 'Clip Art' images (pp. 5, 26, 88, 99, 107, 201) were based on original images obtained from IMSI's MasterClips/MasterPhotos Collection, 1895 Francisco Blvd. East, San Rafeael, CA 94901–5506, USA.

The image of Meg Ryan (p. 143) is a collage, and the image of President J.F. Kennedy (p. 140) is likewise an interpretation, both by the author.

The images of Churchill (p. 140), Nina Rambert (p. 141) and Aubrey Beardsley (p. 141) created by the author, are based on photographs from the National Gallery archive.

The images of war between the Athenians and the Amazons (p. 66), war with the centaurs (p. 67), Assyrians going to war (p. 166), and Conflict (p. 168) are by the author based on friezes in the British Museum.

The images of various gods, Zeus (p. 92), Venus de Milo (p. 97), Mercury (p. 102), Diana (p. 109), and Hermes (p. 143) are by the author, from various statues in the Louvres and other museums.

The images of the Gargoyles (p. 3), Adam and Eve (p. 63), the Good Samaritan (p. 180) and Michael and the Dragon (p. 192) are from Lincoln Cathedral, photographed by the author.

INDEX OF NAMES

Adam and Eve, 63

Adams, Douglas, 9

Alexander the Great, 112, 173

Allen, James, 12, 26, 94, 115, 135, 145, 240, 263

Allen, Warner, 121

Anderson, Julian, 208

Andricopoulos, Yannis, 30

Anka, Paul, 60

Antony and Cleopatra, 35

Aquinas, Thomas, 161

Arc, Joan of, 8

Aristotle, 116

Arnold, Matthew, 54

Arthur [King],112

Auden, W.H., 74

Aurelius, Marcus, 78

Bashô, 194, 255

Beardsley, Aubrey, 141

Beaumont, Francis, 176

Bede, V., 49

Beethoven, Ludwig van, 121

Berryman, John, 173

Betjeman, John, 144

Bettelheim, Bruno, 61, 187

Blake, William, 175, 183, 229, 234

Boom, Corrie Ten, 190

Bortoft, Henri, 120

Buddha, Gautama, 1, 3, 5, 11, 12, 17, 46, 47, 68, 104, 122, 125, 127, 148, 181, 196, 214, 216, 229, 239, 252, 253, 261

Caesar, Julius, 145

Cain and Abel, 65, 66, 67, 68, 69, 71, 72, 197

Campbell, Joseph, 7, 8, 81

Carson, Rachel, 256, 258

Chaplin, Charlie, 138

Charlemagne, 112

Christ, Jesus, 11, 114, 148, 163, 169, 180, 183, 189, 191, 196, 223, 242, 252, 255, 258, 261

Churchill, Winston, 8, 93, 140

Coleridge, Samuel Taylor, 175

Collingwood, R.G., 74, 207

Colquhoun, Margaret, 256

Columbus, Christopher, 138, 139

Confucius, 28, 194

Cummings, E.E., 153, 198

Dahmer, Vernon, 93

David [King], 112,

Dawkins, Richard, 259, 260

Deikman, Arthur, 241

Dostoevsky, Fyodor, 175, 69

Duke of Wellington, 140

Dylan, Bob, 71, 130, 178

Edison, Thomas, 36

Eichmann, Adolph, 179

Elgin, Duane, 7

Eliot, T.S., 121

Emerson, Ralph Waldo, 13, 53, 249

Epictetus, 172, 178

Eschenback, Wolfram von, 72

Fitzgerald, Ella., 207
Flaubert, Gustabe, 175
Fletcher, John, 176
Floride, Athys, 159, 162
Forstater, Mark,131
Frankl, Viktor, 7, 76, 77, 108, 178, 187, 198, 199, 205, 216, 261
Franklin, Benjamin, 175
Freud, Sigmund, 58
Fromm, Erich, 69, 168, 171

Gandhi, 6, 93, 172
Goethe, Johann Wolfgang von, 120, 140, 143, 175, 200, 241, 242, 243, 262
Goleman, Daniel, 191
Graham, Martha, 8, 199, 207

Happold, F.C., 205, 249
Hayden, Robert, 173, 194
Herd, Tracey, 173
Hermes, 143
Hillary, Edmund, 96, 199
Hillman, James, 72, 74, 81, 174, 207
Hinton, David, 47
Hoban, R., 30
Hobbes, Thomas, 205
Hoffman, Paul, 22, 252
Hooker, Richard, 163
Houten, Coen van, 82

Ibsen, 175
Isherwood, Margaret, 225

James, Henry, 156
Jeffers, Susan, 96
Jenkinson, Sally, 204
Jouffroy, Theodore Simon, 64
Jung, Carl .G., 11, 13, 21, 58, 59, 76, 81, 108, 201

Kadmon, Adam, 63
Kant, Emmanuel, 74, 207
Katagiri, Dainin, 135, 137
Kaufman, Stuart, 251, 252, 257
Keats, John, 60
Keenan, Brian, 6
Kennedy, John. F., 140
Kerényi, Care, 113
Kerényi, Karl, 164
King, Martin Luther, 8, 93, 166, 255
Krishnamurti, 116, 183
Kubler-Ross, Elizabeth, 87, 212, 213, 214
Kühlewind, Georg, 68, 93, 194
Kyi, Aung San Suu, 8

Larkin, Philip, 173
Lebentlele, Frank, 9
Lessing, Gotthold Ephraim, 175
Levy-Bruhl, C., 12
Livingstone, Ken, 87

Macbeth, 209
Magdalene, Mary, 97
Maier, Michael, 201
Maitland, Edward, 59
Mandela, Nelson, 6, 9, 10, 26, 46, 93, 191, 199, 253, 261
Manturana, Huberto, R., 134
Mao, Tse Tung, 222
Marley, Bob, 250, 251
Maslow, Abraham, 48, 53, 233
Melville, Herman, 175
Menuhin, Yehudi, 52
Merhav, Shmuel, 155
Merleau-Ponty, W., 55
Mokitimi, Revd., 9
Monet, Claude, 8
Moore, Thomas, 81
Mother Theresa, 8
Mozart, Wolfgang Amadeus, 52, 201

Nefiodow, Leo. A., 15, 31

Nietzsche, Friedrich, 1, 32, 76, 200

Nightingale, Florence, 8

Norwich, Julian of, 1, 249

Novalis, 51, 59, 32, 78, 207, 220, 223, 254, 256

Otto, Walter, 113

Palmas, St. Gregory, 93

Pankhurst, Emmeline, 8, 172

Parzival [Percival], 72, 73, 261

Pascal, Blaise, 48, 139

Paz, Octavio, 62, 63, 64, 215, 216, 225

Pearce, Joseph Chilton, 76

Picasso, Pablo, 60, 95, 250

Pinochet [General], 90

Po, Li, 47

Pope, Alexander, 122

Post, Laurens, van der, 18, 200

Radin, Victoria, 131

Radice, William, 176

Rambert, Nina, 141

Reps, Paul, 247

Rilke, Rainer Maria, 95

Rosenberg, Marshall, 129, 179, 180, 181, 183, 184, 186, 187, 188

Rosetti, Gabriel, 175

Rowe, Dorothy, 16

Rumi, Mevlana Jalaludin, 137, 167

Rushdie, Salmon, 80

Ryan, Meg, 143

Salter, John, 65, 72, 73

Schiller, Friedrich von, 175

Scott, Walter, 175

Seneca, 200, 205

Shakespeare, William, 15, 71, 145

Shelley, Percy Bysshe, 175

Spencer, Stanley, 258

Spinoza, Baruch, 193

St. James, 253

St. John, 259, 261

St. Paul, 201, 259

St. Francis, 8

Steiner, Rudolf, 45, 46, 58, 75, 77, 115, 119, 174, 179, 180, 196, 197, 229, 235, 237, 240, 245, 250

Sterne, Laurence, 44

Stevenson, Anne, 70, 71

Stockdale, Jim, 8

Stravinsky, Igor, 8

Straw, Jack, 90

Tagore, Rabindranath, 176

Thomas, David, 38

Thoreau, Henry David, 152

Tolstoy, Count Leo 175

Truman, Harry, S., 199

Tzū, Che Wen, 262

Varela, Francisco, J., 134

Vogler, Chris, 7

Wagner, Richard, 72, 96

Wagoner, David, 256

Waller, Edmund, 141

Westall, Julia, 73

Whitman, Walt, 45, 70, 71, 119, 170, 185, 195, 197, 198, 213, 246

Whyte, David, 94, 95, 250

Wilson, Colin, 64, 70, 234

Winfrey, Oprah, 199

Wittgenstein, Ludwig, 56, 118, 232

Wolfe, Tom, 73

Wolsey, Cardinal, 71

Woods, Tiger, 239

Woolger, Roger, 210

Wordsworth, William, 72, 175, 205

INDEX OF MEDITATIONS AND EXERCISES

Alexander Technique, 43
All will be well, 249
Ambiguous image (mental exercise),
    117, 253
An emotion-transforming exercise, 193
An experiment in awareness, 54
Ancient Indian meditations, 248
Awareness of sounds, 121

Backache, general health and well being,
    39
Butterfly, 226

Caduceus or Mercury staff, 244
Catnap, 36
Cherokee Prayer, 190
Commitment, 262
Conflict attitudes, 177
Courage meditation, 247, 250

Days of the week, 230–234
Decisions and decision making, 134
Discuss good things together, 151

Equanimity, 128–130
Emotions and feelings, 244

Facing the future with courage, 249–250
Feet, 44
Flexibility, 134

Gaining self-knowledge through daily
    or life-retrospectives, 122–125

Gestalt (mental exercise), 116

Healthy social life, 198
Helix, 245, 262

Ideal or higher self, 242–243
Illness, listening to, 27–28
Internal pressures, 47

Kena-Upanishad, 49

Lifestyles, which are you?, 154
Love, faith and hope, 259

Make appointments with yourself, 155
Mandela (Our deepest fear is not that we
    are inadequate), 10
Meditation that specifically connects to
    God, 243
Meditation, on images, 245
  – steps in, 236–237
  – summary of how, 240
Memory exercises, 133
Michael and Dragon, 193
Mundaka-Upanishad, 57

Natural (Goethean method), 241, 244
NLP, higher perspective, 219
Non-violent communication, 181

Observing living processes, 121
Observing People, 122

Observing your own life (as a source of meditation), 243

Ourobos, 176

Peace, quiet, v, 237

People who have formed us, 195

Plan your weekends, 155

Positivity, 132–133

Recognizing your temperament, 145

Reflection exercises, 45, 227–228

Retrospectives, daily and life, 122–125

Self-leadership qualities, seven practices to develop, 232–234

Self-leadership, 248–249

Setting limits and boundaries for work, 150–151

Spiritual meditations, 246–247

Stress codes, 148–149

Stress signs, 20, 27

Stress reduction action plan, 263

Thinking exercises, 125–127

Thoughts, care of, 46

To enrich thinking, feeling and will, 245

Will, strengthening, 127–128

Ying Yang, 221

Your personal reflections, 228